MW00658568

THE WARREN WAGONTRAIN RAID

· ADOBE WALLS – 1864

SOUTHWEST LIFE AND LETTERS

A series designed to publish outstanding new fiction and nonfiction about Texas and the American Southwest and to present classic works of the region in handsome new editions.

General Editors: Suzanne Comer, Southern Methodist University Press; Tom Pilkington, Tarleton State University.

Other Books by Benjamin Capps

HANGING AT COMANCHE WELLS

THE TRAIL TO OGALLALA

SAM CHANCE

A WOMAN OF THE PEOPLE

THE BROTHERS OF UTERICA

THE WHITE MAN'S ROAD

THE TRUE MEMOIRS OF CHARLEY BLANKENSHIP

THE INDIANS

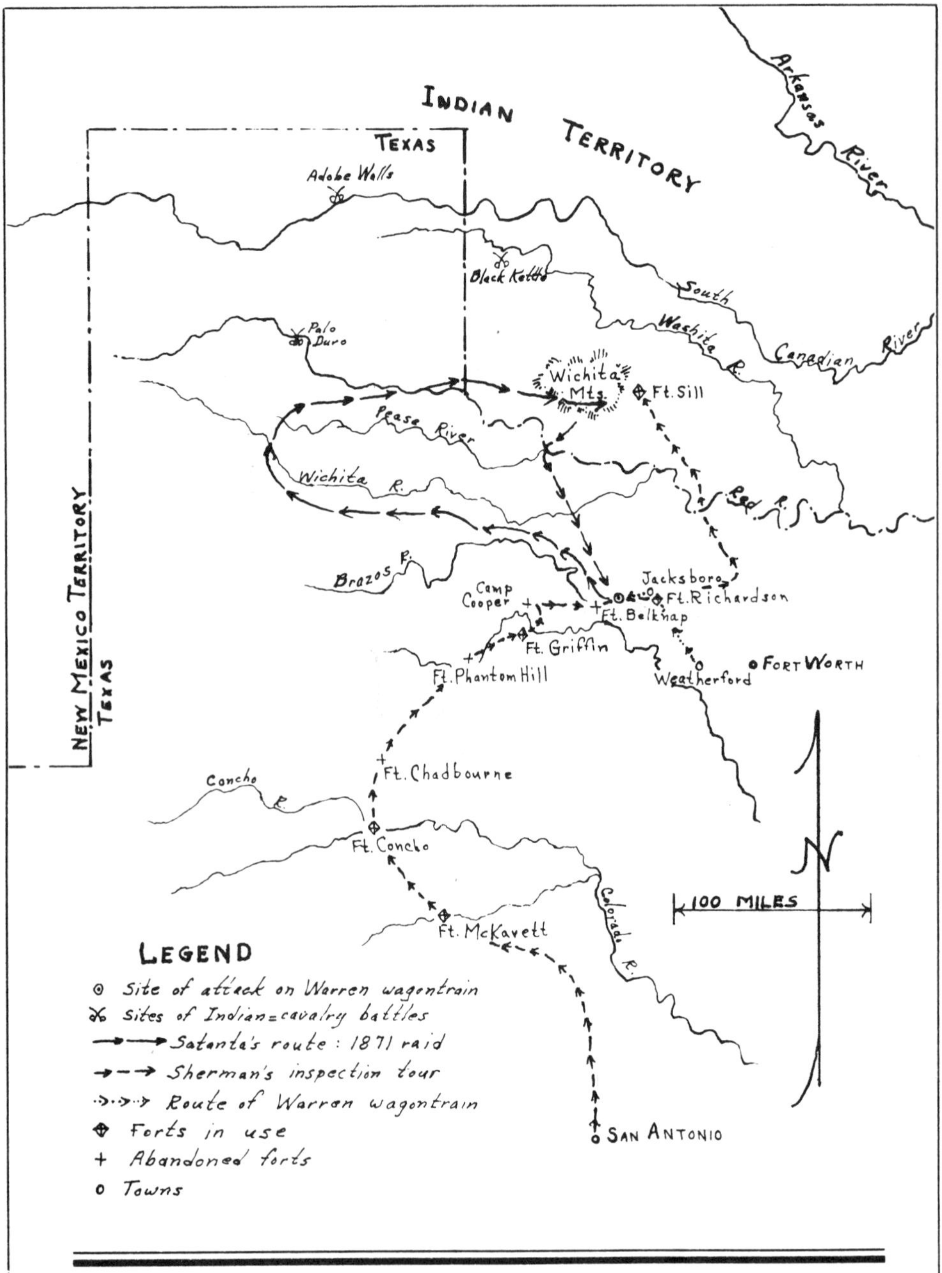

A PORTION OF THE
SOUTH PLAINS — 1871

The WARREN WAGONTRAIN RAID

THE FIRST COMPLETE ACCOUNT OF AN HISTORIC INDIAN ATTACK AND ITS AFTERMATH

BENJAMIN CAPPS

Southern Methodist University Press
Dallas

Library of Congress Cataloging-in-Publication Data

Capps, Benjamin, 1922–
The Warren wagontrain raid : the first complete account of an historic Indian attack and its aftermath / Benjamin Capps.—1st Southern Methodist University Press ed.
p. cm—(Southwest life and letters)
Reprint. Originally published: New York : Dial Press, 1974.
Bibliography: p.
Includes index.
ISBN 0-87074-295-7
1. Kiowa Indians—Fiction. I. Title. II. Series.
PS3553.A59W54 1989
813′.54—dc20 89-42897
CIP

Cover art: *The Attack on an Emigrant Train*, Charles F. Wimar, 1856. Courtesy University of Michigan Museum of Art.

to my daughter Kathleen Marie Capps

CONTENTS

APOLOGIA

It may be that *The Warren Wagontrain Raid* is a useful example to put before graduate students in history and before all manner of would-be scholars, writers, and critics; for the account raises important and difficult questions in historiography. It is not presented as a model, good or bad, but as a considerable problem.

The subject matter of the book is vast, especially to the extent that it succeeds in being a "complete account." It is obvious that General Sherman, who would command the U.S. Army during the heart of the Indian Wars, changed his mind about the Indian problem in the West that spring of 1871. But a more universal subject matter is involved. Here we have native people with a hunter-gatherer economy; such people have for many thousands of years clashed with and often defeated those with a village-farming economy. Then at some point the farmers started winning part of the time—more recently all of the time. The situation may be the basis for the Cain-and-Abel myth. Such Indians as the Kiowas in nineteenth-century America faced whites who not only had crops and domestic livestock, but had an industrial economy behind them.

It has been estimated that there were three hundred mutually unintelligible languages in North America when the European intruders came. Anarchy prevailed in some places as late as 1890. That's not long ago; my own father was born in 1886.

Probably at no time in human history has such a different and various population existed to be followed so soon by such a generally literate and orderly culture. Great university libraries stand today where Native Americans speared buffalo with stone points only three or four lifetimes ago. And machine copies and microfilm make available to the researcher great quantities of primary materials of all kinds. It has been a thrill to me to hold in my hand, for example, an exact replica of a letter handwritten by William Tecumseh Sherman.

The Warren Wagontrain Raid was reviewed in *Western American Literature* by C. L. Sonnichsen in the May, 1974, issue of the journal. As did some other reviewers, including Wayne Gard and William Leckie, he criticized the fictionalizing. He asked whether my method was sound and concluded that it was not. I will not "patronize" him by saying that he is a great teacher, historian, and critic, for everybody knows that, but will only say that he is my friend and will not mind my disagreeing on certain points. We have discussed the matter since then, but I still have not changed the text of the book.

Several questions have been in my mind about the matter. Am I, in this present account, substituting my imagination for historical fact, or am I following fact carefully and merely adding fiction elements which seem true? To whom does history belong? To historians, in a kind of closed circle, or is it a good idea at some point to get out of the ivory tower and produce writings to interest a larger public? Does the general reader deserve and appreciate the documented facts along with interpretation, even thoughtful fictionalizing? Do those who produce strictly "factual" history always get the facts right?

I believe that my account is the most complete and accurate yet written, though the interest of budding historians goes on. The latest book dealing in part with the matter is *Sentinel of the Southern Plains*, by history teacher Allen Hamilton. He confesses that his book is for both the general reader and the serious student of frontier history. In his notes he says that my book is "an apologist's biography of Satanta" and offers the "contemporary and far different" views of Tatum, Carter, and Custer. My own judgment of those sources is thus: Tatum was a good man, naive to the point of condoning fraud in the Indian Service. Custer was as flamboyant as Satanta and had perpetrated savage cruelty against Indians. Carter did not know the difference between history and a dime novel.

The fact that a source is contemporary is surely in its favor, but it still must be evaluated. Nye, usually a dependable source, talked with a participant in the raid in about 1935. That's sixty-four years after the raid. Supposing that the informant was eighty, he was sixteen at the time of the action and not privy to the inner councils of a large war party.

In the area of incidental errors, Hamilton mentions a Captain Mauck and flatly says that it is incorrectly spelled Manck by Capps. Well, I took the spelling from the Post Returns of Fort Griffin, a machine copy, for May, 1871. Now I see that one cannot distinguish in the handwriting between "Mauck" and "Manck." In fact, there in the same handwriting is the word "under," and one cannot distinguish between the first two letters. Hamilton may well be right. The same kind of usually unimportant error may happen from a misprint which is not caught by the proofreader. In the review by Leland Sonnichsen mention above the year of the raid is given as 1877 instead of 1871.

But the big problem is my fictionalizing. Should I have presented it as a novel, with no documentation? Then a number of historians, amateurs or professionals, would have said: "Good writing, but he has the sequence of events wrong. He has more than twenty-four hours between Sherman's passing and the attack, when actually it was only two or three hours. We have Marcy's journal; he was there; he was an official; he was a writer." Of course, Marcy was wrong, as were Nye and others who followed him.

And historians may well have said about it as a novel with no documentation: "Why does Capps use all these real historic names and events, but misspell Woolfork? We have Haley's biography of Goodnight, who knew Woolfork well and certainly knew how to spell his name. We have other evidence, such as a contemporary story in the *Dallas Herald.*" Of course, the distinguished historian Haley was wrong. Young County records have many references to Joe Woolfolk, and the man's grave has a stone with his correct name.

The real people who lived in the American West in the nineteenth century have been victims of too much fiction passing for fact. Lt. Carter produced a blatant example in his article "The Cowboys' Verdict," published in *Youths Companion* in Boston. He set the trial in a log courthouse, with spectators looking in the windows, when he knew well that the courthouse was stone and the trial took place on the second floor. The cowboy jury wore "shootin' irons," when Carter knew well that they were unarmed merchants and clerks. Hundreds of writers in the past hundred years have twisted the facts and the truth about life in the West. It is no wonder that legitimate historians question interpretations. But does that mean that they should condemn the writer who sticks to the facts and adds explanatory fictionalizing?

But back to the main question. Should I have made it straight fact and included nothing that I could not document? Well, the attraction of the subject to me lay in the variety of points of view: the settlers, the Indians, the Indian service, the army. A reader, in order to get the complete truth about the total situation, would need to read several books about the Kiowas and think about them. That some people were not considering any Indian point of view, however, is clear from the sources. Again and again we read that Tsatangya "went berserk" or was killed trying to escape. A seventy-year-old man with manacles on wrists and ankles, surrounded by armed cavalry, gnawed into his wrists and thought he could escape. It is clear that he was thinking about generations to come, about pride in adversity, about ancestors, about the worth of his own life up beside the worth of thousands of Kiowa lives to come.

And, in the thoughts of Satanta, I tried to suggest the dilemma of a fighter and diplomat who was seeing the destruction of the way of life of his people. Surely the whites' killing of buffalo for fun or only for the hides must have seemed beyond reason. The reader who had not studied Native American people and their situation would never see the whole truth of the Warren wagontrain raid.

I'm not an "Indian lover," nor an "Indian hater." In fact, I find them like all people, some good some bad, some dumb some smart, some kind some cruel—like all of us. The big moral problem throughout history is in not seeing different people as human and in following leaders who emphasize the differences.

So, what should I have done in putting out this account a decade and a half after its first publication? We might have called it an "interpretive history." Leland Sonnichsen suggested that I might make it two books, one straight fiction and one an explanation of the research and writing problems. Or I might in an introduction ask the reader to consult the notes in order to understand the validity of the account, as I did in the first place.

In any case, I should admit that I have profited much over

the years from the work of good historians. Their accounts and documentation are invaluable as a starting point for every kind of writing.

Benjamin Capps, Grand Prairie, Texas
December 1988

PREFACE TO FIRST EDITION

The principal people and events which are the subject of this book have been written about dozens, probably hundreds, of times in newspapers, magazines, scholarly journals, books. Unfortunately, the accounts contradict one another and most of them are filled with misinformation. No comprehensive and reliable account has been previously published.

It has been my intention to discover and present truthfully the facts about what has been called the "Warren Wagontrain Massacre," about the trial of Kiowa chiefs Satanta and Big Tree, about connected events and consequences, and about the viewpoints of the various participants. To this end I have studied material from a number of archival repositories as well as a mass of published material, have spent much time evaluating written sources, and have often wished for the aid of a Sherlock Holmes in resolving the contradictions. I invite historians, amateur and professional, particularly those interested in the south plains during the turbulent years of the Indian Wars, to study the notes which apply to each chapter and judge the accuracy of my version.

In the presentation, while I have followed diligently all the facts which can be determined, I have not hesitated to proceed further in interpretation than would the professional historian. However, the discerning reader, particularly if he consults the notes, will easily understand what is documentable fact, what is inferred fact, and what is imagined detail such as reconstructed dialogue. Incidentally, my attempts to see motives and the climate of opinion of the times have led me in a number of cases to new sources, so that what was at first only an informed guess became subject to documentation.

It might be argued that the Warren Wagontrain Massacre was something of a turning point in history, because of the involvement of General William T. Sherman. "I risked my life," he wrote later. To a subordinate general he wrote that such a tour of the frontier as he, Sherman, had made "makes plain what is otherwise incomprehensible." That he changed his mind about the seriousness of Indian activity in the spring of 1871 cannot be doubted. And, of course, it was he who commanded the U.S. Army for the next dozen years, the period during the heart of the Indian Wars. Had he been of a different mind, such a person as George A. Custer probably would not even have held a command.

But I think it is on other grounds that I find this story compelling. So many different factions—the Indians, the army, the Indian agents, the white settlers—saw the events in entirely different lights, and each group had a valid viewpoint; the situation produces a poignant natural irony. In addition, no three men could be better devised to represent the nature and predicament of a people than Tsatangya, Satanta, and Big Tree, who in their actual lives symbolized the Kiowas. They were three distinct generations; the eldest was a master of the old culture, the youngest became comfortable in the new, and the tragic figure of the middle one, Satanta, was caught in between. The story is like a universal allegory. I believe that one of the Fates stirring the brew of history must have been a creative artist.

This book would have been impossible without the response and assistance of many generous people, and I would like to mention particularly the following:

James Auchiah, grandson of Satanta. A painter of murals and other works, he has long been interested in Kiowa history. His wife Celia is the granddaughter of the second Lone Wolf.

Barbara Neal Ledbetter, who lives south of Graham, Texas, and has done exhaustive research in the old records of Young County. Her advice and her loan to me of rare materials saved me much time.

Mitchell Wilder, Nancy Wynn, and Margaret McLean, of the Amon Carter Museum of Western Art in Fort Worth, who were very hospitable in allowing me to use their library facilities and newspaper microfilm files.

Henry R. Small of the Bureau of Records and Identification of the Texas Department of Corrections at Huntsville. He sent me not only copies of appropriate records, but also helpful copies of many newspaper and magazine articles.

Rella Looney, archivist of the Indian Archives Division of the Oklahoma Historical Society. This organization is by federal law the official repository of many old records and letters generated at Indian agencies.

Laura Peacock, chairman of the Jack County Historical Survey Commission, who lives at Jacksboro, Texas.

Oliver H. Orr, Jr., in the Civil War and Reconstruction Manuscript Division of the Library of Congress; Elmer O. Parker in the Old Military Records Division of the National Archives; Richard S. Maxwell in the Social and Economic Records Division of the National Archives; and Marjorie Snodgrass in the Office of Library Services of the U.S. Department of the Interior.

Don R. Swadley, professor of literature at the University of Texas at Arlington, who grew up in the area where the events of this story took place and is much interested in its history.

Marie Capps, who helped in the research, accompanied me on research trips, and typed the manuscript.

To the above people I am truly grateful. The errors and shortcomings of the work are my own.

Benjamin Capps, Grand Prairie, Texas
November 1972

THE WARREN WAGONTRAIN RAID

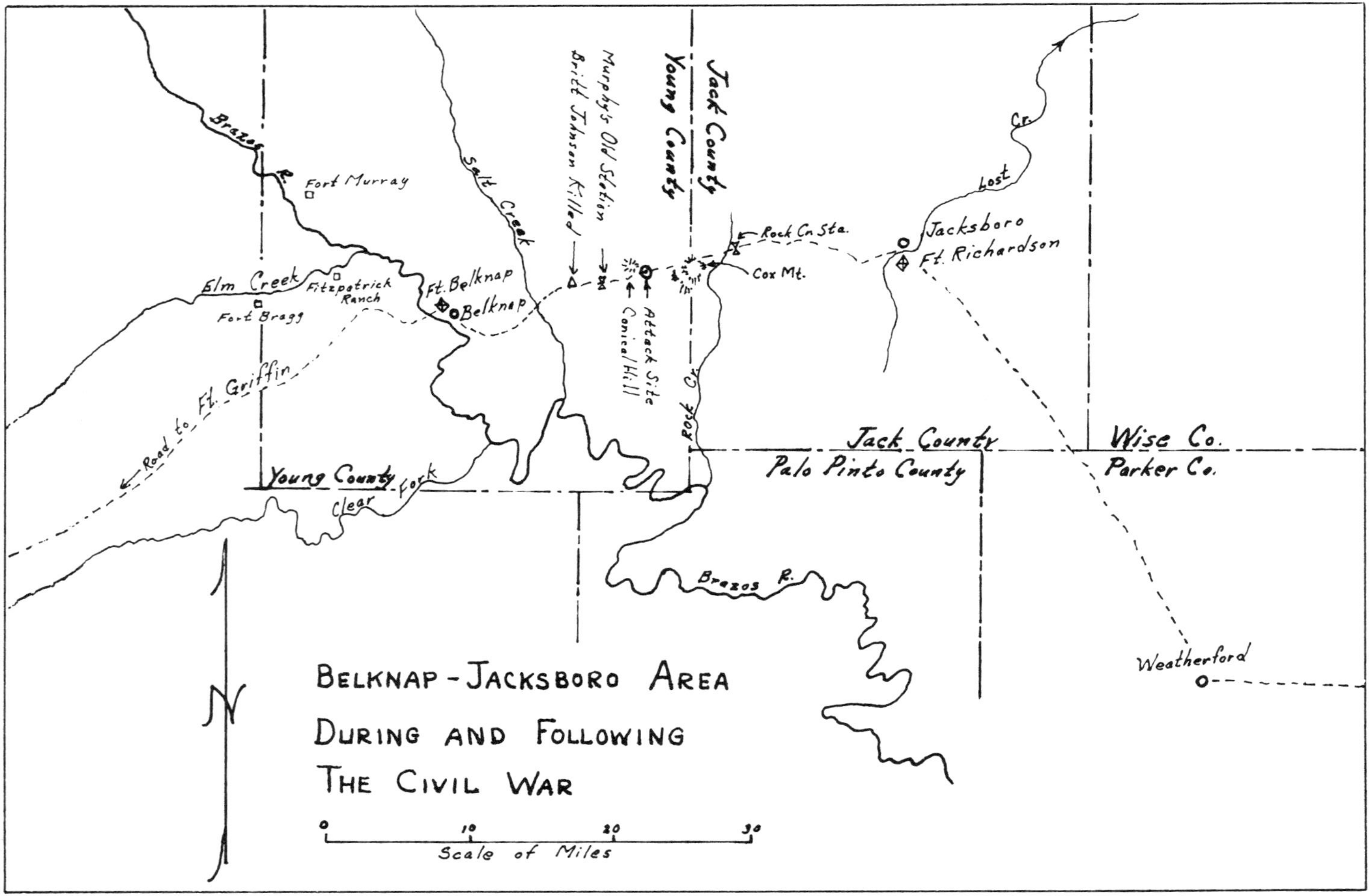
Brazos R.
Fort Murray
Salt Creek
Murphy's Old Station
Britt Johnson Killed
Jack County
Young County
Rock Cr. Sta.
Cox Mt.
Jacksboro
Ft. Richardson
Lost Cr.
Elm Creek
Fitzpatrick Ranch
Ft. Belknap
Belknap
Fort Bragg
Attack Site
Conical Hill
Road to Ft. Griffin
Rock Cr.
Jack County
Palo Pinto County
Wise Co.
Parker Co.
Young County
Clear Fork
Brazos R.
Weatherford
BELKNAP-JACKSBORO AREA
DURING AND FOLLOWING
THE CIVIL WAR
0 10 20 30
Scale of Miles

CHAPTER ONE

THE RAIDERS

In the middle of May 1871, a war party of between a hundred and a hundred fifty Kiowa Indians forded Red River. The streambed was a broad expanse of moulded sand, blown into wavy patterns by the wind, and through it meandered a shallow stream which hardly wet the horses' knees. The irregular file climbed the south bank along a buffalo trail, the hindquarters of their mounts straining with the load up the incline. One young man toward the rear raised his hand to his mouth upon gaining the top and sounded a long tremolo war cry, bringing from those ahead of him a few answering cheers or yips or laughter. They were well aware that they had just crossed a boundary.

They were headed for a strike against the Tehanos, or Texans.

The south bank of the Red had been a boundary long before for the Spanish and French, later for the United States and Mexico, still later for Texas and Indian Territory. For boundaries drawn by other people the Kiowas had little respect. They were entering country which had belonged to their allies, the Comanches. They were crossing a line which their white agent often threatened them against crossing. In fact, the cavalry soldiers who lived at Fort Sill in Indian Territory sometimes patrolled this river, but it was a simple matter to come out here to the west and go around them.

They made a motley parade. A few Comanches rode with them. A few Kiowa-Apaches. Also, a few women, each following closely behind her husband. The bulk of them were Kiowa warriors, each painted with his unique pattern and colors. Some wore single feathers in their hair, a few wore full headdresses. Their mounts and bows and shields carried decorations of paint and fur and feathers and bright cloth. Half of the men bore guns—revolvers, muzzle loaders, here and there a repeating rifle. They were excellent horsemen, riding easily, able to guide their mounts with only a slight knee pressure. Their relationship with their horses was not based on love or even utility; they decorated them for the same reason that they decorated themselves, and they used them as harshly and carefully as they used parts of their own bodies. About the men clung an aura of their wild life; in their faces, in their expressions, were traced certain grim lines, even when they laughed, that came from living under the sky in a land that is hot desert one time and swept by icy blizzard another.

For three-quarters of a century their principal vocation had been raiding and warring, after that hunting, ceremony, trading, diplomacy, the making of instruments for war and ceremony, the making of buffalo robes for trading. In the pursuit of the first business, war, they had ridden with their brothers, the Comanches, west against the Navahos and Jicarillas and Utes, north against the Dakotas and Cheyennes and Pawnees, east against the Osages. To the south they struck the Mescaleros and Lipans and Caddoes and pierced through those tribes like a knife to raid deeper south, to Matagorda Bay, through Durango and Sonora to the Gulf of California. Once they had gone into the

Grand Canyon of the Colorado to plunder the Havasupais. Once they had thrust through Mexico to the tropics to see bright-plumed birds and monkeys in the trees.

At the head of this raiding party rode an unusual man, Satanta, heavy-set, fifty years old, with an air of great strength and vitality about him. His broad handsome face was painted red, in his hair was stuck the longest wing feather of a crane, and around one muscular shoulder hung an army bugle on a leather thong.

It has been written that Chief Satanta was "of that type which today makes gangster leaders. He was brazen and impudent, shrewd at times, yet naive, addicted to violence and boasting." A Texas official called him "the arch fiend of treachery and blood . . . promoter of strife . . . breaker of treaties . . . hideous and loathsome in appearance." A newspaper reporter who studied the chief at the Medicine Lodge Council in 1867 wrote: "It must be remembered that in cunning or native diplomacy Satanta has no equal. In worth and influence Red Cloud is his rival; but in boldness, daring, and merciless cruelty Satanta is far superior, and yet there are some good points in this dusky chieftain which command admiration." Another who saw him at Medicine Lodge wrote thus: "The great chief, Satanta, in delivering his address spoke with a dignity and force that could not but be appreciated. He is a great orator and of unbounded influence in the council." Still another observer noted Satanta's "peculiar dash of manner; a grin equal to all occasions; a remarkable shrewdness," and commented on his "skill in council and diplomacy."

As Satanta rode along he chatted in a jovial manner with those near him. One of them was a young warrior who carried the chief's bow, quiver, gun, sacred arrow-lance, and sacred shield. The latter two objects were highly decorated for use in ceremony as well as war and conferred upon their owner great medicine and prestige. The arrow-lance, or Zebat, had a keen-edged Mexican steel blade; its hardwood shaft was plaited with red and white buckskin; near the tip were tied tassels of red cloth, farther up, yellow-hammer feathers and two white crane feathers. The round shield of flint-hard bull-buffalo hide was decorated on the back with red and yellow strips of cloth, white feathers, and a dried crane's head; on the front was drawn a sun with three rings around it. The ancient shield hung each year in the medicine lodge during the Sun Dance, or Kado. Satanta was the civil chief of the Elks Division of the Kiowas and a senior war chief, but in his mind he was more than that, and he was in fact more.

Three and a half years earlier, when the whites had come in a great caravan of government officials to Medicine Lodge, Kansas, to make a final treaty which would, as they supposed, settle all the trouble with the Comanches, Kiowas, Kiowa-Apaches, Arapahos, and Southern Cheyennes, Satanta had gone to meet them and escort them to the treaty site. Then, when the council began, he had been first speaker for the Indians and had spoken several times later. For the grand manner of his speeches eastern newspapers had dubbed him "The Orator of the Plains." They had been impressed, but to them he had seemed contradictory, an unreasonable combination of militancy and friendliness. They had no idea of the nature of the man with whom they dealt—that he did, for example, speak five languages: four tongues of the warrior Indians of the south plains and Spanish besides, to say nothing of sign language.

The bugle that now joggled against his side as he rode was an apt symbol of his nature—flamboyant, aggressive, adaptable; he was a man of initiative, willing to try any new thing which might have some true use for himself and his followers. He had given fits to the troops of Kit Carson at Adobe Walls out on the Canadian River in 1864 with this bugle, blowing the opposite of every call they blew.

As he rode now at the head of the scattered column a curious set of questions flitted through his mind. How did he look to those who followed him? Did he look both dignified and dramatic? Colorful? Even the petty question: Was his single white crane feather straight in his hair?

Not that concern for personal appearance was anything but normal among them all. A warrior might spend an hour painting himself and require as well the services of two wives to arrange his image to suit his idea of himself. The strangeness of it lay in that he saw himself entertaining the questions when he should have been beyond them twenty years earlier. He had long ago committed himself to making and keeping a bright image. In fact he had long ago earned all the loyalty and admiration which he needed from those who followed him. He thought the questions arose because of the uncertain nature of chieftainship which seemed to be developing among the people, as if all the rules were changing and anything long earned must be earned anew. None of the raiders with him could possibly guess that he had anything but complete assurance; he had played the role too long for that. In truth, he believed with every iota of logic that he possessed that he was a dramatic chief, a shrewd tactician, one in whom the appearance and competence for leadership mated as they should. It was only that his feelings did not always fit with his logic anymore. Even this idea came to him, privately: that this must be a good raid, successful. It must be. He must come out blameless. He must appear successful. They must see him worthy of praise. Or else certain other chiefs not now present—Lone Wolf, Kicking Bird—would rise far above him; then the important understandings he possessed might be scorned by the people. It was crucial to his leadership that he make a good show in this project, and he thought it equally crucial to all Kiowas.

Back there old Chief Tsatangya rode quietly. The questions came to Satanta: Does he follow me willingly? How do I look to him?

He cast the nagging uncertainties out of his mind by beginning his jokes and banter again, and soon he had all those who rode near him laughing as if they were going to a feast.

None of the members of this war party knew so much of Kiowa raiding history as did Chief Tsatangya, a man seventy years old who rode with them, yet seemed curiously separate from them. He wore a thin mustache that curved down past his mouth on either side, as had been fashionable in the past, and its color was that of cotton twine. He wore his hair shoulder length, unplaited, and it appeared straggly from its streaks of gray. His face had a Mongolian cast, the slanted eyes dark and piercing. His left eyelid drooped a bit. His face was marked with age and sorrow and a certain wild distinction akin to beauty.

He wore little decoration other than one item over his left shoulder, a strip of elkskin died black. It was his badge as senior member of the Koitsenkga, the real horses, or crazy dogs, or, as they were often considered, the Society of the Ten Bravest. Each of the ten members wore a cloth or leather sash, and it was the duty of a member, when it became necessary to stand fast in battle, to pin the sash to the ground with an arrow, and there to remain and die unless his comrades released him. The six less-proved members wore red sashes of cloth; the three next higher, red sashes of elkskin; the leader, a black sash of elkskin. Tsatangya had belonged to the group since its reorganization twenty-five years earlier, and in recent years the black sash had passed to him. This simple strip of leather carried a meaning subtly different from the others; it was to be pinned by its owner to the ground when the fate of the Kiowa people depended upon the stand taken by their bravest.

If those who rode near him wondered whether he were too old for his commitment as leader of the Koitsenkga, they did not whisper about it, for Tsatangya was held in extraordinary awe. All of those younger than middle age had heard stories of his achievements in battle when they were impressionable boys. Wherever he rode among them, they made way for him and were careful not to get in the path of his horse.

The raiding party rode southeast. The land looked dry for this time of year, though its semi-desert nature was softened by new mesquite grass and scattered bunchgrass. Here and there rose the stalks of light-green blooms of the Spanish dagger. Some growth of the year before remained, dry clumps of buffalo grass, piles of dark-gray tumbleweeds caught against the bank of a gulley or against a lone mesquite tree.

Satanta chose a short ride for the first day's journey, to make it easy on the horses. He had carefully selected this time, the Moon of Pia Aganti, for the expedition. Horses were weak after winter. If you waited until certain grass seeds were maturing in late spring and did not drive your mounts too hard, you could toughen them and fatten them as you traveled. More important, if you struck south against the nearest settlements of the Tehanos and took some scalps or captives or plunder, you would return just in time for Kado, the Sun Dance, for which all Kiowas gathered; your exploits would be the news of the camps. He was determined to keep this party under his control instead of allowing them to split up, to use his knowledge and experience in order to make sure they captured some worthwhile booty without taking undue risk, and to head them back north in time for the Sun Dance.

Their evening camp amounted to little more than a dozen

small fires over which to broil meat. Satanta passed among the warriors briefly, here and there clapping one on the back, joking with them. He asked old Chief Tsatangya if he could do anything for him and got only a shake of the head in reply. Finally, as they all began to quiet he lay on his back and looked into the night sky.

The raid which he now led did not mean the same to him as raids had once meant, not adventure and excitement anyway. It was rather a means to an end, or to several ends.

Two patterns of thought had run strongly through his life: first, his own career and how to enhance it, a normal concern with the men of his tribe, though few of them had thought about such matters as extensively as he; second, a more subtle, difficult, exclusive set of developing ideas about the relationship between peoples with differing ways of life.

In his youth, in the time when he had been called Guaton-Bain, or Big Ribs, instead of the more dignified Satanta, or White Bear, he had worked up privately a set of requirements for leadership: A man must draw attention to himself, he must show himself to be religious, he must smile, he must learn to hold his temper, he must gain renown in war, he must be a ready talker and a dramatic speaker, he must show that he has confidence in himself, he must have riches and be generous. No sooner had he become a man than he had begun to blaze his name brightly on the warpath, for he had always been strong enough to show up well in personal combat. As soon as his success in raiding had given him the right to speak, he had proceeded to make speeches, dramatically and frequently. He had advanced quickly to the chieftainship of his band; even then his eye had been on the position of principal chief of all the Kiowas. He had waited twenty years for that, meanwhile showing himself capable, leading them in more successful raids than he could count, showing himself faithful to religion and ceremony, leading the herders to hold the buffalo while the tribe made its meat and robe killing, gathering to himself the trappings of leadership such as the sacred shield and arrow-lance and bugle. Then the old principal chief died—it had been five years now—but so much factionalism had risen among the Kiowas that they could not unanimously agree. Satanta had burned to lead them all; he was the obvious successor. For two years it had seemed that he had the position in his grasp. They procrastinated, then compromised and selected another man, Lone Wolf.

Whether that were a permanent choice, Satanta was not certain. Whether the rejection pointed to some shortcoming in himself that he could not see, he was not certain. But in fact, he was beginning to wonder whether during his own lifetime the office of principal chief might become irrelevant.

As early as he had coveted leadership he had been fascinated with other peoples. It began with learning Arapaho speech and ways from his mother, who was an Arapaho captive. Then he had learned Kiowa-Apache from the band which had its place in the great camp circle each year during Kado. After that he learned Comanche from those good allies, who always welcomed a visitor. Finally he had learned Spanish from Mexican captives and the New Mexico traders.

The languages themselves were less valuable than the perspective they gave. He had learned through the years that all people change their ways of life as they come into contact with other peoples. He had developed this understanding: that a people determines its destiny by its choice of friends and enemies, by its ability to remain respected through fear until such time as it can make a peace negotiated between equals.

The intrusion of whites into the plains, from only a rumor at first to an important force today, had come within his own lifetime. They seemed to present a more complicated problem than any other people the Kiowas had dealt with. Their traders were easy enough to get along with, but their peace emissaries who came to bargain for trade routes and to pass out silver Washington medals to important chiefs seemed to assume a kind of hegemony that they had not earned by force of arms. Satanta had decided early that it was well to learn as much as possible about these strange people. He had entertained their traders in his lodge, guaranteeing protection of their goods. He had visited their forts and met in councils with them at every opportunity. He had fought them. He had felt their friendliness, their treachery, the power of their guns. They would not honor weakness, that was sure; they were like the Kiowas in that regard. Their language, English, seemed impossible to learn because of the way they put words together and their peculiar thought patterns.

For years now he had been watching a troubling trend. As whites became thicker, more Indians made more buffalo robes to trade for guns. The buffalo were fewer than when he was a young man. The great herds were still there, but at some seasons a hunting party might search weeks for them. The Indians were undercutting their own way of life, even as they reached out for the strength that would enable them to maintain it. They were running a dangerous race. He accepted change as a rule of life, but what if the buffalo became too few to sustain them before they had enough guns to match the whites and bargain with them on a basis of equality?

His policy toward them was twofold, like the horns of an animal. First, do not avoid them; stay close and study and learn. Second, be militant and peaceful by turns; do not allow them to assume they are superior.

The whites, he believed, were not one people, as some conservative Kiowas thought. They were rent by factions just as Indians were. Even in their army he had found it. He had gone down to the southern settlements one time, killed a white man, and taken the man's wife and four children. He had brought them north and tried to sell them at Fort Larned, but had gotten nothing beyond angry words. He had taken them upstream to Fort Dodge, and there the commanding officer paid a good ransom.

The purposes of this present raid, beyond enhancing his own prestige, were several: Keep probing the differences among the whites, make differences among them, keep the pressure on, try to capture breech-loading guns or something to be traded for them. He was looking ahead to a possibility that some day an alliance would exist between his people and the whites, not the farce of today based on mutual mistrust and forked-tongue talk, but a settled alliance. And he thought that the action of Indians now was determining the nature of that possible alliance, whether it would be as between brothers or as between father and child.

The second day south of Red River they came into an area of fine grazing, open country with wild rye to the horses' knees. The seed heads, full grown, were just beginning to tan. They slowed down to let the horses feed. The beasts gorged themselves, now and then cropping at a lush pile of sour clover or at a wild pepper plant as if to flavor their feast.

Satanta was well pleased with the selection of men who had accepted the pipe to come with him. He had at least a hundred of the finest warriors of the Kiowa nation, several of whom had led their own raids back through the years. Of the younger ones, his cousin Big Tree was outstanding. At the age of twenty-two the young man was already the civil chief of a subgroup of the Elks Division. He had earned it by his daring and horsemanship.

Not large in stature, he seemed nonetheless always eager to get into the center of a fight, and it was said that if a horse had any speed in him Big Tree could get it out. The young chief wore a quiver of puma skin with the mouth and claws still on it. He carried a yellow shield with a streak of black lightning across it. He had things to learn yet about raiding strategy and the handling of warriors, but Satanta could think of no fighter he would prefer to have following him.

As for the old Chief Tsatangya, although he still had a certain grace in the saddle, some question existed as to whether he had any strength for combat. But that had little to do with whether he was useful on a raid. You could hardly have a discipline problem with him along. Some of these men would have preferred to lose an arm rather than be the object of a sarcastic comment from him. He was a tribal institution and his presence alone was enough to put a stamp of authenticity and legitimacy on a project.

Satanta remembered when, at a time when he was only a gangling overgrown boy, Chief Tsatangya had led the warriors in defense of Kiowa territory against the Cheyenne invaders and had brought back the scalps of forty-eight men, who they later learned were the elite soldiers of the Cheyenne Bow String Society. That had been more than three decades ago. But the old man's reputation in war was not all of it; when he took part in a ceremony the event seemed to take on more dignity and meaning for everyone. Satanta had heard him sing to the drum and had heard the other singers drop off one by one to listen; it sounded like the voice of their ancestors calling to them down through the generations. How he had such effect on other people was a puzzle. It seemed somehow that Tsatangya had always known exactly how to conduct himself without even thinking about it, that he knew how to get the good opinion of others without making up rules for himself about it or even knowing that it was an issue.

As for the black elkskin sash, Satanta had two minds about it. First, he believed that sometime in ages past a man such as himself had devised the Koitsenkga. Its purpose was clear—that of defining bravery so that it was useful to all of them, rather than one individual. Warriors who run away do not defend their own lives or those of anyone else. Those who stand are the ones who win, for themselves and their comrades and their families. So you make a dramatic commitment before the battle. It was a shrewd man who had devised the Koitsenkga and the sashes. But the second thing that seemed clear to him was this: that the process was designed for warriors who fight on foot, not horseback. When you pin yourself to a spot on the ground you lose your mobility. So it seemed to him that the impressiveness of old things became somehow contradictory to the usefulness of new things, and he wondered whether sometime his bugle would have a legendary image at a time when it had no practical purpose.

On the third day Satanta led the war party across the red breaks of the forks of the Tsenpa, or Little Wichita River. All the country was dry, and his knowledge of the location of the most dependable springs served them well. He put out scouts that day, on the high points ahead and to either side. Early on the fourth day he selected scouts who knew the country and rode strong horses; he sent them on long sweeps to the east and the southwest, to report to him at a temporary camp ahead. Considering that a few of his men had their women along, that he wanted to keep his party together, make one good strike, and head back north, it seemed necessary to know what was happening in the country. That afternoon they approached the settlements of the Tehanos. Excitement and eagerness showed increasingly in the manner of the younger men. Satanta made a temporary camp, then rode on a few miles with Big Tree, a medicine man named Mamanti, and a half dozen others to a conical hill with sandstone outcrops, a good lookout position. The sun was going down as they dismounted and climbed the hill.

They stood a moment looking for signs of life. A half mile below them ran an ill-kept road, which wound away to the east over an oak-studded hill and to the west into the timber along a small creek. Satanta explained to Big Tree, "This trail was made many years ago by the trader, the one who hauled the rations at the Medicine Lodge council—Butterfield."

He wanted the young chief to learn and remember as much as possible about the lay of the country. Big Tree had been in the area before, but was good-natured about being told things he might already know. Some dozen miles to the south rose hills, blue in the dying light. Satanta said, "Down there through those hills runs a river. They call it in Spanish Los Brazos de Dios."

He pointed west. "On one fork of the river, a day's ride from here, the Penatuhka Comanches had a place to live called by the same white-man's name you heard the agent say, reservation."

Big Tree repeated the strange words after him. Satanta went on. "Back this way, much nearer, the white soldiers had a village called Belknap. That place proves that the whites can be held up and turned back. Once they had big lodges built of red and yellow sandstone, but now the stones are fallen and scattered."

He turned to Mamanti. "Say! didn't you kill those black white men near here? What was that one's name? Britt Johnson!"

About three moons earlier Mamanti had led a small raiding party to this area, and they had killed four Negro men only a couple of miles west on the road they could now see. Mamanti retold the story about the tough fight the men had put up and how one had almost refused to die even though he had arrows sticking in him from every direction. In fact, with his nose and ears cut off and his bowels cut open, that one would not admit that he was dead, but had shown the nerve to pull out a fistful of Kiowa warrior's hair. The scalps of the Negroes were not valuable, of course, because of the short hair, but they had been elated to find that they knew the tough one of their victims. He was a troublesome black Tehano named Britt Johnson, who had the bad habit of coming alone into Indian camps, haggling, threatening, offering inadequate ransom for captives, stealing back captives. He would not cause any more trouble.

When Mamanti had finished the story they noted that it had grown dark. Big Tree pointed to the west and muttered an exclamation. Away on the horizon thunderheads had evidently risen. They could see lightning winking erratically, but the clouds were too far away for them to hear the thunder. They watched it a moment. Being sensitive to the earth, the plants, the dry climate, they were interested in the weather beyond the practical consequences of a possible rain.

Satanta said that he would prefer that it hold off. They might need to stay in this area two or three days before a suitable target could be located. Mamanti offered an impromptu prophecy: He did not think it would rain till their business was concluded. They climbed back down the hill to their horses and returned to the temporary camp.

CHAPTER TWO

THE ARMY

In that same month of May 1871, as Satanta and his warriors rode toward a point on the Butterfield Trail, a small United States military party moved toward the same place, coming from the south, skirting the western frontier of Texas. Their camping gear was carried in covered wagons. Four officers rode in a Daugherty ambulance. These vehicles were escorted by seventeen mounted Negro soldiers of the 10th Infantry, smart in appearance and proud of their present duty.

The country through which they passed was green, as it always is in springtime, but not lush. The few scattered settlers they had spoken to since leaving San Antonio had said that it had hardly rained at all this year and they needed it badly. The open countryside showed little cultivation, so that the land, as the small caravan came upon a rise, appeared vast, endless, empty. They had seen a few longhorned cattle, wild as deer, bounding away so fast that they could not even tell whether the creatures were branded. The road, a winding pair of wagon tracks, was rutted at places where it led up or down hill, and often the teamsters pulled out to one side to find easier going.

The four officers jouncing in the ambulance were an unusual

group for this part of the country. The two lower-ranking men wore the insignia of colonels and were probably lucky to have retained that much rank in an army which six years before had numbered its men in the millions and now had dwindled to thousands.

The third man, Brigadier General Randolph Marcy, now held the position of Inspector General of the Army. Nearly sixty years old, he had graying hair, a flowing mustache, a soldierly bearing, and, on occasion, a stern, reserved expression, all of which qualities were assets in his official position. But men who traveled with him or hunted or fished or explored with him knew him for something different. He was a great teller of jokes and stories, some from his own broad experience, and he loved to raise the glass of good fellowship. He had been in the army forever, it seemed. At one time, well back before the Civil War, life in the service had been hard, with low pay and long separations from his wife and family, but now, thirty-nine years after his graduation from West Point, the army fitted him as comfortably as an old shoe.

Marcy had a famous son-in-law, George B. McClellan, twice head of the Union army and once unsuccessful candidate for President. During the war, with its ups and downs, the "Thanks of Congress" had been given through joint resolutions to fifteen distinguished fighting officers, men like Grant and Sherman and Banks and Burnside and Meade and Sheridan. The name of Marcy's son-in-law, McClellan, was conspicuous for its absence on a roster of these resolutions. Marcy's name was also absent, but not at all conspicuously, for he was not a fighting man; and yet, in a shrinking army where officers were dropping four notches in rank he kept his star. An old career sergeant might have explained it thus: Wars come and wars go, but the army goes on forever. Marcy knew everyone, had been everywhere, knew all the channels and red tape, had written *Prairie Traveller*, a semi-official guidebook sponsored by the army, and *Thirty Years of Army Life on the Border.* In fact, he had explored and mapped parts of northwest Texas into which the small military party was now moving and had laid out the general course of the Butterfield Stage Line over which it was traveling.

The fourth officer in the ambulance was William Tecumseh Sherman, who had become General in Chief of the army two years before. As for the "Thanks of Congress" resolutions, he was the only soldier who had been twice so honored. His country had also lifted him above any petty intrigue of the army by making him a full general. He was held in considerable awe among army people on account of his rank and reputation. Such a flashy general as George Custer, for example, was now a lieutenant colonel; Sherman was a four-star general.

Someone in the army hierarchy was worried about the General in Chief's safety on this present trip. Whoever it was, probably the commander of the Department of Texas with headquarters in San Antonio, was not so confident of the security of the frontier as he had been reporting. It was one thing to risk the lives of a few settlers, another thing to let the biggest general in the country travel that route with only seventeen black soldiers to guard him. The route—through Fort Concho, Fort Griffin, abandoned Fort Belknap, Fort Richardson, and Fort Sill in the Kiowa-Comanche Reservation—would require some eighteen days of travel over the plains wilderness. The thought of William Tecumseh Sherman's lying in that desert with his hair missing was untenable. Arrangements had been made that he be guarded as much as possible, unofficially, without written orders, and without the great general's knowledge.

Sherman was an ugly man, wiry of build, with a long neck. His reddish hair always seemed disarranged and his stubble of beard did not conceal the wrinkles in his face. His eyes burned intensely and his features moved expressively as he talked. He was volatile, with much nervous energy, and he frequently folded or unfolded maps, asked questions, stuck his head out of the ambulance to study the terrain, made blunt comments. He was on a serious mission—to determine in his own mind whether the southwestern frontier was under any serious threat from Indian raiding, to find out as near the grass roots as possible, from men in the scattered posts, from settlers, anywhere he could, what was going on. Reports were contradictory, some certainly exaggerated, all of them filtered through channels. He wanted to know what the hell the country looked like, how the people lived, what they said, maybe even what the Indians said. Something you could put your finger on.

For two years complaints had come to Washington; typical of these was one from a small-town doctor who lived in the village of Weatherford, which lay some thirty miles west of the village of Fort Worth. It had come in January of this year.

Dear Sir.

As I live far off in the wilds of Texas you will be surprised to receive a letter from a stranger from these parts. I therefore write in behalf of our suffering frontier. Can there be nothing done for us? There have been no less than nine persons killed and scalped in the past three weeks in this vicinity, which can be verified by Genl. Oakes of Fort Richardson. We have applied to the military for assistance, and they have rendered all in their power, but are powerless. The Indians are kept at Fort Sill, some one hundred miles from here, and they come down and do their stealing and killing before the soldiers can come up. The pursuit is useless. We see our horses at Fort Sill that have not been stolen from us more than ten days, but it is impossible to get them. I would suggest to the government the only way to stop these Indians from depredating on us is to take their horses from them and suffer none to have any, and never let any leave the reservation without an escort, and those that will not come in and submit to the government to be considered hostile and so dealt with, then we will have peace. They have stolen millions of dollars worth of property in the last four or five years, and near one thousand persons murdered. The Indians that depredate on us are the Comanche, Kiowa, Cheyennes and Wacos. For God's sake see if anything can be done for us. Lay it before the government and ask all who sympathize with suffering humanity to come to our assistance. I have written quite a long letter, but hope you will give it a perusal at your leisure, and think of us in the far off West. Hoping to be excused for this long letter, I remain your most obedient servant.

I. P. Vollintine

That letter, while not as passionate as some appeals, suggested the main elements in the situation. Sherman hardly knew whether to be angry at the reputed ineffectiveness of the army, or affirm it and curse the soft-headed political arrangement which gave Quaker Indian agents all the authority in dealing with Indians up on the Fort Sill Reservation.

He had deep-seated reasons, hardly conscious, for wanting to make a fair evaluation of the facts and do justice to the people of this state. There were places in the South where he could not go, at least not without feeling silent hatred as stifling as the smoke of powder on a battlefield. In Georgia he was equated with Satan. It was said that in places in North Carolina people became sick upon hearing his name. Away back in that time before the war, it seemed a hundred years, he had served as superintendent of a military academy at Alexandria, Louisiana, for some twelve years and had developed a genuine affection for the South. Then in four years of war he had earned the reputation as the man who destroyed it.

It was not a feeling of guilt, nor particularly a desire to gain the love of the people he had fought. They could go to hell if they did not want to understand. Rather it was his conviction that two principles must go together: crushing war and magnanimity. That the second justifies the first. That if you cannot be kind to your prostrate foe, the question is raised whether you were fighting for an ideal or for some strange blood lust. These thoughts had become crystallized around a memory of a conference between himself and two other men six years before. Though he did not analyze himself usually, the vividness of the memory undoubtedly rested upon the fact that one of the men had become America's greatest martyr two weeks after the meeting.

The southern army had made its last major offensive thrust against the Union lines near Petersburg, Virginia, and General Grant had thrown it back in a great victory. President Lincoln had come down to walk over the battlefield and grieve silently over the dead and wounded. He, Sherman, had come up from North Carolina to meet them over headquarters campfires at City Point, behind the lines. His first impression was how much the President had aged, how much the burden of the war showed in that thin, bony face.

They found a curious unanimity—Grant, matter-of-fact, somehow like a bulldog; Lincoln, the brooding philosopher; and himself. The basis of the feeling had not needed explanation. The President had searched for generals who were willing to commit themselves aggressively to a cruel war of attrition, so that a lesser military power should not defeat a greater, and he had found them. The victories of Grant and Sherman had made possible his election to a second term. They had received much opposition, but had been proved right insofar as winning the war. None of that did they gloat over or even talk about; it was an unspoken bond. The President wanted to talk to them about what would come afterward, about watching carefully for white flags and about letting southern soldiers take their horses home to plow with. A way had to be found to make a union worthy of the blood shed to preserve it. Vindictiveness, reprisal, revenge would spoil the victory they were about to achieve. As the man talked, his lean face somber in the light of army lanterns, it was clear that he had meant his words: "With malice toward none; with charity toward all. . . ."

The man had been dead of an assassin's bullet not many days later. Now, much bitterness later, the other man at that meeting was in the White House. Sherman did not allow himself to be sentimental, but there are some things one does not forget. He refused to feel any responsibility for anything he could not control. Still he had felt elation a few days before when he arrived in San Antonio and the German Club had arranged a dinner in his honor. The idea had occurred to him—that Texas is in a sense a key to the good will of the South, because this state with its western frontier has all the same concerns as the nation at large.

He had no intention of being taken for a fool. There could be at least two reasons why the settlers might want more soldiers on this frontier line. On the one hand, maybe they had an Indian problem and needed the protection. On the other hand, maybe they wanted the contracts for building barracks and military roads and for supplying hay and wood, to say nothing of having their country improved at federal expense. Four days northwest of San Antonio the party had come to a spring of water which a fellow had enclosed with a fence, claiming that the land was his and the water was for sale. They had gone in and taken what they needed, of course, without paying, and the fellow could hardly do anything about it in the face of seventeen soldiers. Sherman did not enjoy acting high-handedly, but he did not intend to be taken for a fool.

He could not make up his mind what he thought about this great empty land. It was dusty and windy and damnably like a desert for this time of year. Marcy assured him that it ordinarily looked greener in the middle of May, but farther west toward the Pecos River or to the north along the breaks of the Wichita it *was* a desert in July and August.

They were in good buffalo country. Marcy obviously was itching to do some hunting, but they were not traveling for sport. They were averaging thirty to forty miles a day. Marcy was religiously keeping a journal, noting the mileage covered, the type of countryside passed over, whatever occurred to him.

At Fort Concho, Sherman wrote back to General J.J. Reynolds, commander of the Department of Texas, at San Antonio: "I hear of small parties of Indians stealing horses by night, but up to this point the people manifest no fears or apprehensions, for they expose women and children singly on the road and in cabins far off from others, as though they were in Illinois. Of course I have heard other stories, but actions are more significant than words."

At this fort it happened, or at least it was presented as coincidence, that Captain Clarence Manck with part of his B Company of the 4th Cavalry got ready to travel north at exactly the same time and along the same road as the Sherman party. Manck had orders to change stations from Fort Concho to Fort Richardson. The two parties set out together.

North of Fort Concho they camped one night each at two pre-war forts, now in ruins, and one night at a mountain pass called Buffalo Gap between these forts. At the first fort were stationed a corporal and three men; at the mountain pass, a sergeant and seven men; at the second old fort, another sergeant and seven men. The men said that they were not afraid of Indians, but did not seem as confident as they might have been. They had each a hundred rounds of ammunition, for which they were required to strictly account. Sherman made a note to suggest to Reynolds that the men be given extra ammunition and encouraged to supply themselves with game; maybe that would improve their spirits.

At this third camp out from Concho, Sherman became aware that Captain Manck and his men seemed to have glued themselves to his own party, seemed to be presuming that they were supposed to travel together. Sherman asked him where the rest of his company was. It was already at Fort Richardson. When did that detachment obey their orders and proceed to Richardson? About ten or twelve days ago. And what was the captain doing waiting at Concho? They had to get ready. Sherman exploded. He did not know what the captain thought he was doing or what the captain's superiors thought he was doing, but he, Sherman, was damned well going to determine the conditions of his own trip and if he needed escort he would certainly give orders to that effect. Furthermore, he wanted the captain and his men out of his sight at once; he didn't want to see them hanging around; they had better get on about their legitimate business and cease this nonsense. The officer and his cavalrymen disappeared.

On May 14 the General in Chief's party reached Fort Griffin, a post on a hill overlooking the Clear Fork of the Brazos. It was well garrisoned, though still under construction. From here Sherman wrote back to General Reynolds about a mail wagon which made the trip three times a week from Fort Richardson to abandoned Fort Belknap, down to Fort Griffin, and on to Concho. He observed: "Few or no passengers avail themselves of this stage or light wagon, but it seems to make regular trips and I do not hear of it having been attacked. . . . I have seen not a trace of an Indian thus far and only hear the stories of people which indicate that whatever Indians there be, only

R. E. LEE IN TEXAS

come to Texas to steal horses, and that whilst they approach the frontier in parties of 30 or 40 they invariably scatter to steal and to escape. As against these, troops are almost useless, and the people within a hundred miles of the frontier ought to take precautions such as all people do against all sort of thieves. After I get to Fort Sill I will endeavor to form some definite opinion whether these thieves come from that quarter or whether they come from the Staked Plains."

They rested a day at Fort Griffin, as much as Sherman ever rested. He inspected and asked questions and wrote letters and spent some time along with Marcy and the two aides-de-camp enjoying the hospitality of commanding officer Colonel William Wood and the officers of the post. The inspector general, always at home among a group of men, almost a social buffer for Sherman, was a hero here. In 1854, when this country had been a blank space on maps, he had located two Indian reservations, one just up the Clear Fork a few miles for the Penatuhka Comanches, the other thirty miles east for the so-called Wichita and Related Tribes. He had located an army post, Camp Cooper, about eight miles up the Clear Fork from here, and a more important post, Fort Belknap, some thirty-five miles to the northeast. The reservation experiment had not worked, and both posts had fallen to ruins, but Marcy enjoyed an old-timer's status among those interested in the history of the region.

One of the officers at Fort Griffin, an amateur historian, told some facts and speculation which were, to him at least, a fascinating sidelight on the past of the area. To that small, little-known wilderness outpost eight miles upstream, Camp Cooper, in 1856 had come Lieutenant Colonel Robert E. Lee with the 2nd Cavalry. Some war theorists credited Lee with knowing a lot about the strengths and weaknesses and foibles of northern as well as southern commanders. Well, the amateur historian said, who did Lee have under him out there at Camp Cooper, mind you, living mostly in dusty tents among the rattlesnakes and cactus at the end of the world? George Thomas, George Stoneman, I.N. Palmer, Kenner Garrard, Hood, Hardee, Fitzhugh Lee, Van Dorn, E. Kirby Smith. Nine men under him who would be major-generals in just a few years.

Sherman was amused, but showed no interest. He could have made some comments. But now officer's rank was a touchy subject and he could hardly open his mouth without it sounding like official policy.

He discovered here at Griffin, as he had found farther south, a bothersome situation: None of these west Texas posts were on land owned or leased by the federal government. It went back to some damnable provision in a treaty when Texas became a state; she had to take care of her own public lands and her own public debts. Of course, no one in the War Department had ever worried about the ownership of land beyond the frontier; it belonged to the United States. Here, it seemed, it belonged to private citizens who had obtained it legally through the state land office. The first implication was that the army, after spending big sums on building, might be held up for bigger sums to obtain the land on which the improvements sat. He would have been furious about it except for further possible implications. What else had the government neglected, out of carelessness rather than ill will? He had been a behind-the-scenes power in the 1867 Medicine Lodge peace treaty, which was supposed to settle for good and all the Indian problem on the south plains. The Kiowas and Comanches had been given the right to hunt off their reservations into the panhandle of Texas. It had not struck him till now that Texas should have been represented at that council, though perhaps it would have been impossible only two years after the War of the Rebellion. Kansas had been well represented, he recalled, though she had no legal claim on the regulation of her own public lands. In fact, there had been something in the report—he had not been present at the council—about Indian captives taken in Texas, and evidently nothing had been done about it. It could be that some people of this state had a valid complaint of neglect. That did not mean, of course, that there was an Indian problem of any consequence.

One thing occurred to him when he vowed to himself that he would be nobody's fool in permitting settlers to get rich from army appropriations. Although this Butterfield Trail had been the first stage and mail route across the continent there was no railroad or telegraph within hundreds of miles and even the public roads were scandalous. That's what war gets you, especially if you lose. Or maybe, as some southerners claimed, that was part of what caused the war.

It happened that at this post a certain Captain Joseph Kevin with two companies of the 6th Cavalry had orders to change stations and would be going all the way to Sill at the same time and along the same roads as General Sherman's party. Sherman became as blunt and abrupt as he had been with Captain Manck; he let Colonel Wood and Captain Kevin both know it, short and sweet. This gratuitous, solicitous bull was unacceptable. He'd better not hear or see any more about it.

Early on the morning of May 16, Sherman's party went down the long ramp off government hill, through the unsightly collection of tents and shacks where the Tonkawa scouts and army hangers-on lived, thence across the Clear Fork bridge toward old Fort Belknap. They began to discuss whether it would be difficult to go by the site of Camp Cooper. Marcy thought not. Sherman gave orders and they pulled out of the road and headed west across the rolling country. He wanted it understood that he did not care whether Lee or Attila the

Hun had been stationed at the place; he was concerned about the line of forts from Concho up to Sill in Indian Territory. The line was not straight. He might order some new locations; it seemed reasonable to go west far enough to look down upon the site of the old camp.

If the road had seemed bad, the way out of the road was nearly impossible. They skirted a draw more than a mile before finding a bumpy crossing. The driver wound this way and that, avoiding rocky ground, patches of prickly pear, gullies. They could hardly get lost as long as they could occasionally see the green course of the Clear Fork out to their left. Finally they came out on a ridge from which Marcy pointed out the location, two or three miles distant, where Moss Creek emptied into the river. The route ahead looked as poor as ever, and Sherman had seen enough.

They turned north. Somewhere a road had run from Cooper to Belknap. As they bounced along there was much consultation of maps and some sarcastic comment by Sherman that the maps did not seem to have much relationship to the terrain. The road for which they searched had probably not been repaired in ten years, and since it appeared on the map to cross Elm Creek in two places, a strong doubt arose whether it would be passable. Their only reliable course seemed to lie in trying to retrace their tracks; so much of the day would be gone that they would probably find it necessary to return to Fort Griffin for the night and admit that they had been lost. Marcy, the only member of the party who had been in the country before, confessed with good humor and some embarrassment that he was proving a poor guide.

Luck seemed to be with them, however, for they spotted a man on horseback, and the mounted escort brought him to the ambulance. He said his name was Howsley and he had some cattle up this way. He agreed to guide them east, and in two or three hours had put them back on the main Belknap road. Sherman paid the man ten dollars.

By late afternoon they were fording the Brazos proper. They pulled up the bluff banks and into the desolate town and fort of Belknap, both of which were falling to ruins, though it appeared that two or three families still lived in the town.

The fort buildings of red and yellow sandstone were toppling into piles. The rockwork of two or three buildings seemed intact but their doors and window frames were gone and the roofs had holes in them. Sand had blown in on the rotting floors, where piles of rubble seemed to furnish homes for rats and scorpions. They found a relatively bare area on the old parade ground suitable for a campsite. While the men were pitching the tents Sherman walked with one of the colonels over into the abandoned town toward what seemed to be a general store.

The town buildings, of logs and stone and weathered splitting planks, were in the same dilapidated shape as those of the fort. Here and there was a garden plot or a stock pen fenced with split rails, with weeds grown up waist high inside.

The store appeared to be closed, but two men came from an alley, as if they had been spying on the military party. One of them asked, "You all want some supplies or anything?" They were grim-faced, nervous men.

Sherman told him no, then began to ask questions, casually, about their water supply and the regularity of mail service and the Indian problem. They did not know who he was.

"Can't get no work done," one of them said. "Can't do nothing but stay on the watch day and night. Can't keep no horses."

"I came here to stay," the other said. "They ain't running me out."

The first one said, "Since Nigger Britt and his pals lost theirn three, four months ago my old lady is driving me crazy to get out."

The other repeated, "I come here to stay, myself. I come here to stay."

Strangely, they did not seem to be arguing or appealing, but mentioning things that were well known. Behind their unexplained words lay an assumption that many things had happened, unbearable things, outrages, that had been often reported and were well understood. Sherman thought, could it be possible that these people had been under Indian attack during the war and had been unable to make credible contact with any competent authority in the confusion since the war's end? That would be a total of ten years! He knew how inefficient lines of communication could be; he already knew more about General Reynolds' line of forts than that officer would ever know sitting in San Antonio, and he intended to suggest to that gentleman that he make this same tour of his department. Ten years! But that was impossible. He laid the strange words of the two men to a kind of soured disposition they must have gotten from living so far from civilization.

He and the colonel walked back to see whether supper was ready. They ate in the last light of day after the sun went down. When it was dark, the barely visible hulks of empty buildings lent a sense of loneliness to the parade ground.

"Look," Marcy said, an almost boyish eagerness in his voice as he pointed toward the western sky. "They used to say in this country that rain always comes from the west in the springtime."

Evidently on the western horizon a bank of thunderclouds was rising. Lightning winked in them erratically, like the flashing of distant artillery.

. . .

Captain Clarence Manck had been driven well-nigh crazy that day, chasing all over the country, trying to keep up with the stubborn old fool and not be seen. He did not know how he got into such messes—with definite unwritten orders to do so and so and definite unwritten orders not to do it. That coward Kevin was hanging back at Griffin with two whole companies, under the same impossible orders, and he had damned well better get out here tomorrow and help. How sharper than a serpent's tooth is the ire of a four-star general!

CHAPTER THREE

THE FREIGHTERS

A third party of men was about to head for the same place as Chief Satanta's raiders and General Sherman's inspection group.

The town of Weatherford, forty miles southeast of Fort Richardson, centered on a courthouse square, and the principal business houses faced the county building on four sides across wide streets. The stores, built of yellow pine lumber, were dusted over with the pulverized red clay raised by horses' hooves and iron-tired wheels. The town boasted two hotels, offices of attorneys-at-law, and the banking firm of Couts and Fain, in addition to a blacksmith shop, livery stables, general stores, a stagecoach stand, and a saddlery in which were made saddles with high horns and double girths to supply the frontier trade. The region round about had good farm land with sand or loamy soils, suitable for fruits and grain and garden truck, though watermelons would not make this spring for lack of moisture. Weatherford had more solid citizens than many a western town, fewer saloons, and one of the finest Methodist church buildings west of the Mississippi, a stone structure with a high square bell tower.

At the edge of town sprawled a collection of barns, corrals, and parked wagons called "Captain Warren's Bachelor Roost," a place which added nothing to the dignity of the town—a rough lot of men hung out there and sometimes loud profanity could be heard—but it was tolerated by the good citizens because it was an important commercial enterprise. Here was based the firm of Warren and DuBose, Freighters. The manager, Henry Warren, had come from New York not many years before, but was hardly counted a carpetbagger, for he had come to the state with the same motives as many another, to seek his fortune in the West. An educated and congenial man, he had come first to El Paso, from where the voters elected him to the legislature in 1866, but he had found the transportation so poor between that place and Austin that he had not reached the state capital until the legislature had adjourned. Probably that experience had suggested to him the need for better transportation and he had located finally in Weatherford as a minor gateway to the West. He had talked the bankers Couts and Fain out of a substantial loan. Already he gave the impression of a man of influence and means.

On May 16 he supervised the final preparations of a wagon-train which would haul a load of shelled and sacked corn out to Fort Griffin, via Jacksboro and Belknap. In the late afternoon he left any further arrangements to his wagonmaster, Nathan Long, a grizzled old frontiersman who knew all there was to know about wagons and mules.

That day Long's teamsters had spent some time removing hoop-metal chinks from between the rims and felloes of wagon wheels, taking the rims to the smithy to have them shrunk, and remounting them. It was a hard three-day haul to Griffin and no good place for a breakdown. Ten wagons had been loaded for the trip, three six-mule rigs and seven lighter four-mule rigs. They made other minor wagon and harness repairs and lashed the canvas tight over the bows. About sundown Nate Long gathered them, the ten mule skinners and one nightwatchman, for a final conference before an early departure the next morning.

One teamster, Tom Brazeal, who had bossed some wagontrains for Warren, observed with amusement how Nate handled the men, bluntly, gruffly, and effectively. One of them said, "Hey, Nate. Have we got to listen to another one of your sermons?"

"You mighty right!" Nate said. "You damned tootin'! Get over here! All right, you fellers cut out the mumbling. This ain't no quilting bee. I want to get this over, so's I can get my God-damned beauty sleep."

Brazeal gathered with the rest of them. Most of the men were grinning at Nate.

"Guns!" the old man said. "I done told every man here at least twice and I'm telling you again. They ain't no exceptions. Every man has got to have a long gun that will reach out yonder and a hand gun that will throw out the lead. And shells! Plenty of shells! Carry your damned artillery where you can put your hand on it."

One of them interrupted. "Say, Nate, is half a box of 44's enough?"

"Hell, I ain't counting your shells for you! I ain't checking your mess gear! I ain't seeing if you got coal oil in your lantern! I ain't your mammy! I tell you one thing: They ain't enough Injuns in the country to take us if we get forted up right and plenty of shells. You damned sure can't buy any out yonder on the prairie.

"I don't know if all you men have drove for me or what kind of fool ideas you might have about forting up wagons. I'm fixing to tell you, and if you don't want to listen to it again, that's just your hard luck.

"When I holler to Tom Brazeal, 'Circle 'em!' he's going to turn out the lead wagon. I aim for you to whip up and foller. By God, with the heavy rigs in front you can keep up and you better do it, if you want to keep your hair. Turn where the wagon right in front of you turns, not some place else; you going to mess it up. Quick as Tom catches the end wagon, you watch him, and everybody turn in. Bring them in tight. I want them forty-some-odd Missouri mules all trying to stand on the same spot, staring each other in the eyeballs."

It was growing dark. The wagonmaster stood there glaring at them, as if daring them to ask some silly question. "That's all," he said. "Five o'clock! On the money. Any man shows up drunk, I'll skin him alive."

The men began to saunter off and Brazeal remained behind to discuss with the old man whether there might be any small freight or mail messages to be picked up in town. Nate was in favor of letting Warren take care of any such business. They stood silently a moment pondering whether any detail remained to be done. The parked wagons looked ghostlike, their gray canopies indistinct hulks in the darkness. Brazeal's attention was drawn to the night sky in the west. "Is that lightning?"

They walked up past the wagons so that their vision would not be disturbed by the small light coming from the window of the office shack. They could see a glow rising to the sky from below the far western horizon, as dim and changing as the flame of a candle blown in the wind.

"We might get some rain on this trip," Brazeal said.

Nate Long scratched his gray head, then repeated or perhaps coined an aphorism: "Threaten twice, rain once, they say."

CHAPTER FOUR

ATTACK

When Satanta, Big Tree, and the others who had gone on the short scout ahead returned to the temporary camp after dark they found the warriors eating jerky and pemmican, renewing their war paint, and lounging around small fires they had built in the bed of a dry wash. Shortly, two of the scouts who had been sent on the day-long search to the west came in on sweat-soaked horses. They brought Satanta a strange report.

Down to the southwest, traveling in this direction, was a small wagontrain, including an army ambulance. Seventeen black soldiers were with it, and in the ambulance rode four white officers. But that was not the strange part. Another group of soldiers, who were white, were following the first party and spying on them. The first group had camped at the ruins of the stone fort, and the second had camped a mile away by the river, keeping an eye on the first.

Satanta questioned his men. Did the first party do any scouting? Not at all. Did they seem ignorant of the second group? Completely. Did the second group have any good opportunity to attack the first? It seemed that they did. Did the first group carry any wagon guns? Apparently not. Could it be a trap, with the first group a decoy? Possibly. Satanta talked about it with his senior warriors over a pipe, then pondered it before he slept. His first reaction had been a surge of hope that he was getting evidence of factionalism among the soldiers here, maybe even would witness an armed clash between them. It had been one of his greatest concerns during the past few years, to find a way to more unity for south-plains Indians or toward less unity for the whites and their black allies. But this situation made no sense. They should use caution. He sent scouts out into the night on fresh horses, then slept.

In the dim light before sunrise they awoke. Now they could see a bank of clouds far in the west but no immediate threat of rain. They rode their horses to a spring for water and moved south.

There was no dew on the grass, but the May air was cool as the sun rose. Indian-blanket flowers bloomed in broad patches on the earth in rusty tones of red and brown and yellow, bright on the morning landscape. Satanta could feel the sense of anticipation in his men, and he discussed with those who rode near him the need for patience and caution, and assured them, too, that they would see action in due course. He had decided that the conical hill would be his immediate headquarters because below it the post oaks and blackjack trees opened out into a large prairie, and the lookout spot commanded long stretches of the white-man's road. He gave careful directions for the keeping of their horses on the north side of the hill where they would have a degree of concealment and climbed to the top of the prominence with as many braves as could reasonably be stationed there.

Below them they saw no movement. The only signs of man were the winding road, and a mile to the southwest, the gray, decaying building of an abandoned stage station, half hidden in trees along the small creek. They settled into their patient vigil.

The sun burned straight overhead when the small wagontrain came from the southwest with its escort of seventeen black soldiers. It was as Satanta's scouts had described it. The ambulance looked tiny in the distance. The hooves of the trotting horses and mules raised a film of dust from the bare road. No trace could be seen of the other party, which was supposed to be watching them. Perhaps they were traveling far behind or farther south. The mystery of it was as dark as ever. Satanta heard the buzz of talk proceed down the north slopes of the hill until all his men had heard, then silence. He glanced at the men who lay on their bellies near him, fingered his brass bugle, and studied the small caravan. Once, down in Mexico many years before, near the city of Durango, where the Kiowas had found great sport in personal combat with soldiers, he had approached a Mexican, spear at the ready; but his opponent had cast a lariat and caught him, jerked him from his saddle, and dragged him on the ground. It required the help of another warrior to escape. Several Mexicans had paid for that surprise in later years, and Satanta had never allowed himself to be surprised in any fight since. He knew that those around him now were waiting for a decision. He turned to them and deliberately shook his head. They would wait for a better target.

He heard the buzz of talk again proceed through the men down the hill to the bottom. Those down there, particularly the younger ones, would not be pleased. It had been a long morning for them. But Chief Tsatangya with his stern, sad eyes, would be exerting his powerful, unspoken influence upon them. Having an undisputed choice of any vantage point he desired, he had elected not to climb the hill. The last time Satanta had seen him the old man had been sitting patiently on a rock.

They watched the small caravan an hour as it dipped below

the swells of open prairie, to reappear farther on. Had the prophet Mamanti been able to foretell certain events in the future, possibly Satanta would have raised the bugle and blown the charge. The difference between the shake of his head and raising the horn to his lips would be vast in consequence to the Kiowa people and all the warrior people of the plains; and the difference would be poignantly crucial to Satanta in person, for in the character, temperament, and attitudes of General William Tecumseh Sherman, bouncing in the ambulance, lay his own fate. That one man would determine the conditions of his life for the next seven years and even determine the place of his death.

A story which can only be described as apocryphal tells that a Negro in Sherman's escort called out in jest as they crossed the open country named Salt Creek Prairie, "I see an Indian!" and they all laughed, even the general.

Describing that day's journey of May 17 in a letter the following morning Sherman would write: "The road is across rather rough country and water is very scarce. Of course we saw no Indians. . . ."

But Inspector General Marcy was not interpreting the situation in the same way. He would describe the day in his journal thus:

> May 17—Left Belknap at 6 a.m. and traveled over a timbered section for about ten miles to Salt Creek where we emerged into a more open prairie country, interspersed with timber which lasted to within eight miles of Fort Richardson. . . .
>
> The remains of several ranches were observed today, the occupants of which have been either killed or driven off to the more dense settlements by the Indians. Indeed this rich and beautiful section does not contain to-day so many white people as it did when I visited it eighteen years ago, and if the Indian

marauders are not punished, the whole country seems to be in a fair way of becoming totally depopulated. . . .

At Fort Richardson the most excited person in anticipation of the visit of General Sherman was Second Lieutenant Robert Goldthwaite Carter, twenty-six years old. He was the post adjutant and the post eager-beaver, a young man of great friendliness and gullibility.

He had joined the service from Maine during the great war, served as a private in the Army of the Potomac, and had been mustered out in the fall of 1864, but, in spite of the hardships he had suffered, ever hopeful, fascinated by the pomp and drama which he imagined surrounded the officers of the army, he immediately began to try to get into West Point. In July 1865 they had taken him. He had worked twice as hard as anyone else, and in June 1870 they had given him his beautiful gold bars. Not long afterward he had found himself in the 4th Cavalry on the Texas frontier.

The first lieutenants and captains and majors, who were not old, but thought they were when they looked at Carter, had made life busy for him. They told him great lies about their Tonkawa Indian scouts having eaten a second lieutenant. They maneuvered to have him assigned mounts which had never been broken of bad habits. They tried to get him to order left-handed monkey wrenches and striped paint from the quartermaster, but he knew better than that, having been a plebe at the Point. He knew that they were without conscience in pestering him, but liked them anyway, for they were all heroic Indian fighters, whereas he was only a post adjutant, a pencil pusher. They knew that he was not stupid, but could not help themselves because of his interminable good nature and enthusiasm. The Fort Richardson C.O., Colonel Ranald Mackenzie, and one or two other senior officers stayed out of it.

On May 17 Carter had legitimate instructions to take fifteen men along the road west, meet the General in Chief of the army, welcome him, and escort him back to the post. As he prepared for this unusual duty he got much advice from his fellow officers.

"This is your big opportunity, Carter," they said. "You impress Sherman and your career is made."

"You don't know Sherman, do you, Carter?"

"No."

"All spit and polish. If you've got one fly speck on your boot he'll notice it. May have you cashiered right out of the service. I remember one time old Bill Sherman told me. . . ."

Carter spent half of the morning improving his personal gear, checking the horses and saddles, cautioning the fifteen men. Everything seemed on schedule until one of his brother officers asked, "Have you selected the gun crew to fire the cannon salute yet?"

"The cannon salute?"

"Carter, don't tell me. . . . Listen, this man is a four-star general! There's only three: Washington, Grant, Sherman. What would you do if George Washington arrived at this post? Wave and say, 'Hi, George'?"

"But the colonel didn't say anything. . . ."

"Are you in charge of the welcoming detail or not? Lieutenant, you are an officer in the U.S. Army now. You are expected to know protocol, take initiative, take responsibility, make decisions. You may grin like this is a joke, but if I were you I'd run out one of the field pieces onto the parade ground, swab it out, polish it up, and find me a smart crew who could do it up brown. This is the 4th Cavalry, Carter! The U.S. 4th Cavalry!"

When one of the more serious-minded majors found Carter, the lieutenant was going among the enlisted men trying to discover which of them had ever been in the field artillery and felt qualified to fire a cannon salute to a four-star general. The major muttered a few well-selected words and told the young officer to mount his fifteen men and get out on the damned road west as he had been instructed.

Shortly thereafter Carter led the detail across the bridge of Lost Creek, through the edge of the village of Jacksboro, and out along the Butterfield Trail. As they raced west he recovered his usual eager demeanor. Fifteen miles from the post at an abandoned mail station called Rock Creek he met General Sherman's party.

Quite possibly it was his pink face and broad grin as he delivered his speech that saved him from a severe dressing down. "General Ranald Mackenzie sends his compliments, sir. Welcome to Fort Richardson. General Mackenzie will be honored if you will accept his quarters while you are with us. . . ."

Sherman thanked the young man and politely introduced the officers who were with him. He could not rebuke such an obviously impressed second lieutenant, but he intended to have his way about all this escort nonsense. He said in a friendly but business-like manner, "Your horses are warm, Lieutenant. Remain here and come back to the post slowly."

Carter was not intimidated. The General in Chief could do no wrong. He watched the small caravan disappear and wondered how soon it would be proper to follow it.

Captain Warren's wagontrain proceeded northwest along the rolling divide between the Brazos drainage and that of the West Fork of the Trinity, headed for Jacksboro. A shorter route to Griffin existed, but this one would put them under the protection of Fort Richardson at least for one night. Tom Brazeal, perched on the driver's seat of the lead wagon, felt thankful that he did not have to breathe the dust that rose behind him.

They passed the last ranch house in the middle of the morning and wound on over the hills among the scattered timber, through a land empty of habitation. At noon they let the mules blow a few minutes while they sat under the shade of their wagons, eating from their lunch buckets.

That afternoon the air felt as hot and dry as if they traveled in a giant oven. The sky was clear, with only a bank of clouds in the west. The mules labored, the road being more uphill than down. The beasts began to show patches of sweat and began to smell more rank, their warmth melting all the old dried odors in their hides. Behind Brazeal the other teamsters did less cursing and yelling than they had done in the early morning, though it was necessary now and again to call out to a laggard mule or pop him with a whip in order to keep the train closed up.

The clonking of the wagon timbers, the chink of harness chains, became monotonous. It would have been easy to drowse. When they came upon elevated points in the road Brazeal would scan the country for sign of Indians; the threat of an attack hung vaguely behind every thought that passed in his mind, but it was not a thing you worry about; a man could drive himself crazy if he wanted to worry.

In late afternoon they passed alongside Fort Richardson, which spread out in a curve of Lost Creek, a half mile south of Jacksboro. The army installation and the town were raw frontier outposts, their buildings filmed with dust; the creek, a thin oasis with springs in its banks and holes deep enough to bathe in. They watered the teams, filled up their kegs, and pulled out north of the post to camp.

From the town a string of saloons and houses of entertainment stretched south and along the creek bank, getting as near the Fort as possible. Nate Long not only cautioned his men against getting drunk, but also asserted that he would skin alive any teamster who got in a fight with a soldier. The saloons, however, proved not as wild as usual. A damper had closed on the military's recreation. Some big Yankee general named Sherman had come in. His tents were pitched on the creek not a hundred yards from where they had watered the mules.

That night lightning played stronger in the west. Evidently high thunderheads built up out there, only to fade as they drifted east in the dry air.

The following morning, a Thursday, May 18, they hitched up with the inevitable bustle and noise and headed west in the dawn. They did not water the mules; Nate Long expected to make Rock Creek Station, where there was a tank, before the day became hot. Some question existed whether they would make Belknap before it rained, for the clouds ahead now rose high and solid with angry black areas within them. The air seemed heavy and little wind blew.

They wound through scattered timber. The land looked bright with the low morning sun behind them. In open areas Indian-blanket flowers bloomed. In low shady places white evening primroses spread out, but they would be folding up before midday. Some wild blackberry vines crawled among patches of shinnery on the ground. Here and there beside the road grew the sensitive briar with small puffy flowers of powdery pink; when a mule's hoof brushed a tendril of the plant all of its delicate leaves would fold together as in fear.

They watered at Rock Creek Station and lumbered west. It was already a hot and muggy day. Brazeal noted that the sweat in his clothes would not dry. He felt clammy. Not a breath of wind blew. The clouds had risen higher and pale lightning hidden in them revealed their vast erratic contours. Thunder rumbled over the constant sound of the wagons. The sky behind Cox Mountain, straight ahead, looked so black that the prominence appeared light even though it was covered with dark oak trees; it stood like a giant loaf lying on the horizon.

They went over a small rocky hill, then stopped for lunch. Nate Long searched the sky anxiously as they ate and hurried them back to their wagon seats.

The road led around the north slopes of Cox Mountain, over a series of rocky spurs. The wagon wheels grated and jolted against the stones, and the mules heaved as they pulled. Here grew piles of prickly pear, blooming delicate pink blossoms, and in open places, Spanish dagger. Nate Long was running from one wagon to another like a mother hen as they traveled this difficult section of road, climbing to one wagon seat, then another. He yelled into Brazeal's ear, "It's gonna rain! Try to make it to head of Flint Creek! Camp . . . old Murphy's Station!"

As they came over the last spur of the mountain the open swells of Salt Creek Prairie lay before them. It appeared that two towering thunderclouds were going to pass north and south of them, and others lay dead ahead. A high film of cloud, slate gray, had pushed east across the sky. Now the land seemed to be bathed in unnatural light on account of the diversion of daylight in the clouds and the constant play of lightning. Low thunder came constantly, like a heavy chain dragged over a hollow log. The deathly still air was stirred by sudden small gusts that seemed to come from no direction. Brazeal saw that his mules had become nervous; they were dark with sweat.

He saw a chain of lightning flash ahead, its end striking down tentatively, searching. Trying to estimate how far away it was, he counted off seconds, five seconds to the mile, but when the sound came it was a stuttering and grumbling that went on and on and blended with the rest, so that he could not mark its start or finish. Some of the brief gusts of wind felt icy cold.

A harder wind came toward them. He could see it out ahead, drawing long invisible fingers through the open grassland. It struck a large lone mesquite tree, which suddenly came alive, jerking. It hit with surprising force, as if it meant to tear his clothes off. The mules bowed their heads into it. Features of the land, those not hidden by the veils of moisture streaming from the clouds, stood out vividly in the strange light, thrust out. Ahead to the right, a distance he could not judge, rose a conical hill with sandstone outcrops.

Then began a short, hectic time, some pounding heartbeats less than a minute, during which the grasp of his mind and the quickness of his actions meant everything to himself and the eleven other men of the train.

It began with the notes of a bugle, distant, piercing, incongruous, urgent. After that the rush of horses' hooves, not even as loud as the wind in the grass, hidden when the thunder rose, but containing a subtle rhythm that did not belong to the storm. Brazeal half stood up, not concluding, not even speculating logically, jerking his eyes ahead and to either side. Some of their precious seconds were wasted in trying to understand. He was already making the decision to whip up and pull out when he heard Nate Long screaming.

"Circle 'em, Tom! For God sakes! Injuns!"

The old man's hat was gone and his grizzled hair stood in disarray from the wind. He sprang upon the side step and clawed his way along the canvas tarp as Brazeal flailed the lines against the mules' backs, yelling, "Hyah! Hyah!"

He had handled wagons all his life, but never in such a desperate situation, and the thought surged in his mind how necessary it was to judge a circle large enough for all the wagons. Room to turn toward the center. No second try at it. He lashed at the team and looked back at the others to judge. The mules had caught the excitement and fear; they did not need urging, but were all well-nigh out of control, their heads flinging, their eyes large and white. One of his front wheels caught a joghole with a heavy jolt; the wagon lurched, then righted itself as it bounced on.

Guns cracked out there, above the rising hoofbeats. He stole one look over his right shoulder and saw them pouring from a rise of land no more than four hundred yards away. Easy rifle range. They seemed a thousand Indians. Like a nightmare.

Nate Long was over him on the left, clinging to the front bow, screaming in a voice more shrill than usual something incomprehensible. The old man began firing his Henry rifle, holding it in one hand, resting it on the wagon sheet.

Brazeal's left arm jerked from the strain of trying to turn the charging team. He bowed their six necks by brute strength.

The rear wagon was nearly straight ahead of him when he saw its off leader go down, drop as if all the beast's legs were broken. The wagon stopped in a scrambling tangle of mules and harness. You can hold off a pack of Indians if you get corralled right. Till now his reactions had followed some wild instinct guided by a reasoned plan, but at the sight he felt consternation. The yipping savages were upon them. They were going to cut off the last wagon. Now there was hell to pay.

He strained back, sawing at the lines, yelling "Whoa! Whoa! Whoa!" He had to slow them in order to turn in.

In the bits of time as he pulled against the team, he saw an action that burned into his perception. The teamster came out of the tilted wagon, running, stumbling, toward the moving wagons of his comrades and went down there in the gap before the cruel popping of guns. The first one of the horde of Indians that streamed through had lain low on his horse's shoulder, but as he approached the fallen teamster he straightened and swung his rifle, almost ceremoniously striking the man on the ground. The teamster's body jerked as the barrel struck him. Brazeal's eyes caught it clearly even as he was turning his team; the savage was a young one, exuberant, howling; slung at his back was a quiver of puma skin with the claws and mouth still on it and he carried a yellow shield with a streak of black lightning across it.

As Brazeal came in toward the center he saw that the team straight across from him had a mule down. Then he heard the lead that hit Nate Long and knocked him from the wagon. A sickening sound. He set his brake viciously.

The storm was forgotten. The smoke of burned powder hung about them in the heavy air. The Indians had split and come close by them on either side, wreaking their damage and passing on. The teamsters, trying to snatch rifles from leather boots fastened to wagon beds at the same time that they handled frightened teams, had stopped their wagons in a disorderly pattern, skewed this way and that. Some evidently had taken refuge behind the poor protection of their wagon tarps. Others were throwing sacks of corn on the ground. Four or five teams had mules dead or bloody. The animals were tangled in their harness.

The Indians circled, firing from behind their horses. Some teamsters returned the fire. Brazeal called to the still form of Nate Long and got no answer. He realized that he was firing his rifle and for the first time wondered about their supply of ammunition. He heard bullets and arrows hitting the wagons. The air was full of sound. Away out on the high ground in the direction from which the charge had come some Indian women stood, screaming, beating their palms against their mouths, making a plaintive, eerie sound. Scattered raindrops struck the dusty ground, raising the sweet scent of water on parched earth to mix with the acrid smell of powder. He had seen two Indians go down, one of whom was charging in on foot. Then he saw a teamster rise from behind a wagon wheel trying with both hands to pull an arrow from his shoulder, only to be struck in the head by a bullet and fall. He thought it was John Mullins. The sight produced a certainty in his mind. They could not defend this mess. Impossible. He began to shout to the others to find out how many were alive and to tell them that they must run for it.

Evidently they were all aware that old Nate was dead and welcomed someone telling them what to do. Running and dodging among the teams and wagons they gathered toward him. Where do you run to? Fort Richardson. The cavalry. Nineteen or twenty miles east. "We've got to get out of here," he told them. "They want the train. Maybe they'll let us go." They kept up their fire as they waited for an opening. They numbered seven men.

Someone asked, "Where are the Elliott boys?" and someone else said, "Gone! Jimmy is over yonder with a damned arrow straight in his heart!"

Some of the Indians were dismounting, moving in on foot. Brazeal judged that it was time to go. He yelled at his companions and they ran east. They made two hundred yards before they saw a dozen Indians, then perhaps a dozen more, galloping toward them. The main group still attacked the wagons.

Then began a tedious retreat. The savages kept their distance on their racing ponies, yelling taunts when the teamsters presented their guns, only to charge in viciously when the teamsters ran. One of them went down and the Indians overran him and paused long enough to take his scalp. Brazeal got hit in the foot; he scrambled on, his boot filling with blood. Two others were wounded. As they approached the haven of timber pointing out from Cox Mountain, the Indians pressed closer, knocked down another man, and overran him.

The five came into the edge of the trees, fell to their bellies, and peered back with nervous and desperate eyes. They saw what they had dared to hope. Their tormentors were turning back toward the wagontrain.

Brazeal felt sick at his stomach from running on the wounded leg, but they had to keep moving. With him were Dick Motor, Hobbs Carey, Charles Brady, and R.A. Day. Behind them they left Nate Long, Jim Elliott, Sam Elliott, M.J. Baxter, Jesse Bowman, John Mullins, and James Williams. On the slopes of the mountain the survivors were hit by the procrastinating storm. Rain fell in blowing torrents. Hail pelted them. Drenched, Tom Brazeal felt cold. They had to keep moving east. The distance ahead of them seemed impossible.

Big Tree had made first coup; a warrior named Yellow Wolf, second. The two of them, along with two Kiowa-Apaches, got the credit for cutting off the last wagon.

Or-dlee, a Comanche, dismounted and ran in afoot, dodging, trying to accomplish some daring act in front of all the others. He dropped in the wind-tossed grass, shot dead. He would be their only loss dead on the immediate field. Red Warbonnet, a subchief, was hit in the thigh. A Kiowa-Apache, Light-Haired Youngster, was knocked to the ground and was rescued by two comrades; he had a bad knee wound.

After the five whites escaped to the east, the Indians circled and approached the wagons warily. They were getting no return fire. An eager young Kiowa, Gun-Shot, with no experience, but with stories of bravery burning in his mind, wanted to dash in among the wagons. Wiser heads tried to restrain him but he would not listen. He rushed to a wagon, struck it, and claimed it. As he did so, the wagon tarp rose, and a wounded teamster shot him full in the face. The blast tore off the side of his jaw and they could see the insides of his mouth behind the blood.

The warriors had followed the lead of Gun-Shot, and now swarmed the wagons. They dragged out the one teamster still alive. They jerked the axes from their racks on the wagon beds, began to wreck wagons, slash harness, scatter corn. The fire they built at first to burn the wagon parts, but soon it took on a new function—to torture the wounded teamster. Gun-Shot had become a madman with blood streaming down his clothes. He could not live many days with his wound; he knew it and they knew it. He chained the wounded man to the back part of the running gear of a wagon and pushed him over the fire. They saw Gun-Shot's doom, that he could only demand a price, and they helped him.

The quivering flesh of Samuel Elliott, his nervous system, his consciousness, absorbed the frustration and hatred involved in guerrilla warfare. When he screamed too much the wounded youth he had shot beat out his teeth with the butt of a knife and cut out his tongue, so that he strangled on his own blood as he burned.

Satanta let his bugle rest and sat his horse and watched stoically through eyes that had seen much violence. His mind went back two years to the battlefield where the allied Cheyennes had been struck. He and the other Kiowas camped near Fort Cobb had got the news about the attack and had immediately broke camp and sent runners to establish contact with other south-plains Indians. There would be a great council which would at least provide relief supplies for the remnants of Chief Black Kettle's stricken band. While they waited for the day of the meeting he had ridden up to the Washita River to look over the battlefield where a white named Custer had struck one snowy dawn without warning. He would never forget the sight of bloated Cheyenne women and children, lying so still and cold, even the body of the peacemaker Black Kettle and his wife. Now the thought occurred to him that all the gentle people who ever lived on the earth are fallen before the fierce people. They are all gone, as perhaps they were bound to go, and only their shadows remain with people alive, hoping for a chance sometime to live again on earth.

He saw old Chief Tsatangya sitting as silently as himself. He wondered whether the sight of Texas blood eased the old man's pain over the precious son the old man had lost down here, killed in a raid. But those were airy speculations. Satanta moved in and began to give directions. Cooking gear, clothes, guns, tools would go to the man who took them, but the mules must all go to the New Mexico traders out on White River or the River of Tongues, for white-man money or guns, and no selfish claims. The object—repeating guns for each warrior who needed one.

They carried the body of Or-dlee, the Comanche, solemnly as the storm broke over them, to the top of the conical hill. They found a crevice, placed him in it, and gently laid stones on top to frustrate prowling carnivores. They were pelted with flying hailstones. Then in the rain they led the forty-one mules northwest. Satanta was satisfied. Seven white lives. Six scalps; one of the men had been bald. The guns. The mules. It would be judged a successful raid. He noted with further satisfaction that the deluge would wash out their tracks.

CHAPTER FIVE

PURSUIT

On that sultry Thursday morning, May 18, Sherman inspected Fort Richardson. It was not a place built for defense, but rather a base of operations, a rectangular piece of ground with the grass worn off, buildings lined up around a parade ground on the south half, stables and such to the north. The hospital was a large fine building of sandstone; many of the others were picket houses, the walls consisting of log posts set upright in the earth, the roofs of shingle or canvas or mud-chinked poles. It all had the raw appearance of newly done construction. Sherman chatted with a few of the enlisted men and most of the officers.

Later that morning he sat in the headquarters building and penned a letter to General Reynolds at San Antonio. He had talked enough to the post commander, Ranald Mackenzie, a brilliant young colonel whose opinion had to be respected, that he was beginning to alter his ideas about the Indian situation. He wrote: "I do not doubt that some of the Kiowas and Comanches from the Reservation do come down to Texas to steal horses and they never object to killing and scalping when tempted, but these Indians are in the custody of the Indian

Bureau, and the Army has no more control over it than the Post Office Department has." But he still could not get away from the word "if." He continued: "If the Indians in the Fort Sill Reservation have many Texas horses with brands on, I will find it out at Fort Sill, and will labor to have the thing stopped through the Commissioner of Indian Affairs. Of course it is a great outrage if the Indians who receive annuities from the United States make their reservation a refuge for stolen stock, and when the truth is ascertained some means can be devised to stop it, and of this I will write you from Fort Sill."

Mail came in from the East that day. He got to see copies of the New York *Herald* of May 1, 2, and 3. They were touting him for president. He read with mixed feelings. Grant was going to run again, that was sure, and he certainly didn't intend to oppose him. Maybe in '76. Meanwhile, his main concern should be to keep from giving any impression that he had political aspirations.

By noon it appeared that severe thunderstorms were approaching. He had agreed to meet a delegation of Jacksboro citizens that afternoon. He received them in the headquarters building. The meeting proved to be more than he had anticipated. It seemed that a committee of leading citizens of the area—a doctor, merchants, lawyers—had been working three weeks preparing a stack of papers for him. They presented the material and spoke without equivocation; the situation was unacceptable, unbearable, and it was all because of the Quaker-run Indian Service and the Indian refuge up at Fort Sill.

One of the delegates began to talk about the electors of the county voting on secession from the Union ten years before. The man said the vote in Jack County was fourteen for the Confederacy, seventy-six for the Union. Sherman was upon the point of dryly observing that such facts did not seem pertinent, when the man went on to explain. Many of their young men of fighting age had been called into the armies of the South, even though they had voted against it. Meanwhile, they had been suspect in their own state and had not, he thought, got adequate frontier defense during the war, had found it hard even to get ammunition to defend themselves against Indians. They had evidence that some Union army people in Colorado and Kansas had encouraged the Indians to attack them. Now they were not even allowed to organize themselves into a frontier defense battalion because of being ex-rebels. It seemed impossible. Must they choose between staying here to be the prey of the savages who were the Quakers' pets and leaving, turning their backs on their homes and land and businesses they had worked for?

Sherman flipped through the sheaf of papers they had given him—affidavit after affidavit, notarized . . . a man swore that he had seen horses at Fort Sill he knew to have been stolen in Jack County. Another from a civilian scout for the cavalry expressing the strong belief that the Indians causing the trouble were from Fort Sill. Here was one from a man who had formerly been a member of the U.S. 6th Cavalry, who said that this very spring he had gone up to the Fort Sill area and there he was insulted and threatened by Indians in the vicinity of the Indian trader's store and the Sutler's store, was called a "Teana," until he became alarmed, and he was convinced those were Indians who had depredated in Jack County. Most of the papers began thus: "State of Texas, County of Jack. Personally appeared before me the undersigned personally known to me, who being first duly sworn deposes and says: . . ." Here was one from a man in an adjoining county, a certain Daniel Waggoner, identified as an extensive property holder. The man had lost horses, some fine saddle horses, had followed them north; evidently he had dealt with General Benjamin Grierson, the post commander at Sill, for the affidavit included this: "Gen.

Grierson wholly disregarding his sacred promise made to me failed and neglected to deliver said horse to me whom he knew to be the lawful owner of the horse but contrary to law and good conscience permitted said Indian to keep said horse and affiant has not to this day received said horse or any compensation whatever for said horse."

Also among the papers was a tabular "Statement of Murders and Outrages Committed upon the Citizens of Jack County by Hostile Indians," giving dates, names, numbers killed, locations of outrages from Fort Richardson, remarks about captives and wounded. The first entry concerned the families of Mason and Cameron, nine killed, houses burned, fifteen miles to the northwest. Here was one about a man named Britt Johnson, black, with three others, killed this spring out there on the road to Belknap.

The total killed was one hundred twenty-nine. The tabulation ended with the statement: "In addition to the above great sacrifice of life hundreds have been driven from their homes through fear, and more than Two thousand head of horses stolen. . . ."

The talk of the delegation was serious and businesslike. Sherman assured them that he would give their memorial his fullest consideration, and if some of them wished to accompany his party to Fort Sill they were welcome, and perhaps some horses might be identified and recovered. But the general was not to be let off so easily. Two women had come, matronly, with trembling lips, dark circles around their eyes. They wanted their children. They wanted to beg for his mercy. He knew these females were going to weep as soon as he saw them, and they did as they told him how their children had been captured and taken somewhere into a strange fearful life to be reared as heathen and never know their loved ones again.

One of the women, a Mrs. Fitzpatrick, not only wept, but completely lost control of herself as she told about her infant granddaughter. "Milly! Milly!" she sobbed. "Oh, sir! Sir, you don't know how small and helpless she is!" The damned woman was down on the floor before anyone could stop her, trying to kiss his boots or some such ridiculous thing, begging, "Have mercy on us! Sir, have mercy on us!" As they pulled her out she repeated the child's name as if she were calling someone a long way off—"Milly! Milly! God, have mercy! Milly?"

It was a messy scene. Sherman did his best to express his sympathy without committing himself and was greatly relieved when the women were taken out of his hearing.

Hail, lightning, and blowing rain swept over the military installation that afternoon, and Sherman wrote a long letter to his brother John, now a senator from Ohio. He asked his brother to deny that he had any presidential hopes, and discussed the situation on the frontier, showing by his words that his doubts about the Indian problem were shifting: "Indians in small parties approach, scatter, steal horses, and escape. . . . This has been going on ever since we have had Texas, and now as much if not more than ever. People here, and the officers of the Army here assert that these Indians come from the Indian Reservation, that they carry this stock to the Reservation and are then safe against pursuit." He could not get the two women out of his mind. The questioning cry "Milly?" haunted him. He wrote: "One of the worst practices here is the custom of the Kioways and Comanches, to steal women and children, and I have already had two mothers begging of me their children, as though I could help them.—Of course I promised to do my best, but it is worse than looking for a needle in a hay stack, rather like looking for a flea in a large corn field."

The overly solicitous officers wanted him to move into more

substantial quarters because of the storm, but he would not. Beat the tent stakes down solid, tighten the ropes a bit, he had seen worse quarters. Marcy was evidently drinking with some of the bachelor officers of the post, but the old fellow could certainly take care of himself.

The tabulation of "outrages" presented to Sherman that day had not been quite up to date. Sometime in the small hours between midnight and dawn the next day a lone figure staggered down the muddy approach to Lost Creek, between the two saloons that hugged the military reservation, and across the wooden causeway. His footsteps could hardly be heard on account of the rushing water in the stream. The two soldiers on interior guard duty naturally assumed that here was another drunk coming late from town. They seized him. When the corporal came with the lantern they saw that he was not a soldier, but a deathly pale civilian, cold, exhausted, trembling, seemingly about to faint, trying to tell them something. Tom Brazeal, he said. Warren's wagontrain. Indians. He came to tell them.

Then they saw his foot. They picked him up and carried him bodily into the post, across the flooded parade ground, into the hospital. There the officer of the guard finally came and, upon hearing the words "a hundred Indians, maybe a hundred and fifty," ran to wake Colonel Mackenzie.

The colonel tried to determine whether the teamster was exaggerating, but by this time the laudanum the surgeon had administered was taking effect. He sent and had one of Sherman's aides-de-camp awakened. They got the seventeen men of the escort up to guard the general's tent.

Mackenzie found it hard to estimate what he faced. The men of the 6th Cavalry, which his regiment had replaced here, had talked about some mighty bold mounted Indians who were not afraid of the U.S. Army. Like that damned rebel cavalry back in the war which would strike out of nowhere. What if some rainy dawn a hundred and fifty fighting Indians charged into this unfenced post? My God! He had all his officers awakened. They got some men in the saddle as the gray daylight came, to scout briefly in every direction to the nearest high ground and come straight back.

Inspector General Randolph Marcy came awake in the tent slowly and painfully. It was late to be getting up, but that was the least of his worries. He cursed himself for a damned old fool. Any man his age. . . . That cheap liquor seemed to have settled in his eyeballs. It had probably been caused by the strain of following Sherman around; the fellow seemed never to tire and never to unbend. He had welcomed a jolly session with some of the officers, a glass or two of good fellowship. He had listened to stories of exploration, adventure, hunting, and had told plenty himself, names, names, names of the men in the army in the good old days.

Their mistake had been when some captain suggested that they sample a certain local product which seemed to be called "pine-top" or "white-mule," three dollars the canteen full, straight from the barrel. Their tastes had evidently deteriorated by then, for they did not remember to stop sampling. In fact, he did not remember how he got back to his tent in the rain, off down here in the damned brush where Sherman insisted on camping.

When he raised the tent flap he could see people moving around on the post, one small party of mounted men cantering toward headquarters, flinging up mud behind them. Then he saw the seventeen black soldiers, each armed. He asked what was going on and was told that the fort was under a big Indian alert. It presented an even more awkward situation than he had thought, getting up in the middle of the morning this way.

Marcy made himself presentable and slogged his way up to post headquarters, where he started to clean his boots somewhat before entering, only to realize that such niceties were not being observed today. His intention was to stand around in the various offices and inform himself as fully as possible without asking any stupid questions, meanwhile remaining inconspicuous. It was damnably embarrassing to have something going on, everyone running this way and that, and be completely in the dark. Remaining inconspicuous proved no problem; he found that he, not being in the line of command, had become superfluous. Sherman and Mackenzie had their heads over a map; they were surrounded by the two aides-de-camp and three or four officers of the post.

They seemed to be writing a letter and arguing about the map. Mackenzie insisted that the map was not accurate; Sherman did not like the idea of a map not being accurate. Marcy could see enough of the map in question to determine that it covered an area of northwest Texas, where he had explored years before and gathered map information, some of which was still used. He wished that he had not come in just at this time; he did not know what he would say if they asked him a question. Finally the issue seemed to be settled when Sherman told one of his aides to use Mackenzie's location and words. Mackenzie said, "I'll meet them where the Soloman and the North Fork of Little Wichita unite, or on the high plains just north of there."

Sherman signed something and asked, "Is the sergeant and his party mounted? Let's get this copied and get the sergeant on the road."

An aide-de-camp and Lieutenant Carter rushed the paper into another office. The remaining officers began to discuss what the strength of Fort Richardson would be after some cavalry force departed. Sherman bluntly asserted that all that had been decided an hour before. Cavalry don't defend posts, they ride. He was impatient to get some soldiers into the field.

Marcy wandered into another office and found some coffee which the dog-robber had brought. It was nearly cold, but helped to make him feel a little more human. Not long afterward, he had a stroke of luck. It seemed that after the mysterious letter had been once copied and checked and after the original had been given to a sergeant who galloped west with a small party of cavalry, then still more copies had to be made, these in less haste. Marcy approached the copying clerk, told the fellow to continue his work, that he only wished to look over his shoulder and check a few of the words again. At that time—past mid-morning on May 19—the Inspector General first learned what had happened. The letter read:

Fort Richardson, Texas
Friday, May 19, 1871

Wood, Colonel W.H.
Commanding Fort Griffin
Colonel:

A pretty strong party of Indians have attacked and captured a train of (12) twelve wagons this side of Salt Creek, ten miles this side of Fort Belknap; killed seven men and five have escaped to this post—one wounded. It is all important that this case be followed up with extreme vigor and principally that we find out whether or no the impression be well founded that the numerous robberies and murders on this frontier have been done by the Fort Sill Reservation Indians. General Mackenzie will start at once with 150 cavalry and pack mules with flour, sugar, coffee, salt, and bacon—that will enable him, if necessary, to stay out a month.

I wish you to start out at once, by daybreak of tomorrow, as strong a force as you possibly can, mounted, and let the party strike north-east directly for the head of the Little Wichita; scout around its tributaries and attack any party of Indians there found, and to search for and find General Mackenzie's party and report to him for orders. If your party strikes a fresh trail follow it especially if it lead to the Fort Sill Reservation, and if you don't find General Mackenzie the officer in command should conduct his party to Fort Sill and report to me. I expect to leave here for Fort Sill tomorrow morning and to reach there by the 24th. The men who have come in from the captured train report the strength of the party about one hundred, and that they had their squaws along, who held their horses whilst they made the last charge. They say that they killed several of the Indians, and that they did not abandon their train till seven of their number were dead and about half their mules killed. They then cut their way out and took refuge in some timber till night when they came to this post.

Yours Truly,
W.T. Sherman, General.

P.S. Send your ton-ka-was along and look out for General Mackenzie or his trail about where, on your map, the Soloman and North Fork of Little Wichita unite, or on the high Prairie just north of this river.

W.T.S.

Marcy noted that the confusion on the muddy post increased along toward noon. Women came out in the rain from the officers' houses and from the tents north and west of the post buildings to kiss cavalrymen. Finally the mounted men were formed in companies, A, B, E, and F, and Mackenzie led them west.

Marcy still felt sick at his stomach and did not know but what now, if most of the rush was over, his position might increase in awkwardness; he might become conspicuous again. It struck him that unusual things were happening here and he had been keeping a journal. He thought he remembered all the essential facts. He went back to the small camp in the trees by Lost Creek and got out his journal.

It was with a small prick of guilt that he noted that his last entry was the 17th, day before yesterday. He had kept the log up faithfully until last evening. Well, that was easily fixed. He dipped his pen in the ink and formed the words in his mind: May 18—This morning five teamsters. . . . At that point his thinking was interrupted by some sound or perhaps by one of the Negro escort or perhaps by a further prick of guilt at deliberately thinking the wrong date or perhaps by a subtle warning about the inconsistency between the date and knowing about the five teamsters. But if it was a warning it was lost in the awkwardness of the day and among the facts he was trying to be sure to remember. He wrote in his journal: "May 18.—This morning five teamsters, who, with seven others, had been with a mule wagon train *en route* to Fort Griffin with corn for the post, were attacked on the open prairie about ten miles east of Salt Creek by one hundred Indians, and seven of the teamsters killed and one wounded."

He did not like that sentence. He read it over. As a book writer he was accustomed to working on sentences, but today he was not feeling like a writer. Probably the grammar was bad. It really didn't matter as long as he got the facts straight. He continued the journal: "General Sherman immediately ordered Colonel Mackenzie to take a force of about one hundred and fifty cavalry, with thirty days rations, on pack mules, and pursue and chastise the murderers.

"May 19.—We remained at the Fort to-day. General Sherman examining into the conditions of affairs here."

He immediately knew that the last one was not a good sentence, but he liked it anyway; such a general statement would cover anything. It was a relief to have brought his journal up to date, made it current.

The Inspector General had no idea that he had written an entry which would confuse historians for nearly a hundred years. A strict reader might read that on the morning of May 18, five teamsters had been attacked. Researchers who were aware of the distance the five survivors had traveled might place the attack on the 17th. It would be easy to assume from the entry that Mackenzie got his orders and left the post on the 18th. The most common error that Marcy had originated was the assumption that, since the Sherman party had traveled one day, as he showed in the entry of the 17th, and the five teamsters had come in the next morning, the Sherman party and the wagontrain must have been only a few hours apart on Salt Creek Prairie that fatal day.

The 19th continued to be a hectic day for Marcy. He discovered that certain civilians planned to accompany the party toward Fort Sill, and after a few discreet inquiries of one of the aides-de-camp, found out that a delegation of Jacksboro citizens had appeared before the General in Chief. Perhaps he got the idea that this interview had occurred today, or perhaps he thought he was still writing yesterday's entry. In any case, he continued the confusion of his journal under the heading of May 19.

"During the day a delegation of citizens from Jacksborough, which adjoins the reservation, and contains two or three hundred border people, came to General Sherman to represent the condition of affairs in the country with reference to Indians, and requested authority to go to Fort Sill. . . ."

That was a long day for Marcy. Late that night he wrote for

the third time in his journal. Forgetting what he had written immediately after the heading of May 19, he repeated himself.

"Remained at Fort Richardson. It rained nearly all day. . . ." Then he summarized briefly a communication which had come by courier from Mackenzie at the site of the wagontrain attack and went to bed, glad that the day was over.

The orders which Mackenzie carried with him as he led his regiment west at midday read thus:

Fort Richardson, Texas
May 19, 1871

Mackenzie, General R.S. 4th Cavalry
Commanding Fort Richardson,
General:

I enclose you herewith an official copy of orders to General Wood, Commanding Fort Griffin, to dispatch all his available force of cavalry to the head of Little Wichita to report to you. As you are on the point of starting for the Indians who yesterday attacked the corn train 20 miles east of old Fort Belknap, or about 20 miles west of this place, and as in their pursuit you may have to enter what is known as the Fort Sill Reservation, I hereby authorize you to enter said Reservation and if the trail be fresh and you should overtake the party anywhere within thirty or forty miles of Red River, you will not hesitate to attack the party, recover the property stolen and any other property or stock in their possession and bring them to me at Fort Sill. Should the trail scatter and yet, in your opinion, lead into said Reservation, you may in like manner come to Fort Sill that we may through the Indian Agent there recover the stolen stock and get possession of the party of Indians who attacked this train and killed the seven men as reported.

On reaching the abandoned train this afternoon you can judge of the truth of the statement of the five men who escaped from the train and reported its capture to us this morning. I will probably be at Fort Sill from the 24th to the 27th of May and would be pleased to hear from you there; but in any event I will instruct the Commanding officer there at all times to cooperate with you from that quarter and to supply any party coming from you in the same manner as he would were he within this Department. You may control the movements of the two companies of the 6th Cavalry left at Griffin to escort me, until such time as they can be spared from here when they should resume their march toward their own regiment via Fort Sill.

I have the honor to be,
Your obedient Servant,
W.T. Sherman, General

Mackenzie thought about how neat and matter-of-fact orders could be, not saying anything about the rain. It was like the maps; sitting in headquarters you could see a feature of the terrain—it was right there on the paper—but when you got into the field maybe it was there and maybe it wasn't. The idea that he would reach the abandoned train in the afternoon was another unrealistic idea. The clouds made the day dim; little daylight remained as they approached the site.

The wagons were broken up, some of the wheels rolled far out on the prairie, the heavier parts clustered on an acre of ground where the teamsters had attempted to corral. Some dead mules lay swollen, their legs sticking out unnaturally stiff. The naked bodies of the men seemed hardly human because of their many wounds washed white by the rain. One bald-headed man had not been scalped. Corn, pieces of harness, arrows, rags of grain sack, and clothing littered the place.

Mackenzie set his men to work establishing an overnight

camp, preparing a meal, and scouting briefly on the prairie. He ordered his accompanying surgeon, J.H. Patzki, to examine the dead men and describe them in writing. As soon as he had a tent up to afford a halfway dry place, Mackenzie penciled a letter to be taken back to Richardson. He headed it "Eight miles East of Salt Creek, Tex. 9 P.M." and addressed one of Sherman's aides-de-camp.

> Sir:
>
> I arrived here about dark and found the statement of the citizen correct as regards the train having been corraled. Five mules lie dead among the wagons. The Sergeant in charge of the detail, sent out in advance, found five of the men about the wagons; their heads split open and otherwise mutilated. One was found chained to a wagon wheel and burnt in many places to a crisp; a sixth was found after my arrival some little distance on the prairie, and the seventh will undoubtedly be found in the morning. The Sergeant found Captain Kevin camped at Salt Creek. He at once sent the orders of the General to Griffin. He has not yet arrived. The Sergeant states that he has five Ton-Kaways with him.
>
> From everything I can learn I judge that the teamsters statement that there were quite a large number of Indians, though perhaps exaggerated has nevertheless good foundation.
>
> I have the honor to be,
Very respectfully
Your obedient Servant,
R.S. Mackenzie
Colonel 4th Cavalry

Some time later Patzki handed him the description he had asked for. The doctor had not gone out in the dark to the body on the prairie.

Colonel R.S. Mackenzie,
4th Cav
Sir:

I have the honor to report that in compliance with your instructions I examined on May 19, 1871, the bodies of five citizens killed near Salt Creek by Indians on the previous day. All the bodies were riddled with bullets, covered with gashes, and the skulls crushed, evidently with an axe found bloody on the place; some of the bodies exhibited also signs of having been stabbed with arrows. One of the bodies was even more mutilated than the others, it having been found fastened with a chain to the pole of a wagon lying over a fire with the face to the ground, the tongue being cut out. Owing to the charred condition of the soft parts it was impossible to determine whether the man was burned before or after his death. The scalps of all but one were taken.

I have the honor to be, colonel,
your obedient servant,
J.H. Patzki
Asst Surgeon, U.S.A.

The next morning early, Mackenzie sent out scouts in every direction to attempt the impossible task of picking up the Indians' trail. Meanwhile he set a burial detail to work. They found the seventh body and piled them into a common coffin, an intact wagon bed. The men digging the huge grave had a difficult task. The ground was soaked and the rain still came down. They became muddy from head to feet as they labored. They had to keep bailing out the grave.

When the burial had been completed Mackenzie led his regiment northwest. He figured that Wood down at Griffin would be able to send along about forty cavalrymen. Their orders from Sherman said to start out by daybreak of this day;

COUNTRY SIDE FORT RICHARDSON

that might be easier said than done, but they should not have any trouble joining him. His real problem was rain. He could foresee that they were going to follow wild mustang tracks; they were going to find every creek and two-bit river out of its banks, damned near impossible to ford, and this might well be the most frustrating sortie he had ever had anything to do with.

Sherman's party left Richardson that same day. The officers at the post sent the party east along the lumber road to camp near the sawmill on Big Sandy Creek, thence to turn north to Red River Station on the four-day trip to Sill. The road was not the shortest, but it was the safest, and the general had ceased protesting provisions for his safety. Of these past few days he would write later, "I believe I risked my life." Perhaps that feeling, as well as the attack on the wagontrain and the pleas of the Jacksboro citizens, had caused the dramatic change in his assessment of the Indian situation in this part of the country. On May 24, he would write to General John Pope at Leavenworth, "There is no doubt that the Western Border of Texas has for years been . . . infested by the Indians. . . ."

But now, heading for Sill, he was posing some large questions he wanted answered up there. He was not so much suspicious of the army's part in this ridiculous Indian refuge; their hands were probably tied. But he was thinking that a certain Quaker in the Indian Service had plenty of explaining to do.

CHAPTER SIX

OLD STONE HEAD TATUM

Friend Lawrie Tatum, Indian Agent to the Kiowas and Comanches, looked like a substantial forty-nine-year-old Iowa farmer, which he was. He was bearded and heavy-set, and lines of honesty and seriousness of purpose creased his face. Sometimes, dressed up, he wore a heavy gold watch chain across the expanse of his black vest; beyond that everything about him was plain. His head was bald. The Kiowas and Comanches, quick to apply a nickname, called him "old bald head" or "old stone head."

He did not feel well. Something had gone wrong with his previously iron constitution. Not exactly indigestion, nor hay fever, for he did not sneeze, but some kind of vapors or disarranged humours of the system that often produced a headache or other vague ache. He was sitting in his private office in the agency building, trying to write a letter to Friend Enoch Hoag, the Indian Superintendent at Lawrence, Kansas. But even when engaged in such a simple task as penning a letter he often found himself of late sitting on the edge of his chair, tense, clamping his jaws together, perspiration popping out on his head. He had not speculated either to his good wife, Mary Ann, or to himself whether he were cut out to be an Indian agent, for he did not question himself much, but went ahead and bore stubbornly any tribulation, trusting to the Lord. It was his desire and expectation to be supplied with heavenly wisdom and strength sufficient for the responsible business devolving upon him. His common sense certainly did not seem to be enough.

The appointments of his office were plain. They could hardly have been different with the high cost of transportation to this place out here at the end of the world, two miles south of an unfinished military post called Fort Sill. He had his desk and some simple chairs, in which employees or army officers or Indian chiefs sat when they came to see him. The most burdensome things surrounding him were his ledgers and his files and all the red tape they represented, the reports, accounts, budgets, claims; as much of this as possible he turned over to his clerk; even so, he still seemed swamped with it.

Things were quiet around the agency. Up at the fort they were cleaning up and straightening up in preparation for the visit of General Sherman. Tatum had no inclination to cater to a military man, but he expected to find an opportunity to meet him. He wanted to talk to the general.

From the days of William Penn the Quakers had regarded the Indians as brethren in the divine sight, with souls that needed to be redeemed with the precious blood of the Lamb. At the time of the election of U.S. Grant to the presidency there had been much talk of graft in the Indian service and of turning the whole problem over to the military. Fearing such a development, a committee of Orthodox Friends had called upon the new president and implored him to appoint religious men, humane persons, to the Indian Service, men fearing God and hating covetousness. After due consideration, Grant had agreed, reportedly saying, "Gentlemen, your advice is good. I accept it. . . . If you can make Quakers out of the Indians it will take the fight out of them. Let us have peace."

Lawrie Tatum had not been a national religious leader. He had moved with his family at a young age from New Jersey to Ohio; then in 1844 at the age of twenty-two he had gone out to pioneer on the frontier of Iowa. As that country settled up he had gained the reputation among his neighbors for patience and reliability, and among other local Quakers as a man who would help a runaway slave in his flight to freedom. Early in 1869 he had been farming, concerned about Indians, but knowing little of them, and had been surprised to see in a newspaper story that he had been appointed Indian agent and confirmed by the U.S. Senate. After considering the subject as best he could in the fear of God, wishing to be obedient to Him, he accepted the appointment.

In the middle of that summer he had come here with his staff of Quaker assistants, a doctor, a teacher, a clerk, various artisans. He found himself in charge of an agency which was supposed to serve Kiowas, Comanches, Wichitas, and Caddoes. The previous agent had hired a white farm hand to plow and plant several small patches of land amounting to about seventy acres, and the Wichitas and Caddoes, who had farmed before, seemed to welcome the help. The Kiowas and Comanches thought it a joke; they ate or ruined many of the pumpkins and watermelons before they were half grown. It did not take Tatum long to decide that these two nomadic tribes were, as he would later write, ". . . the worst Indians east of the Rocky Mountains." In a few months those Indians inclined toward agriculture were moved north to a separate agency on the Washita River, but Tatum had remained in charge of those two "worst" tribes, the Kiowas and Comanches.

Not long after he took charge of the agency some Indian commissioners, along with two of the Executive Committee of Friends on Indian Affairs, had come to visit and had held a council with the redmen of the area, proclaiming the new era of peace, friendship, love, Christianity. The dominant Indian at that council had been a strongly built Kiowa named Satanta, who seemed to have no hesitancy toward frank talk. He said that he took hold of that part of the white man's road represented by the breech-loading gun, but did not like the ration of corn; it hurt his teeth. The "good" Indian, he said, who listens to the white man, gets nothing. The independent Indian is rewarded. He wanted arms and ammunition. The commissioners had answered that they would get no arms and ammunition, and if they left the reservation without permission they would be punished; the buffalo came through the reservation twice a year and that was enough hunting. Then the commissioners and Friends departed, leaving sincere, dependable Tatum to enforce their dictums.

He was more fortunate than he knew in being bald-headed. Those people believed, in their unique culture, that a man's virility and pride somehow resided in his hair. He presented an enigma to which they had no answer.

One of his many duties was to regulate Indian traders and approve or disapprove the annual renewal of license for each trader. Not long after taking charge of the agency he noted an item in the traders' stores, a steel spearpoint about a foot long. He saw some of the Indians armed with them; they had fastened long handles to them and whetted the blade to razor keenness. It made a dangerous and wicked weapon. He could not believe that they were used to kill buffalo, but could clearly see that they might be used to kill men, and so he published an order that the item would not be sold on the reservation. He knew that the traders questioned his judgment, but he enforced the order.

Much of the time during those early months he had occupied himself with trying to build livable quarters for his family and the employees and facilities for the operation of the agency business. He had gone to Chicago and purchased a corn mill, a sawmill, and a shingle maker, together with a steam engine to power them. Setting this equipment up, making plans, supervising carpenters and stone masons, he had felt that he was progressing satisfactorily. The trouble was that he could not escape the awareness that such work was only preparation, and his real work, that of patiently and lovingly guiding the Indians into Christianity and civilization, had not begun.

He had been in charge about six months when his Indians committed a shocking and senseless outrage about a hundred miles north in the Cheyenne-Arapaho reservation. A beef contractor named Jacob Harshfield was driving a herd of cattle along the North Canadian River to deliver them to Darlington's agency. A band of wild-acting Kiowas under Satanta drove off the herders and attacked the herd. Like maniacs they shot arrows into the helpless beasts. The animals stampeded and Satanta and his irresponsible warriors chased them with great glee, whooping and laughing and shooting. Before it was over two hundred valuable cattle lay dead or wounded, the others scattered. In actuality, it could not be considered as serious as the killing of a single human being, but it was greatly troubling because of its meaninglessness, its wanton cruelty, its arrogant devilry. Such savagery surely was beyond human understanding.

But that was only a beginning. In the spring—it was a year ago now—his Indians had showed their contempt for their own agency by stealing in one night twenty horses and mules from the agency corral and the neighborhood. The same savages drove his employed farmers from their camp, slashed their tent to pieces, and stole the blankets and clothing from it. One Indian had the audacity to send in a message that he had led the raid and had also scalped a man near the agency. A diligent search did not find a body; no one, least of all Agent Tatum, speculated as to whether the message might be a sly reference to his own bald pate. Savages could not have a sense of humor, could they?

A few weeks later Indians stole seventy-three mules at night from the quartermaster's corral up near Fort Sill itself. The troopers went after them but lost the tracks when the trail was covered by fresh buffalo tracks.

The Quaker employees were getting nervous. Toward the latter part of June that year Tatum and his wife were awakened early one morning by the report of a gun. They still lived then in the old adobe agency building on the east side of Cache Creek. Some teamsters working for the army had camped only two hundred yards away. Not long after the sound of the shot two of the teamsters came dragging another one, seriously wounded by a party of marauding Indians. The man's name was Levi Lucans and the bullet had gone through the lower part of his body from side to side, apparently just inside of his backbone. It did not seem possible that he could live. Another shot rang out to the west. The Quakers could see Indians crossing the creek toward the new mill and houses that were being built, but evidently the savages knew that they were being watched, for they did not remain in the agency area long. Tatum believed it was because they did not know that Quakers do not shoot Indians and also, perhaps, because they were beginning to feel guilty. In the morning the agency people found a Spanish-speaking cattle worker killed and scalped near the beef corral. The same night Indians had killed and scalped still another man, who worked with a woodcutting crew up west of the fort. The Tatums gave a room to Levi Lucans and cared for him while he slowly recovered.

Tatum called a conference of all the Friends working for the government on the reservation. Their labor in this field of Christian benevolence was dangerous. They must search their consciences whether they would remain in the work or return to the states. For himself, he believed that there is One who rules in the hearts of men and whose power is sufficient to restrain the evil intentions and passions of the Indians. They must use their own judgment. He was disappointed that all of them chose to go except the two teachers, Josiah and Lizzie Butler.

About the time they departed he took over from the military all the agency commissary stores, including more than 4,000 cattle intended for issue to the Indians. He employed foremen and herders to care for them. The bulk of the cattle had to be pastured sixty or seventy miles east in the Chickasaw nation to keep them out of the reach of the Kiowas and Comanches. The few which were kept around the agency were sometimes found in the morning standing mournfully with arrows sticking out of their necks, backs, and hips.

Early in August the Kiowas returned about a third of the mules they had stolen from the Fort Sill quartermaster and announced to Tatum that they wished a council to negotiate a trade of a Texas woman and her five children for arms and ammunition. Tatum wanted a council too. He attended with his issue clerk, George Conover, and his interpreter, Mathew Leeper. Colonel Benjamin Grierson attended with an orderly and the post interpreter, Horace Jones. The meeting was held in the council room of one of the long commissary buildings between the agency and the fort.

Tatum led off by reproving the assembled chiefs for their raiding. He explained that they received their annuity goods and rations free because Washington was kind and wished to do them good. The people of Texas also wished to do them good and actually helped to pay for the free annuity goods and rations. The only Texans who came onto the reservation to harm them, as far as he knew, were a few whiskey peddlers. But did they attack the evil whiskey peddlers? No, they went down and attacked the Texans who were helping to feed and clothe them. Washington had sent him to this place for their benefit, and yet they attacked the agency. It was very bad for them to go raiding on the agency where they were fed and clothed and assisted and instructed in what was best for them. He did not like it, and the Great Spirit did not like it, and they had better reform and live as white men do.

He felt that there was some question about the adequacy of the interpretation, for sometimes the Indians laughed.

Chief Lone Wolf said that he did not know what all the complaint was about. All the chiefs were against raiding. As he spoke, Tatum was thinking that so little dependence could be placed in his word that no one could know when he was telling the truth.

Grierson spoke angrily to the Indians. They must give up their warlike ways and take the white man's road.

Satanta, not intimidated, rose and answered in words similar to ones he had spoken before. The part of the white man's road that he understood was the breech-loading gun. Look at the Wichitas and Caddoes. They do as the white man thinks best and get no respect for it. He wished to do as the Kiowas think best. He observed that Colonel Grierson seemed angry but did not think that any reason for concern.

The chiefs had brought their weapons to the council. Tatum noted that one took all the cartridges out of his rifle and slowly put them back again. Another strung his bow, drew out an arrow, and fitted it in readiness. Another, sitting directly in front of Tatum, begun elaborately whetting a butcher knife, turning it over and over, making all the noise and show he could. When the conference was about over Lone Wolf came to Tatum and put his hand inside the agent's vest to feel whether his heart was pounding in fear. Tatum felt revulsion at the touch, and reported later that his heart had been beating as calmly as usual.

The council accomplished nothing. A few days later Tatum ransomed the Texas woman and her five children for one hundred dollars apiece. He could not bear the thought of the woman and the one nearly grown daughter remaining with the Indians.

The trouble continued. On the first of September the Kiowas were about to draw beef rations, and he called the chiefs into his office to tell them that their young men had been misbehaving around the beef pen; he wanted them to attend the issue and supervise the unruly ones. They agreed, but instead went along and assisted in killing a dozen beeves and thirty or forty calves more than they had coming, then proceeded to rob the herders of their provisions and cooking utensils.

He had removed the military guards when he took over the commissary stores, telling himself that the use of soldiers is never justified, that it implies a lack of trust in Christian methods. Now he reinstated them to keep order during the issue of goods and rations and told himself that when soldiers come under a civil officer for duty it is to perform civil and not military duty; the soldiers were not really soldiers.

One of the Indians who seemed even further beyond understanding than the others was an old Kiowa with a thin gray mustache and one drooping eyelid called Tsatangya. By his manner and bearing one would think that he lived in another world and the prospects of making a good Christian of him appeared nonexistent. One day Tsatangya rode a mule to the agency which had been definitely described, brand and all, in the claim of a Texan. Tatum demanded its return. The old man refused; he said that he had stolen the mule down in the country where his favorite son had been killed, and now he loved the mule. But he solemnly proposed a solution to its ownership. He and the agent should go out alone on the prairie with spears; the one who killed the other should have the mule. Tatum declined and he concluded that Tsatangya was probably the worst Indian on the reservation.

After the bulk of the Quaker employees had quit, Tatum found much difficulty in getting the work done. Some houses still needed completion. One day a man named William Wykes, who had been working as a carpenter for the quartermaster, came to the agency office and applied for a job. Tatum told the man to come back in a few days, that he would need to investigate him first.

The investigation revealed that the man was industrious and could work without supervision and could do any kind of carpenter work from building a wagon to building a house, but the man drank and swore.

When William Wykes returned, Tatum charged him with these two vices and said that he could not employ him.

The man said, "Mr. Tatum, I am guilty of both of these habits, and I can't quit them while in military employ. My reason for leaving there and working for you is that I may quit. I know that you don't allow your men to drink or swear, and if you will employ me I will give you my word that I will quit both of these vices."

It seemed an opportunity to secure a good carpenter and

assist a sincere fellow human being at the same time. Tatum hired him.

He proved a first-rate carpenter. Unfortunately, Tatum caught him overcome with drink on two different occasions, but the man seemed so contrite that he did not discharge him.

In December 1870, Tatum was ordered to go north to Lawrence, Kansas, to meet with the other Friend agents, Superintendent Enoch Hoag, and the thirteen men of the Quaker executive committee which nominated agents and advised them. Tatum welcomed the order, for it would give him the opportunity to go on to his home in Iowa, but he felt anxiety about it also, for he would be gone more than two months and the Indians of his agency had not received the annuities due them under the Treaty of Medicine Lodge. The annuities, including clothing and blankets and other supplies needed for the winter, were already two months overdue. It seemed that they were in some warehouse somewhere at Fort Harker in Kansas, waiting hauling by the military, which had its own material to transport and kept delaying the Indian supplies. Tatum felt obliged to go to Lawrence and sincerely believed that he was due the visit to his home. He left his clerk, George H. Smith, in charge. The man was not a Quaker, but was sober and reliable, adept at making out budgets and reports which would be acceptable to superiors in government.

That was an unusually cold winter. One night the mercury dropped to four below zero. George Smith did not spend his time as acting agent in transporting Indian supplies or even in demanding their transport, but went over into the Chickasaw Nation and set up with two other enterprising men a corn-growing business, which they hoped would make them rich. Corn was selling to the army and the Indian Service for two dollars a bushel, and with Smith's connections they would encounter little difficulty in marketing their crop. Tatum did not know of his clerk's business interests, but when, a year later, charges against Smith would be laid before him, he would defend the employee and keep him working for the agency.

As for the meeting in Lawrence, Kansas, the members of the committee were there from New England, New York, Pennsylvania, Ohio, Indiana, Iowa, and Kansas. They discussed with the Friend agents their failures and successes. As Tatum would write later: "The agents were encouraged to use every effort to Christianize and civilize the Indians on the peaceable principles of the gospel, and to deal with them honestly, firmly and lovingly, and so far as practicable to procure religious employees, and look to God for a blessing on their labors."

The blankets and other annuities due the Indians in the autumn arrived the following April, 1871.

When Tatum came back to the agency that spring he took up his many burdens and duties with renewed vigor for a time, having been refreshed by being away from the immediate problems and by the encouragement of his friends in Iowa. One of his most onerous duties, one in which justice was most difficult to achieve, was the matter of claims. His files were jammed with correspondence relative to claims against Indians, some for depredations allegedly done years ago. Typical was a letter forwarded to him, written from the Office of Indian Affairs to Superintendent Hoag.

Sir.

Herewith I transmit to be submitted under your direction, by the Indian Agent, to the Indians in council with a demand for satisfaction in accordance with the requirement of the 17th section of the act of Congress regulating trade and intercourse with Indian Tribes, approved June 30, 1834, the following claims for depredations committed by Kiowa and Comanche Indians. Viz:

Jose Albino Baca, Romualda Baca, and Simon Baca, Depredations by Kiowas on the 18th of July 1867, amount $5,937.50.

Jose Albino Baca, and Romualda Baca depredations by Kiowas and Comanches on the 26th of August 1868, amount $2,745.00.

And so on to a total of $28,336.30. The last paragraph of the letter said: "You will instruct the Agent to present the claims to the Indians, and to report his proceedings to this office, at the earliest day practicable."

He did not know who the Bacas were nor where they lived nor what property they had lost nor its worth nor whether they had proof as to who had done the depredations. What was he to ask the Indians? Had they ever robbed anyone named Baca? Or was he merely expected to charge the Indians with robbing someone named Baca and "demand" satisfaction.

In some cases more details were presented to him. One from Camp Supply, Indian Territory, read:

Lawrie Tatum
U.S. Indian Agent
Fort Sill, Ind. Terr'y.

We enclose herewith our claim for compensation for damages arising from the depredations of the Apache and Kiowa Indians, consisting of the following enumerated papers, viz:

I. Application to you with valuation of lost property and our affidavits.

II. Affidavits of T.R. Curtis, J.H. Richmond and Herm Hanser, setting forth the loss, circumstances and valuation of the property.

III. Affidavit of J.H. Richmond, loss of 16 mules.

IV. Affidavit of Robert Taylor, loss of 16 mules.

V. Affidavit of Amos Chapman, loss of 2 horses.

VI. Certificate of Captain Nolan, 10th U.S. Cavalry, and other officers, certifying to the loss of stock and garden, and that the claim is just and the valuation of the property is reasonable.

Please complete these papers by your certificate and acknowledgment of the Indians, who committed the depredations, or such other papers as you may deem necessary to insure an early adjustment of the claim by the Department—You are aware of the fact that we lost everything by these outrages and as one of us, T.R. Curtis, is the supporter of an Indian family, we would urgently request you to forward the papers without unnecessary delay and also to request Mr. Hoag, to forward them at his earliest convenience—

The mail being so very uncertain, we would thank you for informing us of the receipt of these papers—

By doing so you will greatly oblige

Yours respectfully
T.R. Curtis and J.H. Richmond

In his files Tatum had one list of claims which demonstrated the diversity of claimants and the great amount of monies involved. The applicants were all members of the Choctaw and Chickasaw Nations. Some of their names and alleged losses were listed thus:

Overton Love	$15,200.00
Delphi Rose	365.00
Cornelius	5,100.00
Archibald Yell	550.00
Gabriel	6,580.00
Ah coo chau tubby	13,495.00
Ben Brown	1,130.00

Altogether on the list were 123 names, and the total money requested out of annuities due the Indians of Tatum's agency was

$682,685.00. He was glad the amount was so high. Obviously his superiors would not leave him stuck with the decision.

He had begun to solve part of the problem of proof by taking affidavits himself when the person who had lost property came before him. One such case had been for a modest amount. The affidavit read:

Office Kiowa Agency
I.T. 6 Mo 8—1870

I solemnly affirm that the Indians stole the following property from me on the evening of the 28th of May, 1870, & that I have not attempted to retaliate or obtain revenge. To wit

2 Blankets worth	$10.00
Pants, Coat, & Vest	40.00
2 Under Shirts	5.00
3 Shirts	10.00
2 Drawers	3.00
2 Handkerchiefs	1.50

Jerry Cronan

Affirmed to & subscribed before me this 8 day of 6 mo 1870
Lawrie Tatum
U.S. Ind. Agt

That man had been one of the farmers working for the agency who had been run out of his tent when the agency horses were stolen a year ago. Tatum had not been certain that his handkerchiefs were worth so much, but the man had been so frightened at the experience that Tatum had felt no prick of conscience in recommending that the claim be paid.

One of his troubles from the first had been the old law about presenting the claims to the Indians in council and the fact that his superiors did not understand the impracticability of it. He did not even know half the time where his Indians were, whether out there on the wilderness of the reservation or off the reservation hunting or off the reservation for evil purposes. Sometimes he gave some of them permission to hunt off the reservation, those who would accept permission. In fact, he did not know what the official policy was, whether they were supposed to be allowed to leave the reservation at will, or at all. As to the claims, he could really find no answer, except to pray a lot. He could talk about them to Caddo Chief George Washington or Kiowa Chief Kicking Bird, who was willing to cooperate, or to some friendly Penatuhka Comanche, and then hope that God would understand about any white lie he might imply about having presented the claims in council.

It was not long after he came back to the agency early in 1871 that his nervous headaches began to return. He thought that he might not be able to bear them except for the goodness of his wife Mary Ann, a woman as plain and solid as himself. On one occasion he had been worn out from riding horseback around to take care of agency business, and still had too much paperwork to take care of, and felt he had a dozen impossible decisions to make, and some people from Texas were in the office looking for stolen children and stolen horses. Mary Ann came in and looked at him, put her hand on his forehead, then led him to their quarters and made him lie down in the bedroom. As she went out she locked the door and told the employees that whether the commander of the post or anyone else should call to see the agent he was not to be disturbed until he had rested a while.

That spring rumors were going around about possible Indian outbreaks. Some sources said that the army surveying party on the reservation would be attacked. Instructions and speculations were flowing up and down in the red-tape channels. Tatum received one which read thus:

Lawrence, Kansas, 22nd 2 Month 1871

Lawrie Tatum,
U.S. Indian Agent
Fort Sill, I.T.

Inclosed herewith I transmit copy of letter of Col. Brooks (date 1st. inst) commanding at Fort Dodge, addresses to General Pope com. Division of Mo. date 8th inst by him endorsed to General Sherman and by the latter on 15th. inst. endorsed to Secretary of War and returned to this office through Commissioner of Indian Affairs, relative to anticipated Indian outbreak, on the frontier in early spring. The agent is hereby directed to follow out the requirements of the Commissioners letter (copy herewith) to keep the Department well informed, from week to week, of the disposition and movement of the Indians under his charge.

Respectfully
Enoch Hoag
Supt. Indian Affairs

The best informed he had been able to keep them was to send them guesses and rumors.

He had just attended a meeting up at the Washita Agency, where representatives of thirteen tribes, including those from the East called the civilized tribes, had made long speeches about peace with the whites and their common brotherhood. Ominously absent were such Kiowas as Satanta, who loved councils and speech making.

Now, May 22, 1871, Lawrie Tatum was trying to compose a letter to the Friends committee. Perhaps the impetus for the letter came from the expected visit of General Sherman. Tatum wrote: "I think the Indians do not intend to commit depredations here this summer, but from their actions and sayings they intend to continue their atrocities in Texas." Then he penned a question which implied a daring departure from the policy of loving his charges into civilization: "Will the committee sustain me in having Indians arrested for murder, and turned over to the proper authorities of Texas for trial?"

The following day late in the afternoon a man called at his office, red-headed, spare of build, intense, dressed in civilian clothes, but escorted by various officers, including the post commander. Tatum liked him. No man so homely who had come originally from Ohio could fail to have some goodness in him.

General Sherman had traveled that day and was not visiting for pleasure. He said bluntly, "Down south, sir, they are making serious accusations against the administration of this agency."

Tatum replied with equal directness. "General, I cannot control the Kiowas and Comanches."

Sherman appeared slightly puzzled. "Do you deny that they are raiding in Texas?"

"Of course I don't. I know that they are stealing and murdering in Texas at the same time that they are drawing rations and annuities from the United States. I've not been able to accomplish anything in civilizing them. They pay no attention to my injunctions." It seemed clear that Sherman had expected a defense of the Indians.

The general then launched into an account of an attack on a wagontrain down between Jacksboro and Belknap. Tatum told him that according to his scanty information Satanta and a warrior party were off the reservation. He expected some Kiowas in for rations within three or four days; he would ask if any of them knew anything about it.

The next day Tatum worried about his cooperation with

the military and about the forceful measures he was contemplating. The trouble was that things seemed different sitting among a meeting of Quakers up north and being down here, hearing Sherman tell about a man chained down and burned to death. The following day he wrote to his friend Jonathan Richards, in charge up at the Wichita Agency, and told him briefly about the wagontrain attack. He merely wanted another Quaker in the field to understand what he faced. He wrote that he anticipated that the raid was led by Satanta. That same day he wrote to Superintendent Hoag and repeated the question he had asked three days before: "When I ascertain who commits depredations in Texas will the Department approve of having the guilty parties arrested if they belong to the Indians of this Agency, and transfer them to the Governor of Texas for trial? Please give me an explicit answer as soon as practicable."

CHAPTER SEVEN

CONFRONTATION

Satanta had led his men northwest along the divide between the Brazos and the Wichita drainage, avoiding the flooding streams until he was far enough west to ford them. He left a few of his men to hold the mules and wait for the Spanish-speaking traders, then headed east to join the other Kiowa camps and move with them toward Fort Sill.

He had lost two more men of the raiding party. Tomasi had straggled behind with a few others to hunt buffalo and had been killed by a small squad of cavalry. Young Gun-Shot had gotten screw worms into his massive face wound and had died. No one seemed to believe that any of the three deaths should be blamed on Satanta as leader.

He had been thinking about the scene they had left behind where they struck the train of wagons. When you cut up men in that way what do the people of the other side think when they discover the bodies? The assumption that they are cowed by the ferocity and cruelty, and henceforth will be afraid, be submissive, certainly was an error. Some people might be, but not the whites and not the Kiowas. He remembered that raid by the whites seven years before in the winter when they came from the west and struck the Kiowa camp on the Guadalpa, or South Canadian River, not far from the old adobe trading post. Three things stuck fast in the minds of the Indians who had been there: his, Satanta's, performance with the bugle, which had clearly confused the invaders; the loud devastation of the wagon guns; and the mutilation of the Kiowa bodies in the overrun and burned camp. The Indians who had not been able to escape were the old feeble ones and the babies; they had been slashed to pieces, butchered. Whether the actual ghastly work was done by whites or their Ute and Jicarilla allies did not matter, for it is the thoughtful ones who matter. Always there are people who will act in a frenzy, and there are those who might restrain them, but if they do not, what do they mean? Hate? What good is it to mean mere hate? No, it is a message about the severe difficulty in understanding one another. About the depth of difference. About the worthlessness of words that say "peace" and mean "submission." But if the whites see it done to themselves and see themselves not cowed, can they understand that it might be so the other way around? Would some of them wonder what kind of message lies in such savage acts?

He thought it extremely difficult to get white people to understand certain things. Strangely, some of it seemed to be not mere arrogance, but actual inability to understand. He had made his first serious protest about the buffalo four years ago.

He had gone up to Fort Larned with a few other south-plains chiefs to meet the white peacemakers and escort them down into Kiowa country to Medicine Lodge, for the great treaty councils. The whites came in a caravan of more than two hundred vehicles, people they called "senators," "commissioners," "generals," "reporters," "governors." When they came to a large herd of buffalo, they mounted horses and were charging in every direction among the beasts, shooting right and left. In some instances they cut the tongue from their prey, or hump steaks. Some whites shot animals and left them with hardly a backward glance. Many buffalo were wounded and escaped to die miles away. The hunters shouted at each other and laughed and joked as if they took part in a drunken party.

The small group of escorting chiefs watched in dismay. They were not conservationists, but for over a decade they had seen the prime sustenance of their people decrease wherever the whites came. Satanta noted how much he and the other chiefs were outnumbered; his inclination was to start a war immediately. Then he lost his temper, kicked his horse square into the path of the ambulance full of white dignitaries, furiously shouting recriminations at them. The great caravan halted.

He knew they did not translate all he said and he did not care. Let them wonder. One question the interpreter did apparently get across: "Has the white man become a child, that he should recklessly kill and not eat?"

The general who had charge of the caravan quickly began to attempt to conciliate him. The wanton slaughter was stopped. He was promised that the hunters who had killed more than was needed for food would be punished.

He had thought at the time that he had told them something which they then understood, but if they did they soon forgot it or did not pass on the understanding to others. Up in the northern part of Kiowa hunting grounds where the railroads came whites began shooting buffalo from train windows, not even stopping for the hump steak or to see whether the animals were dead. Indian hunters kept finding carrion, stinking, shot for no purpose, or animals standing weak and forlorn, mortally wounded. And so, a year ago he had begun a policy that was difficult to carry out, based on the determination that for every buffalo wounded, a cow would be shot with an arrow. On one occasion he led a group of warriors against a cattle herd up on the Popa. In full view of the white herders his men recklessly shot and killed two hundred of their cattle, whooping and laughing, imitating white hunters, wounding and scattering the herd.

Sometimes, considering the ridiculous, wasteful policy, Satanta thought, What do you have to do to get them to understand?

It seemed hard sometimes to know whether to mourn or laugh. At that great peacemaking, when all those bearded men would not actually listen, had not really come to negotiate at all, they said it was all settled. A reservation is not a restriction; it is merely a place where the white man cannot come and trouble you, where you can be guided in white ways if you want to be. You can still hunt anywhere south of Sesepa. Besides, you get annuities by solemn agreement owed to you by promise. Then, later what do they do? They want to give you permission to leave the reservation. They want to give you permission to hunt the buffalo. And the peculiar, sweet, serene official from somewhere toward Washington says the buffalo come through the reservation twice a year; that is enough. Tell us how to breathe, how to walk on the earth under the sun, how to look at a cloud, how to love our women, how to ride a horse, how the buffalo move across the land. Tell us what to do about the buffalo.

He knew Kiowa men and women who had said last fall about the time of Agantsanha, the Moon of Cold Warning, that they did not need to make robes for the winter; they would soon get warm blankets from the government, guaranteed by treaty. But for that cold Saigya all they got was promises and excuses and the accusation of being beggars, and but for the generosity of other Kiowas they and their children might have died in the severe weather.

Now he led the band of which he was civil chief east through the southern edge of the Wichita Mountains toward Fort Sill. The other bands moved in the same direction. Satanta had found a chance to talk with most of the other chiefs in short council— about the surveyors on the reservation, about the rumor that claims were being paid out of money due the Kiowas. He knew that all his people were already talking about his successful raid; his influence in the longer councils to be held soon during the Sun Dance gathering would be high. But his mind and feelings concentrated on what lay directly ahead. He felt as if he were about to walk along the edge of a sheer cliff. They were going to the agency to get rations; many of the people had developed a taste for them, especially for the sugar and coffee. For himself, it was an excuse to come close to the whites. Out of admiration? No, out of desperation. He was certain that the nearer a chief stood to them when he showed his defiance, the better for the people who looked to him as a chief. What good is it to be militant if the whites don't know it? Chief Kicking Bird was one who understood the changing nature of human ways, and he had decided that it was time to make peace with the whites in spite of their insane contradictions and lack of understanding. Satanta disagreed with him; he disagreed as fully with those old-fashioned ones who remained hostile and ignorant of the direction the world was moving, expecting to cling to old ways forever. Satanta was determined to be hard and uncompromising with Stone Head Tatum. And he believed that his deliberate course was dangerous. He could not guess whether the white official would be as mild as a doe, as angry as a wounded bear, or as treacherous as a rattlesnake.

. . .

By Saturday, May 27, the Kiowa bands had come with their horses and dogs and lodges and equipment, and were setting up camps on the flats east of Cache Creek, in the broad two-mile space between the agency and Fort Sill. The following day would be Tatum's day of religion and he would not issue anything. Satanta and the other chiefs, with a few young men, went to the warehouse commissary buildings, which stood less than a mile south of the limestone fort buildings. The clerk would not allow them in the commissary room, but said Agent Tatum wished to speak to them in the council room.

The chiefs and the few young men filed into the large room. Satanta noted that Stone Head looked stern. When everyone was seated, on chairs or on the floor, the agent spoke through the young interpreter Mathew Leeper. A wagontrain had been attacked down south and seven men killed. He wondered whether any of them might be able to give some information about it.

There was silence for a minute. Satanta noted that the frowning agent did not look at him, but at the others, as if hoping for a remark that would give some clue.

Satanta rose and told the interpreter to tell Tatum that he had an important speech to make. Then he spoke deliberately, giving time for translation.

"I led the raid you have described.

"We've heard that you have stolen a large portion of our annuity goods and given them to the Texans.

"We have repeatedly asked you for arms and ammunition, which you have not furnished, and made many other requests which have not been granted.

"You do not listen to our talk.

"The white people are preparing to build a railroad through our country; it will not be permitted.

"Some years ago we were taken by the hair and pulled here close to the Texans where we have to fight. But we are cutting that loose now and are going out near the Cheyennes in the Antelope Hills.

"When General Custer was here two and a half years ago, he arrested Lone Wolf and me and kept us in confinement several days.

"Arresting Indians is played out now; it is never to be repeated. I want you to remember that.

"Because of many grievances, a short time ago I took about one hundred warriors, with the chiefs Tsatangya, Eagle Heart, Big Tree, Big Bow, and Fast Bear.

"We went to Texas, where we captured a wagontrain not far from Fort Richardson. We killed seven men and drove off about forty-one mules.

"Three of our men were killed, but we are willing to call it even.

"If any other Indian comes here and claims that he led the raiding party he will be lying to you, for I did it myself."

He had purposely involved the other Indians in the room in his defiance. He felt in a strong position in front of the tribe at this time, and it could be that the sweep of events from this moment would cause all Kiowas to follow the ideas he was convinced of, even though they had not been willing to make him principal chief.

It was impossible to read the face and the manner of Tatum. The agent asked the other chiefs whether they agreed to the truth of Satanta's assertions. They said that they did.

Satanta spoke up again. "Why do you have this policy of denying us arms and ammunition? Why do you want us to be weak while the white man and many Indian peoples have all the guns they want?"

Tatum acted strange. For the first time in a council he did not talk against all guns and act as if there were no possibility of issuing them to Kiowas. He said merely that he had no power to give out guns. He said that a great general from Washington, who was close to the President, was now visiting with Colonel Grierson at the fort. Perhaps the chiefs wanted to talk to him. Then, inexplicably, he said the council was over and he told his issue clerk to issue the rations. He left and went to his nearby office. Satanta observed his actions suspiciously and noted that in a short time a messenger left Tatum's office and hurried toward the fort.

The chiefs conferred as the ration issue started. They agreed that all their warriors should keep their weapons about them and stand prepared to defend their camps or to protect the flight of the old people and women and children. Satanta argued that they should go to the fort and attempt to negotiate with the great general, but the others were dubious. Shortly, Tatum left his office and headed for the fort. Satanta was thinking about the possibility of a missed opportunity—that a person with authority from Washington should talk to the soldiers and the agent and not have the Kiowas' point of view strongly represented to him. He got his horse and followed the agent. He was unarmed and had slung on his shoulder the symbol of his identity, the brass bugle.

It was less than a mile to the quadrangle of stone buildings, but his mind had time for great ranging. The feeling of walking on a cliff's edge rose strongly in him, and behind his thoughts lay an ominous anticipation, as if the next time he stepped on the ground he would feel the slipping of rocks under his foot. But he had said a hundred times in council, if you don't go among them how will you learn the mysteries of their ways? Whether you are going to make peace or war, is not knowledge of them an advantage? And how can they discover that you are reasonable and consistent men who deserve respect unless you go before them?

The light gray buildings squatted peacefully on the rise of ground ahead. He thought of treachery.

Two and a half years before he had ridden, along with Lone Wolf, Kicking Bird, and Eagle Heart, out ahead of the Kiowa warriors to parley with the soldiers. He had carried a white flag on his lance. From the invading white army had come the long-haired general they called Custer and three others. The soldier leaders would not shake hands, and Satanta thought it just as well; the blood of Black Kettle and his people was still fresh on Custer's hands. There was no interpreter and the long-haired soldier's signs were ridiculous. It finally became apparent that the man demanded that the Indians move east toward old Fort Cobb. Satanta, Lone Wolf, and the others were willing. The whites had concentrated at this place a larger force than the Kiowas could handle without their allies. All they asked was that they be allowed to move east slowly in this winter weather and not subject their camps to possible surprise attack until they saw the invading army's intentions. But Satanta and Lone Wolf soon found guns pointed at them; they were prisoners. Custer pretended that he did not know the meaning of the white flag. The two chiefs had been held hostage for two long moons in the soldiers' camps, under heavy guard.

Now, as he approached Fort Sill, he slowed his horse's pace. All the doors and windows of the buildings were closed, and no white women or children were in sight. He could see no activity at the stables west of the barracks. Across the broad parade ground one horse was tied at the picket fence in front of Grierson's house. On the front porch some officers stood. Tatum was with them.

Satanta looked back down toward the commissary buildings and the Indian camps. Some of the people were huddled in groups talking; some women were loading lodges onto travois. It was nearing sunset; shadows stretched long across the land. He ignored his apprehensions, entered the post quadrangle, went to the quarters of Horace Jones, the post interpreter, and took him to the veranda of Grierson's house.

Two or three strange officers were there. Satanta easily guessed that the red-haired one, pacing back and forth, was the chief general. The whites did not appear to see him until his foot was on the porch step; then they looked at him. He realized with a start that they had been waiting for him.

Sherman asked, "Are you the man who led the raid on the wagontrain down near old Fort Belknap?"

"Yes, I am," he said.

The general asked question after question. How many wagons? How many men killed? How many mules captured? At first he answered truthfully; then he noted that two soldiers with revolvers at their belts had placed themselves at the porch steps. The post was entirely too quiet. Where were all the black soldiers? When Sherman asked about the teamster who had been burned, he denied it.

"I was present at the fight," he said. "I did not kill anybody. The young men wanted to have a fight and I went along to show them some things. I stood back during the engagement and gave directions. Three of my men were killed and four wounded. I am ready to call it even and begin anew and see if we can negotiate the differences between us."

The general said that it is cowardly for a hundred warriors to attack a dozen teamsters. If the Indians wanted a fight the cavalry would oblige them at any time. He did not wait to discuss whether any cowardly attacks had been made against

Indian camps, nor to arrange any fight between cavalry and warriors, but began to speak to Stone Head Tatum. The agent seemed to agree and hurried away.

Satanta thought it time to test his situation. He started for the steps. The two soldiers jerked out their revolvers and motioned him back.

He asked Horace Jones, "What is this?"

The general said, "You are not to leave. You will be shot if you try to escape."

A haze of anger blew through his mind. He looked into the cruel eyes of the chief general and saw an uncompromising, narrow-minded fighting man with no shred of diplomacy in him. How simple it would be if you could only meet such a person, man to man, out on the prairie with spears or whatever, regardless of the outcome! His anger turned upon himself. He had been a fool, so sure of his own approach to the whites! But it was a time now for careful action and cool thinking.

He told Horace Jones that his people and the other chiefs would not permit this kind of treachery. The man replied that a messenger and also Agent Tatum had gone to summon all the chiefs to a conference. He thought, I hope they are not as big fools as I was, to come unarmed.

Very soon the chiefs Stumbling Bear and Kicking Bird came. They were unarmed. The general and Grierson sent Kicking Bird to round up more leaders. Old Chief Stumbling Bear sat on the porch, looked at the two soldiers with pistols in their hands and said, "We are going to be killed." The white officers looked grim and nervous.

Kicking Bird returned with ten others, including Chief Tsat-angya. Half of them carried bows and quivers or Colt revolvers. Satanta saw another group of Kiowa braves just outside the quadrangle near where a stone building was being constructed, mounted, waiting. He thought he saw a group of Indians out in the woods to the east toward Medicine Bluff Creek. If only the soldiers were asleep.

Sherman began to question the newly arrived leaders as to which of them had taken part in the attack on the wagontrain. Kicking Bird advised them in a low voice to say no more about it. The dozen Indians and nearly as many white officers stood or sat in a space no larger than three or four tepees.

Sherman glared at them and asserted, "Satanta and the other chiefs who went on the raid are under arrest. They will go back to Texas to stand trial."

Satanta asked, "What right do you have to say that?"

"It's in the treaty of 1867 and you know it as well as I."

"You have not kept a word of the treaty," Satanta said. "I'm not going to Texas. I'd rather be shot right now."

Kicking Bird, trying to ease the immediate tension, began to speak. He said that Colonel Grierson and the agent knew well that he had done everything in his power to prevent his young warriors from raiding, that he had tried to persuade his people to stay in the right path, and for the sake of the good he had done he now asked the great general to release his fellow chiefs from arrest, and he would return the captured mules.

Sherman began to answer, not agreeing, but speaking less angrily, and it was the small possibility of some compromise that prevented a bloody clash in the next instant, for around the corner of Grierson's house marched a column of black soldiers, rifles on their shoulders. The men, twenty of them, stopped square in front of the porch in two lines and turned to face the meeting.

Satanta saw with consternation his worst suspicions being realized. For only a few seconds there had been time to fight and run and perhaps half of them might have lived; he saw the hesitation in his fellow Kiowas, saw their hands go white gripping their weapons, saw them become aware that they had waited too long, that if they fought now all would die. It seemed certain now, also, that no one on this post was asleep.

The chiefs spoke in a melee of voices, bitterly, declaring that the whites had no sense of honor and could never be trusted. Horace Jones could not have interpreted it all, even had he been willing. Kicking Bird said that he had been friendly to the whites, but if war came out of this, he would be on the side of his people. Satanta had wondered about the loyalty of that chief; he decided that Kicking Bird was sincere.

Some Indians were riding around outside the quadrangle, and also some cavalry, which had evidently been hiding in the stables. A scattering of shots rang out from the direction of the trader's store. Shortly a squad of soldiers brought young chief Big Tree, dirty and out of breath, a small wound above one ear dripping blood. The soldiers made him get on the porch with the other Kiowas.

Kicking Bird was sitting where he could see out between the buildings toward Medicine Lodge Creek. He said to Satanta, "I see Lone Wolf out there. Should I motion him to come?"

"If he's going to be our principal chief," Satanta said, "it seems to me he belongs here."

Kicking Bird stood up and made signs. In a minute Lone Wolf rode around in front of the building and tied his horse to the picket fence. He laid two Spencer carbines and a bow and quiver on the ground while he adjusted his blanket at his waist, then picked up the weapons and strode between the soldier guards up to the porch. He gave the bow to Chief Stumbling Bear, who strung it and took out a handful of arrows. He gave one carbine to another Indian, then seated himself, smartly cocked his own weapon, and pointed it at the red-headed great general. The twenty-man guard in front of the porch leveled their guns.

In that moment of tense, nervous expectancy, Satanta's heart swelled toward them. He had competed with these men for honors, prestige, a high place in the tribe. If any of them lived, they would probably castigate him someday. But that did not matter. They were presenting a gift to him and Tsatangya and Big Tree, the three leaders of the raid now present. Their own violent deaths. They would take several forked-tongued, lying, egotistical white officers with them. It seemed that everyone held his breath. The price was too high, of course. He knew that the camps were already in an uproar, some of the women and children fleeing, others desperately packing. Here in this tight place surrounded by enemy guns were nearly all of the dependable and trusted leaders of the people. He sensed that Chief Tsatangya was too proud to call it off. Chief Big Tree was too young.

The sun was down. The sky was darkening. The silence seemed like a question directed at him alone. He held up one hand and said, "No! No!" and repeated more softly, "No!"

The guard raised their sights.

In a moment Sherman began telling Kicking Bird and Lone Wolf that forty-one mules must be delivered up. Suddenly a volley of shots exploded just to the south of the quadrangle. In a minute a young officer came and reported to Grierson. The chiefs demanded information from Horace Jones. He briefly told them. One soldier wounded by an arrow. One warrior killed. The Kiowa camps fleeing west. Most of the warriors were protecting their retreat.

Lone Wolf and Kicking Bird obviously were worried about the turmoil among the scattering people. They agreed to do what they could about the forty-one mules.

The officers became businesslike. They made way and motioned for all to leave except Satanta, Tsatangya, and Big Tree. Some soldiers brought iron bands connected by short chains. The iron bands clicked about their wrists and ankles. As they walked toward the southwest corner of the quadrangle, pushed by the soldiers, the chains jerked at their steps.

A low door at the end of a limestone building was pulled open, creaking. They were pushed down crude steps into the total darkness under the building. Satanta was surprised at the heavy feel of the shackles on his ankles.

CHAPTER EIGHT

THE DUNGEON

Tsatangya was an unusual man. Back at the time of the great Medicine Lodge Treaty gathering when Satanta shone, giving the first oration for the plains Indians, Tsatangya had stayed in the background, waiting calmly, listening. Finally, he had gone to the assembled commissioners when it was time for him to break camp and move south to make a brief talk and say good-bye. They received him formally, impressed by his quiet dignity, and he spoke of the changing relationship between the white man and his red brother, about his hope that wrongs between them would cease, about his understanding that Indians must eventually change, about his own age and the fact that he soon would go the way of his fathers. He said good-bye and went toward the commissioners to shake their hands. They stood up in a line, as if they felt the need to be formal. They were profoundly moved. The newsmen there covering the council were strongly affected also. The correspondent H.J. Budd, an Indian hater, a cynic about the dirtiness and unreliability of the redman, wrote this of Tsatangya's brief talk:

> I have heard the re-echoing eloquence of statesmen, as it warbled through the House and Senate of our national Capitol. I have

> heard and felt the influence of ministerial oratory as it came from the rostrum. . . . But never have I known true eloquence before this day. . . . When the last goodbye fell from his lips, it was not the voice of college culture, of prejudice, of partisan strife; it was the voice of nature and of God.

Of course, all that had been before Tsatangya lost his favorite son, who was raiding in Texas.

For a minute the three chiefs stood near one another, listening, straining their eyes, waiting for the dark place to reveal itself. Only the smell of earth and dank air met their senses. Then from the chinking sound Satanta was aware that Big Tree moved around, exploring the limits of their confinement. Satanta put his hands out and shuffled forward to touch the rough walls. He felt like a blind, crippled man. In a minute, from the other side of the cell where the younger man could be heard, came Tsatangya's voice, "Take care where you step."

The old man had obviously sat down against the wall and did not wish to be stepped on. But the words had a startling effect, coming out of the darkness, calm, not assertive, positive. Satanta had an immediate reaction. What an improper thing, for Tsatangya to be forced to go to Texas to face them! It was sacrilegious!

Then he reacted against himself. The man was old. He could afford to be calm. He had lived the good portion of his life. The Texans were probably going to kill the three of them. What would the Kiowas do in the same circumstances? But what did Tsatangya care? Old and weak. His power gone.

Only it wasn't. Beyond all reason and sense, it was not. His glance had contained, on this recent raid, all the force to compel discipline that it had ever had. He did not even advertise his medicine, but they yielded to him as if he carried the god Taime on his shoulder. Beyond all reason. It had been that way for forty years—calmness, certainty—during all the time that Satanta had watched him. Satanta knew the uses of religion and ceremony and personal medicine, but that old man did not fit the rules. He possessed a strange confidence that was beyond understanding.

After some time of silence, Satanta sat down. He asked Big Tree how he had been captured, and the young man answered, chuckling as he spoke, perhaps being uncertain as to their predicament, perhaps trying deliberately to find something humorous. He had been over in the trader's store dickering with the clerk when a squad of soldiers approached. They came in, started yelling, and rushed straight at him. He wrenched away and dived headfirst through a store window. Outside he was sprinting across a field when the bullets began to spurt around him. One nicked his scalp. He saw that they would kill him, so he stopped and allowed himself to be captured.

Satanta began talking about their situation, partly to reassure the young man, partly as a matter of thinking out loud. When he and Lone Wolf had been held prisoners some of the people had given them up, thinking they were as good as dead. It had required a great deal of talk and promises, willingness to lie like a white man, patience, but it had turned out all right; he and Lone Wolf had come out of it as strong as ever. Even if the three of them were now sent to Texas, all was not lost. Perhaps somewhere down there they could find someone to use diplomacy on, to negotiate with, if they kept their wits about them.

He asked, showing by his tone of voice that he addressed Tsatangya, "Don't you agree?"

The answer came out of the darkness: "I do not intend to go to Texas."

"Why do you say that?" Satanta felt irritation at this lack of cooperation. "Why say that to us. I could understand in a council with strangers. A man might bluff and give the wrong impression, doing what he must to get justice. But there are no strangers here. Why say a thing like that?"

The old man did not answer, and Satanta pressed on. "You have no choice. Unless we can talk them out of it. Why do you say you won't go, when they clearly have the power to make you? I'm ready for the warriors to rescue us if they can, but it's hard for them to know what to do. The people won't stop running this side of Kogaipa; the warriors have got to protect them. Can they spare enough men in time to get organized? We are surrounded by soldiers. Why do you say you won't go? I'm afraid you're going to do something foolish and get yourself killed."

The effect of the old man's answer was strong. The words were almost kind, but as much beyond argument as the honking of geese far in the sky. "Sometimes a man must give up his life in order to save it."

It was hardly the sense of the words, rather the sound, as if it came from no mouth, but from the darkness itself. The feeling of awe toward this great chief returned, and Satanta wished that he had not argued even at the irrationality.

He tried to free himself from the effect of the personal magnetism and to think back, searching for reasons. One of the early stories he had heard about Tsatangya concerned a war party which went far south to the vicinity of Pa Edal. Mexican soldiers rode out to face them, and from their ranks came a trooper armed with a saber offering a challenge to personal combat. The young warrior Tsatangya rode out with his lance. They fought a wheeling, running duel in rising dust. The Mexican was skillful with his blade, Tsatangya graceful and quick. Finally, the onlookers, seeing the wounds of the men and their horses, called them both back. For his fortitude in spite of many saber cuts, Tsatangya's comrades gave him the name of Akia-ti-sumtau, Admired One. He later gave the name away to his nephew.

Thinking of the story, Satanta asked himself why it was so great. He, himself, had killed several enemies in personal combat and the whole tribe knew it. He had not given away any of the honors he had earned, and for good reason. He needed honors to give himself the voice in council, the position of leadership, to put across policies he knew to be right. He was sure that he understood certain matters that other Kiowas did not.

The greatest military victory Tsatangya had accomplished had been done long ago against the Cheyennes, when he, Satanta, was only sixteen. The Cheyennes had begun to press hard on their northern borders, trying to take hunting ground. It was early summer, as they were gathering for Kado, the Sun Dance, out west between the streams Kop Pepa and Aguntapa. A Cheyenne band of forty-eight elite warriors rode down across the prairie in an arrogant challenge. It was a serious invasion, a test of the spirit of the tribe. Chief Tsatangya led the defenders out. He struck the enemy a slashing blow, like an eagle falling out of the sky, and turned them back. He swiftly ordered his forces to cut off their ways of escape. Before nightfall Tsatangya's men had destroyed them, taken the forty-eight scalps, and laid the bodies in a row on the prairie, so that if enemy scouts sneaked down to find what had happened they could count them easily.

But even there, Satanta thought, it was not the victory which was significant; rather it was that, when the Kiowa homeland was threatened, Tsatangya stepped forward, and the warriors followed him. Whatever secret power he had did not come from the victory but preceded it.

The most impressive thing Satanta had ever seen Tsatangya do was not an act of war. Those years of fighting the Cheyennes ended in a great peacemaking on the upper Sesepa not far from Bent's trading house. He, Satanta, had been nineteen at the time, much interested in all the preliminary meetings and negotiations. When his band came into camp on the south side of the river and he looked across the shallow stream to see hundreds and hundreds of Cheyenne and Arapaho lodges, he had been greatly impressed. It was like a Kado gathering of nations rather than bands. Cooking fires smoldered among the trees for miles up and down the valley. More than ten thousand Comanche and Kiowa horses grazed over the hills to the south. One afternoon he had gone with his mother to visit some Arapaho kinsmen. The next day, while the various chiefs were feasting one another, he went into the edge of the Cheyenne camps out of curiosity, made friends with some of them, and spoke with signs to those who during his lifetime had been deadly enemies.

Rumor said that the Kiowa chiefs offered to return the forty-eight warrior scalps taken by Tsatangya's party three years before, but it was decided that it would be best not to be reminded of old troubles. Gifts should be of a more practical nature. The day after the feasting of the chiefs, the nation of the Southern Cheyennes, men, women, and children, waded the river, bringing ropes as they had been advised, and sat down in long rows before the camps of their new allies. In front of those who sat near the Kiowa camps passed Chiefs Dohasan and Tsatangya in a ceremonial giveaway, the most liberal anyone had ever seen. From bundles of counting sticks, each stick representing a horse, Tsatangya passed out one or more to every man and woman, as many as six to some of the chiefs. The magnanimity of it sent a thrill through all of them.

The young man Satanta, watching, kept asking himself, how does he know how many to give each one? It would seem like a problem requiring discussion and consultation, yet Chief Tsatangya handed out the sticks without hesitation, assured, his movements simple, yet perfect. He knew how many to give each one without even thinking about it. Or was it that Chief Tsatangya by his bearing and manner caused everyone, Cheyenne and Kiowa alike, to accept what he did as proper whether it was proper in any reasonable way or not? It was near magic.

That afternoon the Cheyennes exchanged the sticks for horses out of the herds south of the river. They had not brought enough ropes and had to drive them away in bunches. They hastened to show themselves equally generous, giving trade guns, blankets, kettles, beads, calico. Also, they gave a giant feast, including food brought from Bent's Fort—dried apples, corn meal, sugar, molasses. There was much good humor, horse racing, gambling, trading.

Chief Tsatangya had been in the prime of his manhood then, yet somehow ageless. Sitting here in the dungeon now pondering it, Satanta thought it a great irony that he, himself, had probably thought more about diplomacy, about the place and ways of varying people on this turbulent earth, than any other redman; yet that old man—Tsatangya had begun to mumble prayers in a passionate, unintelligible voice—that old man had filled a perfect role in a great successful peacemaking without appearing to give it any thought at all. Of course, that irrational, old-fashioned, ceremonious approach was useless now three decades later.

Sitting in the complete darkness, feeling the discomfort of the cold hard floor and the weight of irons on wrists and ankles, listening to the mumbling of the prayer across the cell, Satanta again thought that the old man was weak, even ridiculous. Wearing his black sash that showed him to be the leader of the Koitsenkga, the Society of the Ten Bravest, long outmoded in a world of horses and guns, about which the whites knew nothing and cared nothing, with all that presumption he was as helpless as a baby.

But such an impression hardly had time to form itself before an opposite one began to replace it. The calendar keepers, those historians who drew pictures to represent the years, why had they named years after Tsatangya? The Winter Tsatangya's brother was killed. The Winter Tsatangya was wounded in the mustache by a Pawnee. The Winter Tsatangya's race horse Red Pet was stolen. The Winter Tsatangya brought home the bones of his favorite son. People died every year, were killed in war, did brave acts, yet the calendar keepers name a year after a small wound the old man gets in the upper lip. It seemed almost as if they thought he represented the Kiowa people, not the leadership, but themselves, the best in them, or the best that they had been in the ancient past.

And so Satanta's impressions alternated, and he could not resolve his questioning.

The nights and days dragged slowly in the dungeon. The soldiers brought food for them to eat in the halflight that came in the door. Once they were taken up the steps to talk through the interpreters to the officers. It seemed to Satanta that they came not to talk, but to gloat. Tsatangya insisted to the interpreters that Caddo Chief George Washington, a trader somewhat trusted by the whites who sometimes sold guns to the Indians, be sent to them so that they might send messages to their families.

When the thin-faced Caddo was brought they were fortunate that no interpreter was present, and they could converse with him in Comanche in front of the soldier guards. They plied him with messages and questions. The principal news he was able to relate was that the soldier chief Mackenzie had arrived from Texas three days before with many cavalrymen, and the three of them were to be taken south the next day.

Tsatangya said to him, "I want Kiowas here to say good-bye to us."

Caddo Chief Washington said, "That may not be easy."

Tsatangya went on as if the objection had not been voiced. "And children," he said. "Children who will live and remember a long time. Do you understand?"

Washington was mutely agreeing as if he were hypnotized.

"I want the hunting knife you carry in your belt. Embrace me and pass me the knife. Say good-bye loudly in English for the sake of the guards."

Washington did as he was bade, and the guards evidently suspected nothing.

CHAPTER NINE

THE MEMBER WHO WORE THE BLACK SASH

John Charlton was corporal of the guard that day, June 8, 1871, along with Corporal Robinson. Lieutenant Thurston of E Company was officer of the day. The regiment had orders to head back to Fort Richardson, traveling with all precautions. Charlton was thinking: The colonel didn't give us what you might call a real long rest, three lousy days, after leading us around in the mud and rain nearly three weeks; I guess he figures if some of the boys get rested too much they'll get to fighting with these colored cavalry boys.

Rumor had it that the Kiowas had gone west, but how far? They couldn't be sure. If it looked like the prisoners were going to be taken away from them or escape, orders said to shoot them dead. And rumor said *that* order had come from *the* general, not Bad Hand Mackenzie. After the slick way old Sherman had tricked the Indians and captured three of their head men, no telling what they might do.

The two wagons came, heavily loaded, three spans of mules on each one, up to the end of the long company quarters building. Charlton was thinking, It'll be a cold day in July before we have quarters for enlisted men like that at Richardson. He watched a Fort Sill officer and some black soldiers bring the prisoners out of the cellar to deliver them over to the 4th Cavalry. All of them had to stoop away down to come out of the door, as if coming out of a hole in the ground. The three Indians blinked and squinted at the light and took short steps to keep from jerking the chains on their leg irons. A bunch of officers, including Mackenzie and Grierson, stood around with their hands on their hips to watch the prisoners being loaded.

The three Indians wore blankets wrapped around them. The old one with stringy hair and mustache seemed nervous. After blinking a bit he saw Grierson standing there and stumbled or lurched toward him. The other two caught him. It had seemed as if he had recognized Grierson suddenly and started to shake hands with him. The three were talking in that weird, sputtering language they have. Charlton was thinking: I'd give two to one the old one is cussing and the middle-aged one and the young one are begging him about something.

Lieutenant Thurston said, "Corporal Charlton, you and Private Beals put these two in the rear wagon with you."

Then he said to Robinson, "You and Private Cannon take the old one in the first wagon."

Charlton wondered whether the officer had decided beforehand on such an arrangement or made up his mind on the spot. He was thinking: They say the way to make corporal is learn to read a lieutenant's mind, but the way to make sergeant is learn a lieutenant can't even read his own mind. Here the man has given me and Beals one Indian apiece and has given Robinson and Cannon only one Indian between them, and that an old one. Well, ours is not to wonder why.

They motioned to the two of them to get into the rear wagon, and the two Indians gave no trouble but allowed themselves to be boosted in. The canvas was open, tied back to the rear, and the bed loaded nearly level with sacked corn and oats and bundled fodder.

The old one up ahead wouldn't budge. Four of them picked him up and hoisted him into the front wagon. He looked wild. He began chanting some endless song in a high-pitched voice.

Some of the troopers led off, then the pack train. As the lead wagon rolled out the interpreter Horace Jones, standing alone, observing, said to Charlton, "You all better watch that old Indian, Corporal."

He asked him why.

"He means trouble. He's singing his death song."

He didn't have time to ask the interpreter any more about it. Death song? What the hell is that? The teamsters got them moving, and the wagons rumbled down the hill south toward the stone quarry and the agency buildings and the crossing of East Cache Creek. A few Indians stood near the fort, watching but pretending not to watch, stoic, and with them was a man Charlton took to be an agency employee. He didn't know what kind of Indians they were. He thought: When they get to hanging around an army post, they get to looking all the same. Thank God, they're not armed!

On a little rise not far from the road stood some Indian children, eight or ten, dressed in shirts and trousers that didn't fit.

Farther out to the west, maybe half a mile, he could see a single mounted Indian who looked naked. Just sitting his horse. Some more could have been down to the left among the timber, and there seemed to be a few ahead at the agency buildings. He figured the one out west alone was a scout for the wild ones. George Washington, a chief of the Caddoes, rode beside the wagons.

The old prisoner in the wagon ahead never let up. He would

yell at the sky, duck his head under his blanket a few seconds, jerk it out, and yell at the people around him. The Tonkawa scouts riding nearby grinned at him and chattered among themselves. The troopers laughed nervously at the old man. They didn't know how to take it, or thought it was some kind of horseplay. The nearest trooper squirted a mouthful of tobacco juice toward the old Indian. Sergeant Miles Varily shouted to the trooper to cut it out and conduct himself like a soldier.

The old Indian seemed to get more worked up the farther the caravan went. Charlton was thinking: I'd give a purty to know what's in his mind.

» «

Help me, oh, Taime. Help me! I am too old to do it! My flesh is weak and wasted and I am fit only for sitting by the fire and letting others tend my wants. Help me! I am too old for it!

Oh, Sun, you remain forever, but we Koitsenkga must die!

Oh, Earth, you remain forever, but we Koitsenkga must die!

That fool George Washington has brought me only Caddo children to watch. The Kiowas stand far off and I don't even know them with my dim eyes. And these pale-faced . . . very strange . . . people. Who will remember? Who will know? I am too old, Taime! Help me!

Oh, Sun, you remain forever, but we Koitsenkga must die!

Oh, Earth, you remain forever, but we Koitsenkga must die!

You! Yes, you, you damned Tonkawa! Can you understand Comanche? You can have my scalp. The hair is thin and stringy, but it will be the best you ever got!

Oh, Grandmother, I'm too old for this! Help me! How can these old tired bones. . . ? How is it that my hands burn so? And sting? When I am so old? I cannot find my strength, but pain finds me so easily! Only a little more flesh and the irons will slip over. The blood helps to slip the irons. Help me, Grandmother, please! Help me find strength. Give me, for only a minute, the strength of my youth!

Oh, Sun, you remain forever, but we Koitsenkga must die!

Oh, Earth, you remain forever, but we Koitsenkga must die!

You! Yes, you, Caddo! Tell my people that my bones will be lying beside the road. Come and get them.

Son, make ready. My favorite son! My departed son! I am coming to see you. I have grown old and weak, but we shall see each other today. Make a little feast for me.

Oh, Earth Mother, where are my people? I have never lied to you in all my life. I need your help. Earth Mother, who will remember? Someone. . . . May someone see and understand! If this is the last. . . . If we are come to the end of our way of life, let those who live on know about the Koitsenkga. Somewhere out there . . . a hundred winters . . . my people will need to know! Help us, Earth Mother! Help the Kiowas! We are come into a great confusion. Let them know our weaknesses if you will in that far-off time, but let them know our ancient strengths also. Let them feel all our hopes and reasons for the Koitsenkga. Let them forget my name, if you will, but let them remember this day when the man who wore the black elkskin sash took his stand before alien soldiers.

You chiefs! Satanta! Big Tree! See me? I am a Kiowa warrior of old! See the tree ahead beside the road? I will not go beyond it!

Oh, Taime! how the flesh rebels against my teeth! It hurts! I am too old for my task. Give me strength. Give me strength! Please give me some of the strength of my youth!

I must loose the sash first, then reach for the knife. Grandmother, may someone see me fasten the sash. Help me gather all the power remaining and use it in these brief pieces of time, now.

Oh, Sun, you remain forever, but we Koitsenkga must die!
Oh, Earth, you remain forever, but we Koitsenkga must die!

» «

Listen, I'm going to tell you the God's truth. That old Injun was crazy as a loon. He acted raving crazy. Ain't no two ways about it.

I don't deny I spit at him. It didn't mean a thing. It was just a joke or like a that. If a man gets aggravated, you josh him a little. I never spit in five feet of him. Fer one thing I'd done been in the army long enough to have sense enough not to spit tobaccy juice on no government property, no government wagon, no government floor, ner nothing else claimed by the government.

After I spit at him, which didn't mean a thing, I commenced to keep my eyes on the old coot. First time he come out from under that blanket that's when I started in to keep my eyes on him. Had blood on that scraggly mustache.

I says to myself, how come he's got blood on his mouth? If that's what it is? Ain't nobody hit him or cut him or like a that. Looked like he been eating a bloody piece of raw meat. And them sounds! Crazy as a loon!

Not that I was skeered of him, mind you. He was old. Look at a man's neck; that's where you can tell. Hell, he was seventy, eighty, if he was a day. Double ironed. And like the sarge told me: Look out on the prairie, soldier. Could be they will come whooping and hollering in here, charge us, and try to take the prisoners. Only when I seen the blood on his mouth and got to noticing them sounds, not like English, weird sounds, no sense to them. . . . Damn near like he was praying, if an Injun could pray. Then I commenced to keeping my eye on him.

Right before he rose up, nobody else seen it or didn't say so if they did, tears ran out of his eyes while he was singing. If you want to call it singing. It was high talking or chanting or like a that. Made no sense. But tears come out, just streaming, and run down onto the blood on his mouth and chin.

I commenced to think, my God! Old man, take it easy. What's eating you so?

They was something else I don't believe nobody noticed but me. He had on a long suspender like. Over one shoulder. Made out of rawhide. Deer or something. Dirty, like it had charcoal on it. I'll tell you what he done with it.

I'm riding along there and he drags his head out from under the blanket for about the fourth time. Looks at the sky and screams. Next thing I know he's whacking that knife into Corporal Robinson's leg. He's slashing at Cannon, and both them soldiers go tumbling head over heels out of the wagon. I'm riding along there, my eyes bugging out, looking straight at him and saying, he can't be loose! My God! He can't be! He *is* loose.

That's when he does this queer thing with that strap or suspender or like a that. What's he doing? If you think about it? Taking on the U.S. Army! But he takes time out, calm and slow-like.

He pins that suspender to the wagon box with his knife!

Then he rises up with Corporal Robinson's carbine, working the lever. Throwing a cautridge in the chamber.

This is all going fast. Hell, the two guards are rolling in the dirt away from the wagon wheels and my horse is spooking and the team, some is shying this way and some that. Tony Bordello, sitting on the near wheeler is scrambling to keep his seat and yelling, "Whoa! Whoa!" Lieutenant Thurston commences to yell, "Shoot him! Shoot him!" And the boys—they all been scanning the prairie—now they're jouncing around trying to unlimber their guns and see where the enemy is at.

I think the old Injun screams twice. It makes chills run up my back. He's holding that Spencer carbine in his bloody hands and jerking the lever. I reckon a round was in the chamber and the extractor never took hold. Maybe it jerked loose when Robinson dropped it. Anyway the old Injun can't get the action closed. He's turning around to all of us.

Lieutenant Thurston gets his military bearings and quits yelling "Shoot him!" and goes to yelling, "Fire! Fire! Fire!" I don't know who all fired. Too many. We had a full-scale battle there a mile south of the post, just west of East Cache Creek, right out from the long agency buildings. You can see bullets hit a man close like that. I seen one catch Tony in the head, knock his hat off, plow a red furrow in his hair, and knock him off the near wheeler. I seen them strike that old Injun and shake him like tall grass in a hail storm.

He goes down in the corn sacks and you can't see him for the sideboards. Maybe Lieutenant Thurston tells them to cease firing.

But he rises up, that old Injun. Like a damned ghost! The tears and blood on his face shining. He's trying to scream some more, but ain't got no air. He's give up on the lever. Finger ain't even on the trigger. But he's pointing it. Swinging around and pointing it at every son-of-a-bitch in the U.S. Army!

I don't know if the lieutenant says "Fire" or what. They cut him down. They cut the side out of the wagon with lead. They knock the old man over, his belt comes loose, and he falls into the dust in the road. The team shies away out of the road, and some mother's son gets enough sense about him to ride over and catch the bridle of one of the lead mules.

The boys are jerking their eyes all around across the prairie to see where the big attack is coming from. Their guns are smoking. I guess we follow Lieutenant Thurston. Anyway, we level our guns on the second wagon. Trying to be ready for whatever the hell is happening.

The one they call Satanta—his fists are clenched tight in front of his iron cuffs and his face looks like a chunk of red granite. The one they call Big Tree has put his hand on Corporal Charlton's arm, and I hear him say in Mexican, "Por favor, no!" Fifty muzzles are pointing at him, but Charlton's gun is still pointing at the old one in the dirt, and Big Tree says, choked up like he's got a cold, "Por favor!"

The general, Old Bad Hand Mac, is galloping down hell for leather, him and the officers that waited to gossip with Grierson.

If I spit at that old Injun I'm sorry. I never understood what he was commencing to do. One thing I'll say: When the ruckus died down to where a man could think, I checked my gun. The barrel was cold and seven cautridges in it. I never fired a round at the old man and I'm glad.

» «

The colonel yelled, "Deploy for the main attack! Where is the main body of warriors?"

The troopers and Lieutenant Thurston were jostling around, confused and embarrassed.

The colonel said, "Lieutenant, what in the hell is going on?"

"We couldn't help it, sir. He had a knife and he got a carbine, and . . ."

"A knife! Who searched him? Later! Later! Captain, we cannot stop here. Get some flanks out farther! Get some scouts out ahead! Let your sergeant lead F Company and you come back here.

"Surgeon!"

"This teamster is badly wounded, sir."

"I can't help it! Come here and examine this Indian!"

They dragged him out of the loose dirt which was cut up by hoof tracks and wagon tracks. They leaned his gray head and his shoulders against the trunk of a pecan tree, for his eyes still shined and sometimes his chest shuddered as if he took a deep breath.

"Can this Indian live?" Colonel Mackenzie asked. "Look, Patzki, I want a positive answer. We've got to get out of here."

"No, Sir, he can't live."

"Examine him! Examine him! You've got to be right, man! Here, Sergeant, ride fast up to General Grierson. Tell him I urgently request him to come down here personally. Tell him I said immediately please. He'll need an ambulance to carry a dead man and a wounded man. Hurry!

"What the hell's the matter with that soldier? His leg!"

"He was stabbed, sir. It's not . . ."

"It's damned well bleeding!"

"It's not deep, sir."

"Put him in a wagon. Patzki, what's the answer? Can the Indian live? I don't want any of your medical theories! I've got to know for sure! We can't move till we know. And we've got to move! They could hit us anytime!"

"The Indians that were sneaking around and the children—they seem to have drawn off, sir."

Assistant Surgeon Patzki said, "I see a dozen fatal wounds, sir."

"Dammit, man, look under his clothing! A little blood won't hurt you. Don't you see that we have to be positive?"

"What do you want? An exact count of his fatal wounds?"

"I don't want any smart-alec nonsense. Do just exactly what I say, and if you have any questions or complaints we will take them up later. Captain! Please listen carefully. Captain Davis,

I seldom get orders straight from the top, if you know what I mean. In the event that it hasn't come clear to you: We didn't look worth a damn chasing these Indians. Now we've got a simple task from the same authority. Transport three prisoners to Texas. I would hate to look like a fool twice in a row. I want this outfit moving. Take charge of it. I want to camp away down on Beaver Creek tonight. That mule over there is out of his traces. Find you a teamster among the men. Get it straightened out and start rolling. Move like you were in enemy territory. Patzki, what's the answer? Captain, I'll wait here for Grierson."

Assistant Surgeon Patzki said, "I count eight fatal wounds, sir. Twenty-seven that might not be fatal. Or would not be if they were separately sustained and treated in time."

"Oh, hell . . . do you think he's dead?"

"He's very dead, sir."

"You better go back to Bordello. See what you can do for him. I wish that damned Grierson would get down here."

Two of the Tonkawa scouts rode back, dismounted, left the reins dangling, and walked up to the colonel smiling.

"What do you want?"

One of them made the sign for scalping.

The colonel frowned at his scouts a moment. Tsatangya's blanket lay there, holes in it, dirt sticking to the bloody spots on it. He picked it up, tossed it to the Tonkawas, and motioned them to go on and join the caravan.

Colonel Mackenzie, his wagons, and men approached Fort Richardson from the north, and their road led through town. The wagon canvas was pulled forward and lashed securely, concealing the two prisoners. The men had orders to say nothing to the citizens of Jacksboro.

The eager-beaver post adjutant, Second Lieutenant Carter,

had been occupied with paper work while the colonel's troops had been engaged in their glorious three-week adventure. He was impressed with the prisoners, so much so that an image of Satanta would stick in his mind and he would write of the Indian chief long years later: "He was over six feet in his moccasins, and . . . seemed to be even taller than he really was." Little did the lieutenant know the falsity of the first half of that statement or the truth of the last half or what it would reveal about his own susceptibility to impression, for Satanta measured exactly five feet, nine and one-half inches, as would be determined later. That description, inaccurate as to detail, but poignantly right in its revelation of effect on a young mind, continues thus: "His coarse jet black hair, now thickly powdered with dust, hung tangled about his neck except a single braided scalplock with but one long eagle feather to adorn it. His immense shoulders, broad back, deep chest, powerful hips and thighs, contrasted singularly with the slight forms of the Ton-ka-ways. . . . The muscles stood out on his gigantic frame like knots of whip cord, . . . his perfectly immobile face and motionless body gave him the appearance of polished mahogany. . . . Every feature of his proud face bespoke . . . disdain. . . ."

The post guardhouse was full as usual with soldiers who had attempted to desert, those who had been too obviously drunk, those who had been guilty of affray. Behind the large stone hospital sat a house which was the post laundry; its small rear room was the post morgue. Here Satanta and Big Tree were brought for confinement, still in their chains.

The colonel sent a messenger that evening to find Jack County Sheriff Michael McMillan, or, should the officer not be in town, any official of the county.

They already knew something of the matter in question, for General Sherman had written on May 28 to the temporary commanding officer of Fort Richardson, "We now hold Satanta, Satank [Tsatangya], and Big Tree, three as influential and as bad Indians as ever infested any land," and had added in a postscript, "Let the Jacksboro people know of this." Now Colonel Mackenzie wished to inform the county officials that he had two Indians instead of three and they were being held securely awaiting the action of the state of Texas.

Another question which had already been bothering the colonel was also mentioned in that same letter from General Sherman: "They must not be mobbed or lynched, but tried regularly for murder and as many other crimes as the Attorney can prove; but the military authorities should see that these prisoners never escape alive, for they are the very impersonation of murder, robbery, arson, and all the capital crimes of the Statute Book." The colonel discussed with the officers of the post the necessity of guarding the prisoners with perfect security against rescue or against illegal action by settlers, and he believed that he had adequate authority to keep the two murderers in military custody while the civil procedures took their course. He was determined that Satanta and Big Tree should be given a fair trial by a jury of their peers, strictly according to law, and duly executed.

CHAPTER TEN

THE SETTLERS

On Friday, June 16, 1871, the *San Antonio Daily Express* ran a story on the arrest of the Kiowa chiefs and plans for their trial. The editor was not yet aware that one of the three chiefs had been killed. The paper said: "Instead of bringing these three wretches back to Texas to be tried by a civil tribunal, they ought to have been tied to the mouth of a cannon and blown into their happy hunting grounds, and their whole tribe made to follow by the same expeditious conveyance. This is not cruelty, it is justice. . . ."

The *Express* was a radical Republican newspaper, given to violent solutions. It believed, for example, that the failure of the United States to execute the leaders of the Confederacy had been a blunder. It believed that the Indian problem should be solved by exterminating the "red devils." Many white settlers on the frontier agreed.

But certain white authorities on the frontier, no less determined that the raiding must cease, saw that the problem was more complicated, requiring more than belligerent assertions or acts, requiring shrewdness and finesse.

In the latter part of June His Honor Charles Soward sat in

his office in the red brick courthouse at Weatherford, where he made his headquarters for the far-flung Thirteenth Judicial District over which he presided. He was thinking about his upcoming trip to Jacksboro, not about the rougher atmosphere in that soldier town, but about the problems which would certainly arise in the unique trial to be held there.

He wished for a moment that he were the District Attorney in the case rather than the judge, then realized that it could be worse; he could be defense counsel. That reminded him; he had to appoint someone. Briefly he thought of the possibility that the Indian Bureau might defend the two chiefs; it would save a local lawyer the embarrassment. There was not much precedent. But, no, you never know what you might get into. It was a ticklish business. The defense had better be left in the control of local people. This case could well be the turning point on this frontier, as an example and the first in a series of trials. It was a God-sent piece of fortune. Long overdue. He had better appoint as defense counsel a man, or two men, who could conduct a decent defense, but who knew the nightmare of Indian raiding and would not expect technicalities to stand in the way of a larger justice.

The problem he faced was not his alone. He had been appointed by Edmund Davis, the reconstruction governor of Texas, not at all beloved by the citizens of the state, but who had found much common cause with the responsible authorities on the frontier, District Attorney S.W.T. Lanham, the sheriffs of the various counties, the lawyers and business leaders of the communities in his district. Soward, like the others, took satisfaction in the spread of Roman-English law over a land where it had never before existed. That movement had been stopped in northwest Texas; in fact, it had been turned into a retreat. Jack County, in which was situated Jacksboro and Fort

Richardson; Young County, to the west of it, in which Belknap had been the county seat; and Clay County, just to the north of Jack, had all three been organized fourteen or fifteen years ago. Clay had folded up from Indian attacks nine years ago. Young, six years ago. This backing up of civilization seemed intolerable to a man trained in the law.

How do you convict a couple of Indian chiefs? But he did not face the problem alone. Lawyers and officials on the frontier found it necessary to cooperate thoroughly on account of the difficulties of transportation, of gathering evidence, securing witnesses, serving papers. He knew at least eight lawyers in this town of Weatherford, including the D.A., whom he could trust. He had no intention of carrying the delicate burden by himself.

During that week of June 18 through June 24, 1871, Judge Charles Soward had a series of conferences or talks or chats. The purpose of the conferees was to probe all facets of the unusual situation they faced. They generally agreed on a policy informally embodied in ten points:

1. First and foremost, convict and punish these so-called chiefs, Satanta and Big Tree. Make an example of them.

2. Cloak the trial with all the legality possible. Else there may be no more such cases and the raiding will continue. Federal officials and other outsiders do not believe in the validity of legal processes on the border, but it is possible to convince them otherwise. James Robinson, clerk of the Jack County District Court, had been on the citizen's committee which presented the appeal to Sherman a month ago. They had swamped the general with affidavits in legal language, properly notarized, and the man had been impressed.

3. Whether the upcoming trial is in fact legal is not the issue. We are at war with these Indians.

4. It could be a touchy business. Outsiders will be trying to look over our shoulders. We have one agent named Tatum on our side for the present, but his superiors in the Indian Bureau will surely object to the trial.

5. Be as cooperative as possible with the army; they are on our side now.

6. We do not want a change of venue for several reasons: Move it off the frontier and you might not get a conviction; move it and you might have meddlesome people judging the legality; move it away from Fort Richardson and you cause the army trouble.

7. We don't want physical custody of Satanta and Big Tree until it is time to hang them. A lynching or escape or rescue would spoil everything. But to put the sure stamp of legality on it we will pretend all along that we have full custody and full jurisdiction.

8. We should not give the federal government or anyone else any substantial records on the trial, only legalese.

9. It will be impossible to get a proper murder venire in Jacksboro, considering all the valid challenges for cause that can be made on account of prejudice against Indians. You probably could not get a good jury out of a hundred veniremen, but we are going to empanel twelve one way or the other and try these savages.

10. There is not going to be any appeal or review of the case.

After the informal conferences and meetings of the minds among the lawyers of Weatherford, it appeared that some considerable burden still rested on the shoulders of Judge Charles Soward. Who, after all, is responsible for the legality of a trial? What if they could not prevent a review, either in the near future or by historians? What, finally, could the judge fall back on? How about "extenuating circumstances"? Make it seem so hard to hold a trial that the judge is a hero doing his impossible job. And so, though the lawyers of the town knew perfectly what was in the mind of the district judge, and he what was in theirs, they presented him a petition. He would refuse the petition of course. It read thus:

> To the Honorable Charles Soward, Judge of the Thirteenth Judicial District of the State of Texas.
>
> We, the undersigned members of the bar, practicing attorneys, most respectfully request and petition your honor not to hold the next ensueing term of District Court at Jacksborough, Jack County, Texas; and state as reasons therefore that it is a well known and indisputable fact that the County of Jack and the whole country between this place and Jacksborough is to an unusual and very dangerous extent infested with large bands of hostile Indians, and that on this account travel between this and Jacksborough is unusually dangerous, that owing to the great number of Indians in this country, we do not think it would be humane and just to force litigants and jurors of Jack County to leave their families and attend court, we therefore hope your Honor will not hold said at Jacksborough.

The petition was dated June 22, 1871, and signed by S.W.T. Lanham, A.J. Hood, J.L.L. McCall, R.J. Mackenzie, O.W. Bolls, J.C. Stone, H.F. Hensley, and Thomas Ball.

The judge chose the last-named on the list, Thomas Ball, a fine orator, as one defense counsel. For the other he chose a man who had not cooperated in the meeting of the minds, Joseph A. Woolfolk. It seemed a safe appointment. Woolfolk had been a county official out at Belknap before Young County had been closed down by the Indians, and he had been an officer in the frontier battalion for defense against Indians. But the man was not quite what they thought he was.

Even as Satanta had studied the whites and looked forward to a distant day when white men and red men would have an alliance as brothers, so a few whites transcended the fierce urgency of the times and wondered whether it must not be true that there is more to the Indian than appears, if one could only understand them. Joe Woolfolk was a strange lawyer. He believed that counsel should take the side of the client, that the American system of partisan pleading should prevail, that every human being is due his day in court. He was up against a tough combination, but the trial would not be so much a cut-and-dried proposition as the vested authorities had planned.

A piece of evidence had been spread in a messy way before the people of Weatherford. A handful of arrows from the scene of the attack on Warren's wagontrain had been brought here and displayed as a curiosity. Local Indian experts had identified them as having been made by three different tribes: Kiowas, Comanches, and another uncertain tribe. Well, the word had come that the two chiefs awaiting trial were Kiowas. Arrows make a beautiful courtroom exhibit. Judge Charles Soward and District Attorney Lanham consulted whether it might be possible to throw away the other arrows and get an expert to identify the remaining arrows as Kiowa. It could be done if they needed the evidence. They agreed to wait and see what evidence was available.

The Judge knew a hundred stories of Indian fights and raids out in that country to the north and west. Every soul who lived out there knew them. Indian trouble had been the story of their lives for the past dozen years, bigger to them than the Civil War, bigger than the twisted politics of Reconstruction. This upcoming trial would take its meaning and, indeed, its character from the fears and hatreds which had arisen in those turbulent dozen years.

One raid in particular the Judge was reminded of because of the bugle blowing. One of these Kiowa chiefs, Satanta, when he was taken prisoner had worn an ordinary army bugle slung around his neck, and rumor from the Fort Sill area said he often wore it and knew how to blow calls on it. In what the settlers had come to call the Elm Creek Raid, out west of Belknap, an Indian had blown a bugle. There would be no way to tie the two together, but a person could not help wondering. The Elm Creek Raid had happened seven years before, in 1864; its consequences still continued. It had made a hero out of a black man, Britt Johnson, and only this spring the Indians had taken revenge on him out there on the Butterfield Trail near where Warren's wagontrain was attacked. One other thread of consequence might remain. Several captives had been taken along Elm Creek and all but one had been recovered, a tiny girl named Milly Durgan. Whether there were still any hopes for her, no one knew.

Elm Creek headed out west toward old Camp Cooper and ran into the Brazos upstream of Belknap. By the spring of 1864 settlers in that area were few and scattered, but they had built two small private forts where they could concentrate for protection, Fort Murray north of the river, and Fort Bragg, some six miles south on Elm Creek. On October 13 of that year a large party of Indians, several hundred, swooped down from the north. The settlers learned their peril at different times depending on where they lived, but those watchful ones whose eyes were frequently on the horizon saw smoke columns, evidently the signal to attack, rise at eleven o'clock on that cool autumn morning.

A cattleman named Peter Harmonson, who had been the first "chief justice" of Young County, and his son Perry had ridden out to hunt some of their stock that day and were among the first to encounter the Indians. The two raced their horses to a grove of timber and dismounted to make a brief stand not far from the mouth of Elm Creek. They wounded one of the attackers, then mounted and dashed west to a thicket on the small streambed called Rabbit Creek. Fortunately, they were well armed. One of their horses was killed, but it would have required some risk and delay to flush them out of their hiding. The Indians turned back toward where Elm Creek ran into the Brazos from the south. Harmonson, with a minor wound, and his son rode their remaining horse two miles farther west to Fort Murray to give the alarm.

Francis Peveler had set out that morning with his brother's Negro slave called Seth with the intention of making a long trip east to a mill near Fort Worth before winter weather set in. He rode horseback and the old black man drove their ox wagon. They saw smoke rising near the mouth of Elm, but did not believe it could be Indian signals because it was too near the settlements. They came into Fort Murray and ate lunch, but did not continue their planned trip, for shortly thereafter Harmonson and his son came in with the news of Indians.

Then Lieutenant N. Carson, in command of a detachment of Texas Cavalry stationed on the border, came in breathless. He had fought a pitched battle with the redskins. He brought a couple of women his men had rescued from the ranch of Isaac McCoy. He said the country was "alive with Indians."

In his official report of the engagement, Lieutenant Carson stated that two of his men, Fields and Jones, had started on the thirteen-mile trip to Belknap, had been attacked by Indians, and had returned to camp for reinforcements. He had taken fourteen of his twenty men to investigate. They came upon a high point and saw two of the savages, whom they chased for more than a mile. It was an ambush. Suddenly three hundred concealed Indians rose up within fifty yards and charged in. The lieutenant yelled for his men to fire and fall back. They acted with unexampled coolness and bravery, but five of them were shot from their saddles and overrun. The men killed were Jones, Snodgrass, Neathrey, Walker, and Blue. In the retreat Brison's horse was shot from under him, but he was saved. Buckingham was thrown from his horse but made his way to Fort Murray. Fields took a wound in the thigh. The horses of McGuire, Wallis, Wimberly, and the lieutenant were wounded. Near the McCoy ranch the border cavalrymen took a stand against the hotly pursuing invaders long enough to rescue Mrs. McCoy and her niece; the men of the family were away from the house at the time. The cavalrymen took the women up behind their saddles and escaped north to Fort Murray.

Someone reported that the Indians had discovered the horse herd belonging to the people in the fort. A short sally out on the prairie revealed that the settlers had waited too long. Their main horse herd was cut off and taken.

Francis Peveler and young Perry Harmonson, the son of Peter Harmonson, took a telescope and climbed on top of the crude building of Fort Murray. They saw countless Indians plying through the mesquite brush. Peveler, squinting two miles south across the Brazos, said, "They are killing old Isaac McCoy and his son right now." Perry prevailed upon him to be quiet about it, for there was nothing to be done, and the womenfolk of that family were among the anxious crowd below.

All that afternoon they watched toward the east and the south through the telescope, seeing bands of Indians, and once Peveler reported seeing so many pack horses loaded with plunder that he could not count them. He said they had even brought their dogs along. The settlers moulded bullets and carried water to hoard, filling every bucket, jar, churn, and pitcher. They waited nervously, but the attack against Fort Murray never came. Perhaps, since it had been built only that year, the Indians did not know about it; perhaps they were seeking easier targets.

After having chased Peter Harmonson and his son Perry, one large force of the invaders turned back east to the mouth of Elm Creek. There they caught a man named Joel Myers, whom they killed and scalped. Then they turned southwest up the creek valley.

At the large ranch house of the widow Mrs. Elizabeth Fitzpatrick they struck their strongest blow. With her lived a young son and grown daughter, two small granddaughters, and the family of Negro Britt Johnson. Britt had gone with a neighbor to haul supplies from Weatherford. The grown daughter, Susan Milly Durgan, and the eldest Negro boy, Charles, about twelve, and a little brindle bulldog came out to defend the home. They lost their lives. Taken captive were Elizabeth Fitzpatrick; her son Joe, thirteen; granddaughter Lottie, five; Britt's wife Mary; and his little boy and girl, Jube and Cherry. The house was set afire. The older Negro boy was left where he was shot down. The grown daughter Susan was stripped naked and scalped. The small bulldog lay in the doorway, filled with arrows. Young rancher Charles Goodnight, who came by the following day, said that the savages had ripped open Mrs. Fitzpatrick's feather mattresses and pillows and scattered the downy feathers. A north wind blew them southward to cover an acre or more, where they looked like snow fallen on the autumn foliage.

But in the last moments of violence and confusion, the house ablaze and filled with smoke, a warrior found a tiny girl still inside, crawling out from under a bed where she had been hidden. He snatched the child out of the burning house and took her on his horse. The girl, Milly Durgan, about eighteen months old, would be separated from the other six captives.

From the Fitzpatrick ranch the Indians moved upstream toward the home of Thomas Hamby. His son Thornton had been wounded in the Confederate army and had come home on furlough to recover. Also living at the Hamby place were Doc Wilson and his family. The three men had been branding calves that morning at a nearby stock pen. They heard the guns firing at the Fitzpatrick ranch and saw great numbers of Indians in the distance. Evidently the settlers had given thought to the difficulty of fighting and warning others while trying to protect families, for the first thing the three men did was conceal the Hamby and Wilson women and children in an obscure cave in a rocky cliff overlooking the creek. They then fled west to warn other settlers, aiding two more families of women and children to hide.

Finally the three men, with the raiders hot on their heels, came to the ranch of George Bragg, called Bragg's Fort, though it was only a two-room picket house. They piled off their horses and ran for the door. As they were scrambling inside, Wilson was struck in the chest with an arrow. He pulled it out and fell dead.

Thomas and Thornton Hamby found the place poorly defended. Besides George Bragg, an old man, there were only five women, a bunch of children, and a near-grown Negro boy and girl. A desperate fight ensued. The Indians charged to the notes of a bugle; they were driven back again and again by gunfire from the small fort. One warrior came to the very wall and was trying to dig out one of the picket posts when he was detected; Thomas Hamby fired through a crack with his revolver and killed him. The Indians did not realize the effectiveness of their attack and the small number of defenders. George Bragg was wounded so severely that he could not fire a gun. Thomas Hamby was wounded three times. The Indians gathered their dead and wounded, blew retreat on their bugle, and pulled away.

That day the invaders altogether killed eleven settlers, wounded about the same number, and carried away seven captives. They also plundered nearly every house along Elm Creek, drove away every horse they could find, and took as many cows as was convenient.

Guerrilla war seems peculiarly cruel and uncompromising, but sometimes in the confusion of events dominated by flame and blood an act can be seen that strangely does not belong. Such a thing happened that October day in Elm Creek valley. John Wooten was caught alone. His horse was shot from under him. In the fall his gun jammed into the mud so that it was clogged and useless. He ran carrying the gun, two Indians chasing. He turned and pointed the weapon, but one Indian yelled, "Don't shoot, Wooten! You run!" One of them knew him and spoke some English. Wooten took the advice and ran. He had helped issue beef to the Indians on the Brazos years before. When he turned again the Indian yelled, "Run, Wooten, run!" They ran him out of the path of the other invading redmen, then turned away and allowed him to escape. Whether he had done some kindness years before or whether they simply could not kill a man they knew has not been explained.

When Britt Johnson came back to the burned Fitzpatrick house to find one son killed, his wife, Mary, and little Cherry and Jube carried away, one thought began to burn in his mind: They could not have his wife and children. He intended to get them back.

Britt was an unusual man by any standards. Born a slave, now about forty-one years old, he had moved with the Johnsons to this part of the world and had demonstrated by his ability, perseverance, character, bravery, that the question of who-owns-whom was actually unsettled on the frontier. Apparently he shared ownership in the Johnson family's cattle business, lived with his own family in the large Fitzpatrick house, and acted as foreman of Elizabeth Fitzpatrick's ranch. There were free black people in Texas. Perhaps the Johnsons had not settled in their own minds the slavery business, but Britt trusted them and himself.

At the time of the raid on Elm Creek, the country to the north and west of the Texas frontier was wilderness, nearly unknown. It was peopled by warlike savages who would scalp you for fun; they had even more contempt for a Negro than for a white. A group called Wichita and Related Tribes and one band of Comanches, the Penatuhka, had agreed to a reservation up there. The United States government had lost control of the area and the Confederacy had only halfway established its own control. But the Kiowas and most of the Comanches had never agreed to anything with the whites or their black allies. No town existed between Jacksboro and Denver, six hundred unknown miles away. A man would need to be mad to go out there alone. Britt Johnson took the best horse on Allen Johnson's ranch and set out.

He had two things going for him: what he was, himself, and an attitude in the souls of his enemies, that they could not help respecting audacious courage. He spied on Indians, walked boldly into their camps, let them dance their war dances around him without flinching, showed them his expert marksmanship and ability on horseback. He used diplomacy. He asked questions. Some of them wanted to adopt him into their tribe. He located horses that he recognized as coming from his home area near Elm Creek. Then he found Mrs. Fitzpatrick, who was willing to give all her property for freedom for herself and her granddaughter Lottie. Her son Joe had been killed, and she did not know the whereabouts of baby Milly. Britt journeyed back to Texas, got the horses and goods for ransom, and gained for her and Lottie their freedom.

He learned that his Mary and little Cherry and Jube were with the Kiowas. In the late spring of 1865, about a year after her capture, he was allowed a short, poignant interview with his wife. He went back to Texas and brought what he could, blankets, sugar, silver dollars, pistols, to use in courting favor with his family's captors. In all he made three trips north. During this time he located two captives from Montague County, Texas, and got their freedom. Finally, when he knew the land well enough, knew enough of the redmen, and when the time was right, he stole back his wife and two children, outran the Kiowa pursuit, and brought them back to the northwest frontier of Texas, which he considered home.

No similar case is recorded in western history. The man had gone among the most feared warriors of the plains and, over a period of many months, had brought back seven captives. The settlers were not always broad-minded, thoughtful, humane, but they understood determined bravery. He became a walking legend.

He paid the price seven years after the Elm Creek Raid. The Kiowas caught him out there on the Butterfield Trail between Belknap and Jacksboro in February near where Warren's wagontrain would be attacked three months later. Britt's body was surrounded by a hundred and nine spent cartridges; Indian hair was clenched in his dead hand. Reports said that the Kiowas must have recognized him, for his body was more mutilated than those of his three companions.

The hero had become a martyr. The *Dallas Herald*, not known as being a pro-Negro newspaper, said of him on March 11, 1871: "For these acts of chivalry he never asked any remuneration. He was one of the best shots, with a rifle, on the frontier, and was a stranger to fear. He lived at Fort Griffin and was an excellent Indian guide. All . . . regret his loss and say that he was a noble hearted man."

With his death the strings of consequence of the Elm Creek Raid were nearly ended, but not quite. Certainly not for the ransomed grandmother Elizabeth Fitzpatrick. Was little Milly still alive? The last time she had seen Milly, the little one had been encircled by the bare copper arm of a rider, savage but careful. The thing bore heavily on the heart of Elizabeth because she had carried on disagreements amounting almost to a feud with her daughter Susan, and upon the cruel death of Susan the arguments had been too suddenly resolved, without time for apology or decent compromise. The result was that Elizabeth Fitzpatrick poured her mixture of remorse and grief into love for the missing child; that was the reason she had lost control of herself when she appealed to General Sherman at Fort Richardson. Now, in the early summer of 1871, Milly would be nine. It was unbearable to think about.

On Sunday, June 25, the officials of the Thirteenth Judicial District took the stage to Jacksboro. The regular term of court was scheduled to open the next day. Various cases were on the calendar, civil and criminal, which could be disposed of before the major business, the trial of the two Kiowas. Soon after arriving at Jacksboro, Judge Soward and District Attorney Lanham went out to the fort to call on Colonel Mackenzie. Yes, indeed, the colonel did have the two savages, right over there across the parade ground behind the big hospital building, chained up in a room they sometimes used as a morgue. He would cooperate in every reasonable way. He expected to attend the trial in person, but saw no particular reason to testify himself. He would give them an old Indian-fighting sergeant who could identify arrows, who had helped bury the teamsters, and who had witnessed the scene of carnage on that rainy evening of May 19.

The judge and the D.A. realized that they had little evidence, and they must get something from Fort Sill and the Kiowa-Comanche Agency. Could they get some testimony about the two chiefs being absent from the reservation? About possession of the stolen mules or perhaps camping supplies of the teamsters? The most important thing would be to get witnesses who had direct knowledge of Satanta's confession.

The colonel wrote a letter to Agent Tatum requesting his cooperation. The commander at Fort Sill, Grierson, would certainly help, since he knew Sherman's interest in the matter.

Five solid citizens of Jacksboro volunteered to make the trip north to Sill to get everything they could in the way of paper evidence and witnesses. The judge and the D.A. instructed them; it was necessary to build an overwhelming case if possible. The five men left on Monday, expecting a three-day trip up, one day with Tatum and Grierson, three days back.

Satanta and Big Tree sat on their bunks in the eight-by-twelve stone room. They wore their ankle shackles secured by chains so that they had little movement, enough to lie down, enough to go to the chamber pot. There were two windows and a door in the room.

Satanta could see that his younger companion was more patient than himself. It was not easy for either of them. The iron on their legs caused sores; it made a man hunt an easy position and then stay still until he must move. The lack of movement, the restriction, was hard. It had not been nearly this difficult when Satanta had been held prisoner in the tents of Custer three years before. It really did not seem proper to live inside a stone wall, even had he and Big Tree not been accustomed to ruling their domiciles as chiefs.

Throughout the boring and difficult and strange circumstances he tuned his senses and all his intelligence to try to find out as much as he could about the predicament of himself and the younger chief. The armed soldiers who checked frequently and brought food would say nothing, only gawk or smirk or make silly faces. A few times officers had talked to him in poor Spanish; from them he had gained a few vague ideas about a council called in English a trial, where the nature of the acts of himself and Big Tree would be studied and their fate decided.

His finely tuned senses noted another thing. Beyond that solid stone wall of their room was something called a laundry, and they could hear in there women's voices, laughing, joking, gossiping, chatting, when they worked. The words were meaningless, that guttural English nonsense, but the total impression of it was poignantly true. The women sounded like Kiowa women tanning skins, cutting a tepee cover, making pemmican. They were women working together. Women. Not whites. Women.

How often he had seen women at their work without thinking much about it—he had himself five daughters, besides his wives and three sons. He could easily see in his mind a group of Indian women stooping and kneeling over buffalo skins, stripping off the thin dried flesh, chipping at the hides to make them even in thickness, kneading in a tanning mixture of brains and manure and liver and tallow, flexing the hide, stretching it, pulling it around a tree limb until it was soft, all the while making a hard task lighter through the company of other workers. Or he could see them gathering wild plums, pushing their

Satanta

General William Tecumseh Sherman

BRADY COLLECTION, THE NATIONAL ARCHIVES

Satanta or White Bear

SIGNAL CORPS PHOTO, PRINT FURNISHED BY JAMES AUCHIAH

Mary Ann Tatum

Lawrie Tatum

Inspector General Randolph Marcy
BRADY COLLECTION, THE NATIONAL ARCHIVES

General Ranald Mackenzie

BRADY COLLECTION, THE NATIONAL ARCHIVES

Tsatangya or Sitting Bear
(Note that a portion of the little finger is missing. Kiowas often cut off a finger in grief at the death of a family member.)
SIGNAL CORPS PHOTO, THE NATIONAL ARCHIVES

Addo-Eta or Big Tree

SIGNAL CORPS PHOTO, THE NATIONAL ARCHIVES

Forage.
X
To Jacksboro.

A photograph of Fort Richardson taken in 1872. In the foreground is the road to Jacksboro and just behind that, but hidden from view, is Lost Creek and the bridge over which the wounded teamster Brazeal stumbled. Sherman's campsite, not shown in this picture, was across the stream and to the left, near a spring.

SIGNAL CORPS PHOTO, THE NATIONAL ARCHIVES

3

A view of some of the officers' quarters at Fort Richardson, taken from the parade ground.

SIGNAL CORPS PHOTO, THE NATIONAL ARCHIVES

Fort Sill with its broad parade ground.
On the right are the officers' houses.
SIGNAL CORPS PHOTO, THE NATIONAL ARCHIVES

Fort Sill, a well-built post, had even its corrals constructed with limestone walls.

SIGNAL CORPS PHOTO, THE NATIONAL ARCHIVES

The officers' quarters at Fort Sill.
Satanta, Tsatangya, and Big Tree were arrested on the porch of Colonel Grierson's house, the third from the left.

SIGNAL CORPS PHOTO, THE NATIONAL ARCHIVES

way into the thicket with their baskets and bags, talking. Or he could see them scattered out on the prairie with their digging sticks, searching for wild turnips, calling often to one another to keep in touch.

He thought a person could tell a lot about the women in a group by listening to their voices if one studied them enough: which ones knew the most about the work they were doing, which ones were learners, which had confidence in themselves, which were respected, which were best-liked, which were good-humored, which had family troubles, which liked to tease or be teased, perhaps which were loved by men.

He wondered briefly whether, should a time ever come when Kiowas were farmers, their women would do the plowing and planting and harvesting. To many of the men of his people this was the great issue. They feared that if they took the white man's road they would have their manhood compromised by drudgery. They would have to give up their freedom to do great and difficult and dangerous acts in war and hunting, get off their spirited horses and hook the beasts and themselves to either end of a plow. Many men would rather die than do it. To him, that was not really the issue. The whites with their never-ending supply of guns and ammunition and their increasing population simply did not respect Indian farmers; they respected Indians who were fighters. They would become indignant at warrior people, but they would listen to them. His own audacious militancy had put him and Big Tree into this serious plight, but he still believed in the principles that had been behind his action.

Another sensory impression sometimes struck him as he sat in his chains, that of baking bread. When the wind was right he smelled it. These palefaces had some good ideas about cooking food, practices that the Kiowas would do well to learn. The whole matter of different peoples learning from one another was infinitely interesting to him. His people had learned much from the Crow people away up north. One of the oldest true stories he had ever heard had to do with another people, who lived in caves and whose name he did not know. The Kiowas had learned to kill buffalo—this was before horses; their burdens were carried or dragged by work dogs. They killed buffalo by driving the great animals over cliffs or into snowdrifts. They came into an area where many buffalo lived and the hunting was good. Up in the hills around about lived strange people in caves; they did not know how to kill buffalo and lived a hard existence. They spied upon the Kiowas, and the Kiowas upon them. The Kiowa people did not know whether the cave people considered this their land and whether they were angry and whether they might fight to defend their land, so they developed a policy of carrying buffalo meat up to some flat boulders and leaving it there in great chunks. When they came back the meat would be gone. The cave people never attacked. Thus the two peoples talked with one another without sounds, without hand signs, as long as the Kiowas stayed in that area.

It had been a simple arrangement, not nearly so difficult as relations with their present good allies, the Comanches, and simpler still in comparison to any accommodation he could foresee with the whites.

Neither he nor Big Tree had any illusions about the serious straits they were now in. They discussed the probability that the whites would kill them. If it had been Utes, they would have been food for buzzards weeks ago. But they were not ready to give up hope either. If death were certain they would resist as they could. But what was a trial? Could it be that it was a kind of talking time? Would they really talk and really listen at a trial? Did they know that they had in captivity the greatest orator on the plains? One who had melted the hearts and swayed the wills of Kiowas and Kiowa-Apaches and Cheyennes and Arapahos and Comanches? If words, grand images, gestures could move these people, Satanta could provide them.

He had seen the shortcomings of talk at places like the Medicine Lodge Treaty councils. But what if he went deeper into the whole matter and spoke frankly? Told of the grievances the Indians had? Their fears for their own existence? How the Kiowas had children and loved them and wanted descendants who knew themselves as Kiowas and had a choice in their way of life? Suppose he explained more fully why he had been killing white men's cattle, for example? Suppose he told them that Kiowa men would rather die in battle than be treated as children? These Tehanos were warrior people. Wouldn't they understand that?

But what language should he use? Perhaps he was a little better in Kiowa. On the other hand, this country here was Comanche country and had been for more than a hundred years. Comanche seemed the proper language of this country. Still, the Arapaho people had a reputation for being reasonable and peaceful; perhaps their way of speaking would be more acceptable to the whites.

He'd already found that Spanish was no good. He began to try other languages on the guards and on those who brought food. He smiled and spoke calmly to them. He got no response.

What is a trial? He looked forward to it and studied his own mind and his own past, putting his thoughts into five languages, trying to find a way to tell how it happened that a band of warriors he had led had been justified in attacking a train of wagons. Surely they would let him speak and would help him find some way to be understood.

. . .

In a Jacksboro hotel room, less than a mile from where Chief Satanta was chained, District Attorney S.W.T. Lanham also worked on a speech. He committed his to paper and he had no doubt about what language to use. He had been presented with the most golden opportunity ever given to an ambitious young politician and had no intention of letting the opportunity fade for lack of effort on his own part. The beauty of the situation was that it was his duty to prosecute as hard as he could, which was exactly what every qualified voter in the district wanted him to do; he could hardly be called to account for the legality of the trial. Further, an added bonus, he believed in what he was doing.

Lanham lacked a few days being twenty-five years old, but he was in no sense innocent or boyish. He had indeed been a boy when he had entered the Confederate army from his home near Spartanburg, South Carolina, but his energy and ambition had quickly raised him to the position of second sergeant of his company in the Third South Carolina Regiment. Soon after he came out of the defeated army he married; then, late in 1866, headed for Texas, which seemed to promise a chance for a young man of intelligence and zeal. Two years he taught school in east Texas, studying law at night. Then he headed west. He taught school in Weatherford and was admitted to the bar in 1869. His teaching experience had revealed something to himself: He could get along with people and was a good public speaker.

The people of west Texas liked his style. In the fall of 1869 he ran for District Attorney and won.

The case of the two Kiowa chiefs seemed made to order for him. He had learned to expect more success than another man might consider reasonable. It had been unreasonable to think that he could be sergeant over older, more experienced men. It had surely been unreasonable to think that he could be elected

D.A. at twenty-three. The coming trial would help his reputation. He meant, eventually, to be more than D.A. in a frontier district. He intended to sit in the U.S. Congress. In fact, he intended to be governor of this, his adopted state. (He would be elected to Congress in 1882; to the governorship in 1902.)

He was writing his speech of summation to a hypothetical jury for two purposes. First, it was a good way to plan a case; try to imagine going over the evidence at the end of a trial and you will show yourself how much of a solid case you have, whom you must talk to in the way of witnesses, what facts you need to develop further. Such a tentative speech is a plan of action. Second, he was searching for the rhetoric, the beautiful words, the powerful passionate words; he understood that if your listeners strongly agree with you, then you cannot overdo it in the way of oratory.

In the last days of June 1871, in a hotel room in Jacksboro, District Attorney Lanham wrote thus:

> This is a novel and important trial, and has, perhaps, no precedent in the history of American criminal jurisprudence. The remarkable character of the prisoners, who are leading representatives of their race; their crude and barbaric appearance; the gravity of the charge; the number of victims; the horrid brutality and inhuman butchery inflicted upon the bodies of the dead; the dreadful and terrific spectacle of seven men, who were husbands, fathers, brothers, sons and lovers on the morning of the dark and bloody day of this atrocious deed, and rose from their crude tents bright with hope, in the prime and pride of manhood—found at a later hour, beyond recognition in every condition of horrid disfigurement, unutterable mutilation and death, lying
>
> Stark and stiff
> Under the hoofs of vaunting enemies!

This vast collection of our border people; this "sea of faces," including distinguished gentlemen, civic and military, who have come hither to witness the triumph of law and justice over barbarity and assassination; the matron and the maiden, the grey-haired sire and the immature lad who have been attracted to this tribunal by this unusual occasion, all conspire to surround this case with thrilling and extraordinary interest! Though we were to pause in silence, the cause I represent would exclaim with trumpet-tongue!

Satanta, the veteran council chief of the Kiowas—the orator—the diplomat—the counselor of his tribe—the pulse of his race: Big Tree, the young war chief, who leads in the thickest of the fight, and follows no one in the chase—the mighty warrior athlete, with the speed of the deer and the eye of the eagle, are before this bar, in the charge of the law! So they would be described by Indian admirers, who live in more secure and favored lands, remote from the frontier—where "distance lends enchantment" to the imagination—where the story of Pocahontas and Logan, the Mingo, are read, and the dread sound of the war-whoop is not heard. We who see them to-day, disrobed of all their fancied graces, exposed in the light of reality, behold them through far different lenses! We recognize in Satanta the arch fiend of treachery and blood—the cunning Catalin—the promoter of strife—the breaker of treaties signed by his own hand—the inciter of his fellows to rapine and murder—the artful dealer in bravado while in the pow-pow, and the most abject coward in the field, as well as the most canting and double-tongued hypocrite when detected and overcome! In Big Tree we perceive the tiger-demon who has tasted blood and loves it as his food—who stops at no crime how black soever—who is swift at every species of ferocity, and pities not at any sight of agony or death—he can scalp, burn, torture, mangle and deface his victims, with all the superlatives of cruelty, and have no feeling of sympathy or remorse. They are both hideous and loathsome in appearance, and we look in vain to see, in them, anything to be admired or even endured. Still, these rough "sons of the woods" have been commiserated; the measures of the poet and the pen of romance have been invoked to grace the "melancholy history" of the red man. Powerful legislative influences have been brought to bear to procure for them annuities, reservations and supplies. Federal munificence has fostered and nourished them, fed and clothed them; from their strongholds of protection they have come down upon us "like wolves on the fold." Treaties have been solemnly made with them, wherein they have been considered with all the formalities of quasi nationalities; immense financial "rings" have had their origin in, and drawn their vitality from, the "Indian question"; unblushing corruption has stalked abroad, created and kept alive through

> . . . the *poor* Indian, whose untutored mind
> Sees God in clouds, or hears him in the wind.

Mistaken sympathy for these vile creatures has kindled the flames around the cabin of the pioneer and despoiled him of his hard earnings, murdered and scalped our people and carried off our women into captivity worse than death. For many years, predatory and numerous bands of these "pets of the government" have waged the most ruthless and heart-rending warfare upon our frontier, stealing our property and killing our citizens. We have cried aloud for help; as segments of the grand aggregate of the country we have begged for relief; deaf ears have been turned to our cries, and the story of our wrongs has been discredited. [Here, Lanham, who had not yet investigated enough to understand the sequence of events on May 17 and 18, was about to make a false assumption about Sherman. Lanham would, of course, correct his understanding in the days to come.] Had it not been for Gen. W.T. Sherman and his opportune journey through this section—his personal observation of the *debris* of the scene of slaughter, the ensanguined corpses of the murdered teamsters, and the entire evidence of this dire tragedy, it may well be doubted whether these brutes in human shape would ever have been brought to trial; for it is a fact, well known in Texas, that stolen property has been traced to the very doors of the reservation and there identified by our people, to no purpose. We are greatly indebted to the military arm of the government for kindly offices and co-operation in procuring the arrest and transference of the defendants. If the entire management of the Indian question were submitted to that gallant and distinguished army officer who graces this occasion with his dignified presence, our frontier would soon enjoy immunity from these marauders.

It speaks well for the humanity of our laws and the tolerance of this people that the prisoners are permitted to be tried in this Christian land, and by this Christian tribunal. The learned court has, in all things, required the observance of the same rules of procedure—the same principles of evidence—the same judicial methods, from the presentment of the indictment down to the charge soon to be given by his honor, that are enforced in the trial of a white man. You, gentlemen of the jury, have sworn that you can and will render a fair and impartial verdict. Were we to practice *lex talionis*, no right of trial by jury would be allowed these monsters; on the contrary, as they have treated their victims, so it would be measured unto them.

The definition of murder is so familiar to the court and has been so frequently discussed before the country that any technical or elaborate investigation of the subject, under the facts of this case, would seem unnecessary. Under our statute, "all murder committed in the perpetration, or in the attempt at the perpetration, of robbery is murder in the first degree." Under the facts of the case we might well rest upon this clause of the statute in the determination of the grade of the offense. The testimony discloses these salient features. About the time indicated by the charge, the defendants, with other chiefs, and a band of more than fifty warriors, were absent from their reservation at Fort Sill; they were away about thirty days—a sufficient length of time to make this incursion and return; that upon their return they brought back their booty—the forty mules, guns, and pistols, and camp supplies of the deceased; that Satanta made a speech in the presence of the interpreter, Lawrie Tatum, the Indian agent at Fort Sill, and Gen. Sherman, in which he boasted of "having been down to Texas and had a big fight—killing seven Tehannas [Tehanos], and capturing forty mules, guns, pistols, ammunition, sugar and coffee and other supplies of the train; that he said if any other chief claimed the credit of the victory that he was a liar; that he, Satanta, with Big Tree and Satank [Tsatangya] (who were present and acquiesced in the statement), were entitled to all the glory." Here we have his own admission, voluntarily and arrogantly made, describing minutely this whole tragic affair. Then we have the evidence of one of the surviving teamsters who tells of the attack upon him and his comrades, by a band of over fifty Indians—of the killing of seven of his comrades and the escape of four others, with himself. Then we have the testimony of the orderly sergeant who, himself, is an old Indian fighter, and familiar with the modes of attack and general conduct of the savages. He, with a detachment of soldiers, went out from Fort Richardson to the scene of blood, to bury the dead. He describes how they were scalped—mutilated with tomahawks—shot with arrows; how the wagon master was chained to the wheel and burned, evidently, while living—of the revolting and horrible manner in which the dead bodies were mangled and disfigured, and how everything betokened the work and presence of Indians. He further describes the arrows as those of the Kiowas. We learn from him the interesting fact that Indian tribes are known by the peculiar manner in which their arrows are made like civilized nations are recognized by their flags.

The same amount and character of testimony were sufficient to convict any white men. "By their own words let them be condemned." Their conviction and punishment cannot repair the loss nor avenge the blood of the good men they have slain; still, it is due to the law and justice and humanity that they should receive the highest punishment. This is even too mild and humane for them. Pillage and blood-thirstiness were the motives of this diabolical deed; fondness for torture and intoxication of delight at human agony impelled its perpetration. All the elements of murder in the first degree are found in the case. The jurisdiction of the court is complete, and the state of Texas expects from you a verdict and judgment in accordance with the law and the evidence.

CHAPTER ELEVEN

THE TRIAL

Lawrie Tatum felt as harried as ever. He had thought that he had surely satisfied the Texans in the matter of Satanta and Big Tree; now five men were here from Jacksboro wanting evidence and testimony. Whatever else, he did not want to attend the trial; already his colleagues and superiors, Friends, were beginning to question his part in this whole matter, and going down south to that ex-rebel, anti-Indian place would be almost like consorting with the enemy.

He had agreed to send his interpreter, Mathew Leeper, for a witness, as requested in a letter from Colonel Mackenzie. The five Texans had insisted on more evidence, and he had suggested that they should be able to find in the files up at the fort a letter he had written to Colonel Grierson immediately after Satanta's confession; the letter told of Satanta's assertion, told what other Indians were implicated, and was signed by himself. It should be perfect evidence.

He had been getting letters from influential Quakers, expressing sympathy for him and assuring him of their prayers, but containing subtle disagreement and also inconsistencies. One from William Nicholson said, "I do not know that any better course could be adopted than the arrest of the ring-leaders, provided they could be held in confinement. It is not probable that they would cease their raiding until something more stringent than mere talk and threats was put into execution." What did that word "provided" mean? That, if the Texans hanged the two Indians, then he, Tatum, had not been justified?

Typical of the letters was one from John Garrett of Philadelphia. It read thus:

> Dear friend
>
> Lawrie Tatum,
>
> partly to express my sympathy with thee in thy responsible service for the Master—but more especially at this time to encourage to use every proper effort to secure for Satanta and his companions in crime a punishment consistent with the precepts of Christianity. I rejoice that there is a prospect of their trial by civil process, and that these unread Kiowas are likely to learn that wrong-doing on their part will bring upon them the same penalties as like conduct would bring upon the pale faces.
>
> But how earnestly so I desire that their lives may be spared, and Christian influences brought to bear for their conversion and Salvation.
>
> Will not the effect upon the tribe be far better for these criminals to be held in close confinement during their natural lives than for them to receive the common penalty for murder in the first degree?
>
> I am quite unfamiliar with the law of Texas, but suppose it provides the death penalty for such crimes. But cannot thou, or cannot we, secure through the Governor of the State, or otherwise, a commutation to imprisonment for life?
>
> I am apprehensive that the feeling of the white frontiersmen is such that they will demand immediate trial, conviction and ex-

ecution—but in hope that I can strengthen thy hands in some little measure to use every exertion to secure for them a punishment more consistent with our sense of right, as well as more politic for the nation—and desiring the Lord's blessing upon all thy labors for the advancement of the Indian toward a Christian civilization—I pen this hasty note.

Very truly thy friend
John B. Garrett

Mr. Garrett apparently rejoiced that wrongdoing on the part of unruly Kiowas "will bring upon them the same penalties as like conduct would bring upon the pale faces" and also supposed that the penalty for murder in Texas was death, yet strongly supported a commutation. Also, what does "strengthen thy hand . . ." mean? To Tatum it seemed more like putting pressure on him.

Mr. James Rhoads of Germantown proposed in a letter that perhaps when the chiefs were convicted the governor might decline to sign the death warrant, as might succeeding governors, and thus the Indians could remain prisoners for life, though under a sentence of death. Mr. Rhoads closed his letter thus: "May the Lord give thee wisdom in all things! And in his mercy order all to the glory of the name of our Blessed Savior and to the extension of his kingdom." Such blessings seemed to Tatum to increase his frustration.

On Thursday, June 29, Tatum wrote a letter to District Attorney S.W.T. Lanham, which the Jacksboro citizens would carry back with them. He urged the D.A. that the Indians not be given the death penalty for their crimes. He expressed his convictions that we should ". . . leave to God his prerogative to determine when a person has lived long enough." But he also made the pragmatic argument that two traits of Indians are to seek revenge and a great dread of imprisonment. He said, "... it would be a more severe punishment to confine them for life . . . and it would probably save the lives of some white people. . . ."

The five Jacksboro citizens had found the letter for evidence in Grierson's files at the fort, but they were not satisfied with it. It read thus:

Fort Sill, Ind. Terr.,
Office Kiowa Agency
5Mo. 27, 1871

Col. Grierson,
Post Commander,

Satanta, in the presence of Satank [Tsatangya], Eagle Heart, Big Tree, and Woman's Heart, has, in a defiant manner, informed me that he led a party of about 100 Indians into Texas and killed 7 men and captured a train of mules. He further states that the chiefs, Satank [Tsatangya], Eagle Heart, and Big Bow were associated with him in the raid. Please arrest all three of them.

Lawrie Tatum
Ind. Agent.

Tatum asked them what their objections were against the letter.

"Where's the evidence against Big Tree?" they asked.

"I know Big Tree was in it," he said.

"But the letter doesn't say so."

"I talked to my interpreter and to Chief Lone Wolf and I'm confident that Big Tree was on the raid."

"Then why didn't you say so in the letter?"

"All you have to do," he proposed, "is copy the letter over and insert the name of Big Tree. He's guilty, I'm sure."

"Well, Mr. Tatum," they said, "we need legal evidence, not just a copy. It will have to have your signature."

He copied the letter over for them, thus:

> Col. Grierson
> Post Comd.
>
> Satanta, in the presence of Satank [Tsatangya], Eagle Heart, Big Tree, and Woman's Heart, in a defiant manner, has informed me that he led a party of about 100 Indians into Texas, and killed 7 men and captured a train of mules. He further states that the chiefs Satank [Tsatangya], Eagle Heart, Big Tree, and Big Bow were associated with him in the raid. Please arrest all of them.
>
> Lawrie Tatum
> Ind. Agent.

He made a mental note to search his files and also check with the records of the fort to be certain that no copy of the original letter remained in existence; someone might not understand. The vague unidentified illnesses which plagued him became worse from dealing with the Texans. He understood that Colonel Grierson was willing to send Horace Jones, the post interpreter. As far as any information about Warren's mules or camp supplies of the teamsters, people did not seem to realize what little control he had over the Kiowas and how little opportunity he had to note what they had in their possession.

If Stone Head Tatum worried about ever having to answer for the fraudulent letter, he undoubtedly thought it would be at the Last Judgment, for all earthly sign of the true letter was destroyed. Was it not? Perhaps if he had not been so harried he would have thought of the possibility that a history-gathering general had taken a copy of the true letter north with him and that the brief missive would wind up in the Sherman Papers in the Library of Congress.

In the latter days of June and the early days of July the regular term of the District Court proceeded at Jacksboro. The grand jury, under foreman S.W. Eastin, a local merchant, indicted Satanta and Big Tree for murder, and the item was set on the docket for July 5 as Case No. 224.

On a Tuesday, the fourth of July, the court issued an order for a special venire of fifty good lawful men of the County of Jack to serve as jurors in Case 224. It was simply a matter of form. No one could expect the sheriff to travel over the county searching out and giving summons to that many qualified jurors. District Court Clerk James Robinson made up a list of twelve, mostly businessmen of Jacksboro, easily accessible, who were willing to serve.

Lawyer Joseph A. Woolfolk, a slight, blond man with a beard, had not liked his assignment to this case from the first, not so much that he did not wish to defend Indians, for his own reputation and experience were such that his good name would not be damaged by it; but it was all so cut-and-dried, such a foregone conclusion. When he saw the list of jurors, on it the name of Peter Lynn, it seemed too much. Did they know who Peter Lynn was, the brother of Mary Mason, a bloody victim of an Indian attack? Yes, the judge knew. And, no, there would be no jury challenges allowed.

As the day of the trial approached, Woolfolk argued with the judge and the others. They could not believe that he was serious in his objections, for if anyone knew the plight of the settlers in this part of the country it was Joe Woolfolk.

In the central square of Jacksboro sat a new courthouse. It was a big hulk of a box, with no architectural pretension, but it was made of stone, two-story, symbolizing the determination of the people that whatever a courthouse means, it is here to stay. Stored in it, under the keeping of the proper authorities, were the records of Jack County. But also, improperly, incongruously, were stored there the records of Young County, of which Belknap had been the chief town; they were in dusty cobwebby boxes and crates, waiting.

The attack on Warren's wagontrain had actually happened across the line in Young County, so that the location of these misplaced records had a peculiar pertinency.

Had one gone into the records, he would have found something ironic, even pitiful, in the official language, which had no room for the word "Indians," which had between its lines vast vague spaces, begging explanation, with no suggestion that here the crude fingers of western civilization were reaching out to touch strange people and that the fingers were cut and burned so that they could not feel.

The records showed that at the first session of the Fourteenth District court sitting at Belknap, a district comprising sixteen frontier counties, there was given a license at law to Joseph A. Woolfolk, this in the fall of 1858. A year later the minutes of the Commissioners' Court of Young County had this entry: "The court have this day appointed Joseph A. Woolfolk, Esqr. attorney to attend to civil suits in which the county of Young may be a party—and to be paid the sum of $150.00 per year from date and to be paid to him quarterly."

Two years later the office of County Clerk had been vacated for unexplained reasons and Joe Woolfolk was appointed to the job. For many months the records of the county are in his handwriting, matters pertaining to the probate of wills, the certifying of voters and jurors, the posting of bonds, the payment of county funds for schoolteachers and officials and their legitimate expenses.

In the records of 1861, people begin to disappear. John

Williams is a sheriff by appointment; only a month later Alfred Woodman is posting a bond as sheriff. In October of that year a vacancy in the office of J.P. is noted. In November a commissioner resigns.

The Young County Commissioners' Court meets February 17, 1862, and among other business notes this: "It appearing that J.A. Woolfolk was absent it is therefore ordered that Edward L. Barry be appointed clerk, pro. tem." At that meeting the county treasurer tries to resign and they talk him out of it. From somewhere Woolfolk reappears in time to copy the minutes of the meeting, as was his duty.

But by early March 1862, there is presented in a special term of the court "holden in A.H. Latimer's office" the resignations of the Assessor and Collector of Taxes and two county commissioners. By March 29, 1862, Woolfolk is missing again; to be missing has become so usual that no notice is taken. The court of that date records this: "Special term holden in courthouse, town of Belknap. The court being notified there was no chief justice in the county. It is therefore ordered that the office be declared to be vacant. The presiding officer of the various prect. be required to hold an election on April 12 for the election of one Chief Justice and one county treasurer." Two days later the court notes the vacancy of the office of District Surveyor of Young Land District. In June they have a temporary chief justice, and on August 3 a properly elected one and are proudly recording: "Be it remembered that August Term of Court opened in due form of Law at the Courthouse in the town of Belknap. Presiding: Honorable Pleasant Tackett, Chief Justice."

That fall the commissioners are begging of the state for some of the powder and lead and caps bought in Mexico. They levy a tax on all the property owners of the County of Young each to pay what it might seem proper and possible. The county is not paying out much money now; in February of 1863 they record: "Ordered by the court that Alfred Woodman be allowed $11.50 for services rendered the county as sheriff; that Hon. P. Tackett be allowed $15.00 for holding four terms of Hon. county court of Young County and that the clerk be required to issue county Script for the same. . . ."

On August 31, 1864, the court notes: "Bond of W.S. Cox as sheriff of Young County, Texas, approved and ordered to rec." By October 11, 1864, less than a month and a half later, they are approving the bond of George B. Dobbs for sheriff. At least Cox got a mountain named after him, that prominence in the eastern part of the county where the Indians caught him, once called Sugarloaf Mountain, the same rise of ground that Tom Brazeal and eleven other employees of Captain Henry Warren would traverse shortly before they were attacked seven years later.

Early in 1865 the court records: "Being notified that there is no sheriff in the county, It is ordered and declared vacant. Election on April 10, 1865 for one sheriff, one commissioner, one justice of the peace for Pre. #1 and one justice of the peace for Pre. #2."

But they could not continue. On the date for that called election, those dusty records in the neighbor courthouse at Jacksboro showed this resolution:

State of Texas
County of Young

In county court called in session Monday April 10, 1865. It being considered by the county court of Young county that the clerks office and the court house of said county was unsafe to keep the county records and papers pertaining to said county, it is therefore ordered by the court that a place be selected and that a house be built for the safe keeping of said records, and it is further ordered that Flag Springs be the place selected by the court.

There being no further business before the court it is therefore ordered that court adjourn until the next regular term in course.

M. V. Bowers, Chief Justice
Young County, Texas

The officials must have left that last meeting with heavy hearts. Flag Springs was a cow camp, a place where armed and mounted men met, men with nervous eyes. No house would be built. They could bury their records in the manure, or they could take them east to Jacksboro and ask those people to take care of them; they chose the latter course. No officials of Young County would meet again for nine years.

When Joe Woolfolk disappeared from county records he showed up in others. In the spring of 1862 he became a second lieutenant in Captain J.J. Cureton's company of the Texas Frontier Regiment. Along with such cattlemen as young Charles Goodnight, a private, he ranged out of Belknap against the Indians. It was a war which was only a shadow of the great war in the east, a matter of brief fights, long scouts, and patrols. Woolfolk came to know the poorly charted canyons and high plains to the north and west, to know the frustration of trying to fight the redmen on their own soil, to know the impossibility of stopping the raiding with the inadequate forces of the Frontier Regiment.

In 1863 Woolfolk was made an officer in the regular Confederate army and ordered to Tennessee. There he joined Morgan's Raiders, and took part in the Ohio raid in midsummer that year. They invaded Indiana and Ohio in an audacious and exhausting ride, fighting the federals again and again, averaging over twenty hours a day in the saddle for over two weeks. The raiders were unable to get back to southern lines; Joe Woolfolk spent the remainder of the war in a Union prison.

After the southern surrender he went back to his original home near Louisville, Kentucky, where he married, briefly practiced law, tried to farm. Then in 1867 he headed back west, settling this time in Weatherford. He traded some in cattle and practiced law. It seemed to him a hundred years since he had left this part of the country, but the trouble on the frontier was as bad as ever.

He was not quite the same Indian fighter who had gone away. Perhaps it was the time in a Northern prison. Perhaps he had gained an insight into the minds of people who go on raids. Perhaps he had come into a curious sympathy with people who fight for lost causes.

Now, Judge Soward and the other officials could not believe it. On the day before the scheduled trial of the Kiowa chiefs, this slightly built, blond-bearded lawyer Joseph Woolfolk had presented the honorable court with a Plea to the Jurisdiction, claiming that Texas had no right to try the Indians at all. To his protestations that the planned trial was a travesty, a farce, they insisted that it was necessary to convict and punish the chiefs with every appearance of legality so that the government would allow and cooperate in this kind of solution to Indian raiding. Woolfolk suggested that if this was the kind of law they intended establishing here, perhaps it would be as well to let the Indians have the country. They had him outnumbered and they talked him down, hoping that he would sleep on it overnight and see that his rebellious ideas could lead to nothing but the ruin of his own career. He did not withdraw his official Plea to the Jurisdiction.

On July 5 the dusty streets of Jacksboro became busy at an early hour. The hotels and most of the respectable places of business sat across the street on four sides of the large courthouse square. The hitchrails became crowded with saddle horses and buggy horses. The people, men, women, and children, dressed in their best clothes, milled about, maintaining decorum in spite of the undercurrent of excitement and anticipation. They were determined that now, at last, justice would catch up with at least two Indian monsters. In their minds were many stories of outrage, some of them exaggerated in repeated telling, of torture, of gang rapes of white women on the prairie, of the callous killing of children. But they understood also the strategic situation, that if revenge could be taken legally, this day might be the beginning of the end of a dozen years of trouble. By eight A.M. any merchant who had opened his doors closed them. The people's attention turned to the new sandstone courthouse.

The main duty of Sheriff Michael McMillan and his deputies consisted of selecting which people should enter the courthouse and which must remain outside. The courthouse, on the second floor, would accommodate about 150 people if mothers and fathers would take children onto their laps and if some spectators were willing to stand. The sheriff and deputies tried to judge who might be boisterous or unruly and tried to be diplomatic about admitting people; they used the excuse, when they needed it, that room must be left for certain officials and for a delegation of officers from the fort.

The sheriff had a list of jurors, and these men he admitted without question as they came. One was Thomas W. Williams, who would be the jury foreman, for he was one of the most respected townsmen. He had built the first house in Jacksboro, or Mesquiteville as it had been first called. He had worked as a carpenter and builder and contractor, had taken part in civic affairs, even having served as county judge from 1864 to 1868. In that county convention when the citizens had voted orally on the ordinance of secession from the Union, his vote had been not merely "yea," or "nay," but "For the Union forever!" And so had his vote been recorded for posterity. He also had helped in planning this proud stone building in which the trial was about to proceed.

Another juror who came was Peter Lynn. His sister Mary Mason had been an early victim of the Indians in what had been called the Mason-Cambren massacre. Old Isaac Lynn had gone one day in the spring of 1858 to visit the ranch of his daughter and son-in-law, only to find them both dead and to find his tiny grandson, with his clothes drenched in his mother's blood, trying to nurse at the dead woman's breasts. In that same raid several of the Cambrens were killed and one child who cried had been silenced by an Indian who rammed a spear down its throat. The whole business had well-nigh driven old Isaac Lynn mad; he had begun to collect Indian scalps and once had gone on foot hundreds of miles following the Frontier Regiment, hoping to see a great killing of Indians. Now, as Peter Lynn entered the courthouse and climbed the stairs to the second floor it occurred to him that if his time had come for vengeance it would be more for his father's ruined life than for his long-dead sister.

Still another juror who came was William Hensley. His sister's husband, a man named Youngblood, had been killed by Indians and scalped. The marauders had been pursued by rangers, who caught up with them, retrieved the scalp and returned it, so that it was replaced on the dead man's head just before he was lowered into his grave.

Among those who, along with jurors and officials, had unquestioned entry to the courtroom were two citizens who had agreed to assist the D.A. in the prosecution, the five men who had made the trip to Sill for evidence, and witnesses such as the interpreters Mathew Leeper and Horace Jones. Teamster Tom Brazeal entered, grim-faced. He was wishing it over with, so that he could put it out of his mind; still, he wanted a chance to say publicly that he and the other survivors had felt certain that Sam Elliott was dead that day when they ran, leaving him at the mercy of the Indians.

Colonel Mackenzie came and spoke to the sheriff about how many soldier guards would be permitted in the courtroom. The prisoners would, of course, remain in the custody of the army. For the colonel a front-row seat among the trial spectators had been reserved. He would be an observer, as it were, for the federal government.

Shortly after eight o'clock the procession came from the fort, winding along the dirt road and up onto the central square. Satanta and Big Tree, dressed in army fatigues, the shackles still on their wrists, but not on their ankles, sat in the center of the wagon, three guards perched in front of them and three behind. Twenty mounted cavalrymen rode surrounding the wagon. As the prisoners were taken into the building the people stared in silence. This was their first glimpse of their enemy in chains.

The courtroom occupied most of the second story. It was adequately lighted on this July morning by eleven windows. At one front corner a small room had been partitioned off as chambers for the judge. Two tables crowded in front of it, for the prosecution and for the defense. At one side two benches were already occupied by the twelve who would become jurors. The filled room was decorous, but alive with a buzz of whispers. At eight thirty a deputy rapped the wooden mallet on the judge's desk and ordered everyone to rise. Judge Soward came out of the small room and took his seat.

Case No. 224 being called, the State versus Satanta and Big Tree, there first came on to be heard the exceptions of the D.A. to defendant's Plea to the Jurisdiction. Lanham ridiculed the plea. A capital felony had been committed in this judicial district. He quoted the Constitution of the United States, Article Six: ". . . accused shall enjoy the right to a speedy and public trial, by an impartial jury of the State and district wherein the crime shall have been committed. . . ." Of course the court had jurisdiction. Surely counsel for the defense would not insinuate that Jack County jurors could not render a fair and impartial verdict?

Judge Soward announced that, after due consideration, the court had determined that the law was with the plaintiff, or State. It was therefore ordered and adjudged that the plaintiff's said exception to the plea be sustained.

"Your honor," Woolfolk said, "let the clerk note that defense takes exception to the ruling."

He did not sit down, but immediately informed the court that defendants also took exception to the indictment. Lanham argued it with a calm manner of slightly strained patience. Judge Soward announced that the law was with the plaintiff; it was therefore ordered and adjudged that the defendants took nothing by their exception.

"Your honor," Woolfolk said, "let the clerk note that defense takes exception to the ruling."

The D.A. stated that if distinguished counsel was finished with his delaying tactics the State was ready for trial.

"Your honor," Woolfolk said, "in view of the difference in age of the two defendants, we ask a severance. We are ready for the trial of Big Tree."

The judge was caught unawares, and everyone in the courtroom knew it. It was not that he gasped or made any great change of facial expression, but it was the way he started to speak and did not, staring at Woolfolk, glancing at Lanham, back at Woolfolk. He was silent for some long seconds.

The room was quiet from the armed guard of soldiers on the front row back through the spectators standing in the rear. At the defense table Satanta watched them all. His brown eyes moved around from one face to another. The greatest event of recent days for him had been when he saw Mathew Leeper and Horace Jones from the agency and Fort Sill enter this room; now he had some possibility of getting in touch with these whites. He had been interested to note that the war chief Mackenzie sat as if he had no part in it. He had guessed that this skinny white man with the blond beard who had been sitting near him was on his side. Now the man had said something important. What had he said? That white men shoot buffalo out of train windows up north? That the whites butchered Kiowa women and children and old people out there near the adobe walls? That the whites had twice taken Satanta prisoner through deception? What could he have said?

Judge Soward cleared his throat and said, "Counsel will approach the bench, please." But as Woolfolk, Ball, and Lanham came forward the judge glanced around, obviously displeased with the lack of privacy, tapped his gavel, and said, "Two-minute recess."

The three of them followed the judge into his small crowded "chambers." At once Soward's public dignity disappeared, but his sense of authority evidently did not. "Joe," he said, "what in the hell do you think you're doing?"

"A hundred or a hundred and fifty men commit murder," Woolfolk said. "You think you've got the leaders. That Satanta is about fifty. That Big Tree is not much over twenty. Any decent lawyer would ask a severance. I don't know what else I'm doing, but at least I'm going to try to save the young one's life."

Soward said, "You think I'm going to tell Mackenzie to double up his guard and take one back? Haul them back and forth one at a time? After the army's started cooperating with us."

"That's your problem," Woolfolk said. "You may represent the colonel, but I represent those two damned Indians sitting out there."

"We can separate the trials," Soward said, "but I want to know the meaning of your exceptions for the record."

"You know the meaning. I'm going to appeal this case."

"No, you're not going to appeal."

"You wait and see if I don't."

"Indeed, I will wait and see if you do or don't. I'll see if you have any records upon which to base an appeal. Woolfolk, you must be crazy."

"If you want to kill them," Woolfolk said, "why don't you go get your shotgun and blow their brains out. It would be an honest thing to do." The slightly built lawyer was angry and trembling. The other three were clearly ranged against him.

"Listen, Joe," Ball said. "We are besieged. After this Indian war is settled we can go back to law and procedure that is meaningful. To partisan pleading. Appeals. We're fighting for our lives. We are besieged."

Woolfolk said, "How do you know they don't think they're besieged?"

The D.A. did not enter the argument; he could not lose.

Soward said, "You must be crazy, Joe. Wasn't Dr. Vollentine in your Frontier Regiment? Didn't you fight Indians alongside him? He lives in Weatherford today. Ask him. Ask him about Mrs. Woods and her two younger sisters! They killed the woman and passed the two girls on the prairie! Dammit, man, do you know what that expression means? They passed the girls on the prairie! The girls lived. Vollentine took care of them for weeks. Ask him. You are defending animals! Beasts!"

Woolfolk trembled visibly. He said, "Did the girls identify Satanta and Big Tree? If one group of Indians did something, are all Indians guilty? Vollentine doesn't even know Indians did it! You are talking about primitive revenge! Not law!"

Lanham interposed, "Let's have law. Bring Sheriff Cox, your old colleague in the Young County government. Is he available or has something happened to him? I hope nothing has happened to him."

Woolfolk became angry at the sarcasm, and his voice became charged with emotion. "They are human beings! Look in their eyes! They are intelligent! How do you know what they think or why they do what they do? You can't even talk to them!"

Soward suddenly became businesslike. "All right. We've got to settle this. They are waiting out there. What do you want, Woolfolk? Don't pretend you have a strong position. If I go out there and announce that we cannot try the Indians because you object, you won't get out of Jacksboro alive! They'll tear you to pieces! What is it you want?"

"I want a severance and . . ."

"Dammit! I told you that you could have a nominal severance!"

"If either one of them, or both, are sentenced to hang, I want two months before the execution and I want you to write Governor Davis and ask for clemency."

"Woolfolk, you're going too far."

"Take me off the case."

"You know I can't take you off the case at this stage of the game."

"Then I want your word you'll write the governor. And I want time to appeal."

"You'll not appeal," the judge said. "I'll agree to write the governor if you'll cease this nonsense and let Ball do all the talking."

"You'll ask for clemency?"

"I'll ask for a commutation in my own way, in my own words. And you will keep your mouth shut through the rest of these proceedings!"

They filed out of the cubicle and took their places in the larger room. One of the deputies had opened the windows on account of the warm July air, and two or three spectators were leaning out of these openings to call the news to people on the ground below. Judge Soward tapped his wooden mallet and took a moment to assume his authority, then announced, "The severance is granted. Because of the peculiar difficulties in guarding the prisoners, both will remain in the courtroom and maintain their present seats. Proceed with the arraignment of the defendant Big Tree."

The indictment was read. Ball entered a plea of "not guilty." Ball also waived as to venire service of fifty good men of the county and accepted the twelve men already seated on the jury benches, Thomas W. Williams, John Camron, Evert Johnson, H.B. Vernor, S. Cooper, William Hensley, John H. Brown, Peter Lynn, Peter Hart, Daniel Brown, Lucas P. Bunch, and James Cooley. Ball also waived defendant's rights in regard to the length of time the indictment had been in existence. The jury was questioned and tried and empaneled and sworn to truly try the issue joined and true deliverance make according to the law and the evidence.

The first witness called to the chair was Tom Brazeal. The D.A. led him through the facts of that stormy day, May 18, through his story of the attack and escape. Brazeal persisted in saying that he had been sure Sam Elliott had been dead when they ran from the wagons.

"You mean that you *thought* he was dead," Lanham said.

"We felt sure that he must be."

"You did not see that he was dead?"

"No, sir, but we felt sure he was. I shouted to everybody and he didn't answer."

"Let me ask whether the situation was something like this," Lanham said. "The thunderstorm was making noise. Indians were all around yelling. Guns were firing. You called out to your comrades, then made your desperate escape. Because of the confusion and noise you could not tell whether Sam Elliott heard you or whether he answered. You did not see him killed or wounded. You did not know whether he was dead or not. You *assumed* he was dead, because you certainly would not have left him behind to a cruel fate if you had had any idea he was only wounded. Is that your testimony?"

"Yes, sir."

"I want to ask you one more thing about the bugle that some Indian was blowing. It was an ordinary army bugle such as one might hear sounded out here at Fort Richardson?"

"Yes, sir, it was."

On cross-examination Ball asked only one question. Could the teamster identify any of the Indians in the attacking party?

"No, sir," Brazeal said. "The one that led the first charge was a young one. It could be that one there, but I don't know."

The second witness called to the stand was a sergeant, one

who had ridden out with Mackenzie on May 19 and had been in charge of the detail to bury the dead. Lanham established him as an experienced Indian fighter, then led him to describe all the grim particulars of the wrecked wagons, bloated mules, and cut-up human corpses, with special emphasis on the appearance of the body of the teamster who had been burned. The D.A. unwrapped the Kiowa arrows which had been lying in a bundle on his table, got the sergeant to identify them as being of the kind which lay about the massacre site and as Kiowa arrows, and introduced them as evidence.

Ball asked a few harmless questions.

The third witness called was Mathew Leeper. He testified that Big Tree had not been seen around the agency up on the reservation for about a month previous to May 27, upon which day he entered the agency council room with Satanta and other Indians, that Satanta confessed to leading the raid and named Big Tree as another participant, to which Big Tree agreed, that Big Tree was a Kiowa and a subchief of the Elks Division of that tribe. Leeper testified that Satanta had worn an ordinary army bugle around his shoulder at the time of his confession. When Lanham brought out the spurious letter, Leeper testified that Agent Tatum had written a letter to the fort after Satanta's confession, then identified the signature as that of the Quaker agent. Lanham entered the letter as evidence and rested his case.

Ball's questions were harmless and unproductive. He had no witness or material evidence to introduce for the defense.

Judge Soward consulted with Colonel Mackenzie about the logistics of the noon recess, how the prisoners might be fed and allowed to go to the toilet, charged the jurors that they must not discuss the case with anyone, and dismissed the court for a long lunch period.

After the noon recess the sheriff and his men had the same problem about what spectators to admit, but by 2 P.M. the courtroom had assumed its previous air of decorum.

Judge Soward directed Lanham and Ball to begin their summations.

The D.A. was not denied his oratory. The fine phrases he had created, the quotations he had planned, all the beautiful speech he had written a week earlier, he delivered as he paced in the limited open area at the front of the room. His summary of the evidence was not quite the same as he had first written it a week before, but the rhetoric worked; all he needed to do was apply it to one Indian instead of two. He was quite aware that the crucial trial was this one; if he could put Big Tree in a noose, Satanta would be a pushover. His voice rose in powerful sarcasm as he described romantic ideas about Indians, anticipating the defense, and he jabbed his finger at the younger Indian at the defense table as he described him as a "demon" who would stop at no crime, who "pities not at any sight of agony and death," a man who could "scalp, burn, mangle, torture and deface his victims," with no sympathy or remorse.

Lanham had the jurors and spectators in the palm of his hand and knew it. He was telling them, in better words than they could ever find, what they already believed. He played to them, back and forth between the noble Hiawatha and the stark reality of Indians as they knew them, between a hypocritical "Indian Ring" of easterners who loved Indians and made corrupt fortunes through them and the frontier people who had lost untold horses, cattle, and property through Indian raiding.

The last paragraph of the speech he had written earlier required little change. "The same amount and character of testimony were sufficient to convict any white man. By their own words let them be condemned. Big Tree's conviction cannot repair the loss nor avenge the blood of the good men he has slain; still it is due to law and justice and humanity that he should receive the highest punishment. This is even too mild and humane for him. Pillage and blood-thirstiness were the motives of this diabolical deed; fondness for torture and intoxication of delight at human agony impelled its perpetration. All the elements of murder in the first degree are found in the case. The jurisdiction of the court is complete, and the state of Texas expects from you a verdict and judgment in accordance with the law and evidence."

Ball rose and did well what was expected of him. He spoke of the simplicity of Indian people who have not had the blessings of civilization and about the white man's burden and about mercy. They wanted him to say such things and did not hold it against him, for the spirit of the courtroom was a feeling for impartiality and legality, as long as it did not go too far; every criminal should have a defense before he is hanged.

Judge Soward charged the jury at some length and the twelve men, accompanied by the sheriff, picked their way through the spectators to the stairs. They would make their decision in one of the offices on the ground floor.

The half-hour wait seemed interminable. The buzz of talk rose again in the courtroom and again people leaned out of windows to call to people on the ground outside. When finally the jury came back and settled on their benches, quiet passed like a wave among the people.

"Have you reached a verdict?"

Old Thomas Williams stood up. "We have, your honor."

"Hand it to the clerk."

Clerk James Robinson took the paper and passed it to the judge, who briefly scanned it.

Judge Soward said in a commanding voice, "I want no demonstrations. This is a court of law, not a circus. No yelling. No clapping. Let the clerk proceed to read the verdict."

Robinson read, "We the jury find the defendant Big Tree guilty of murder in the first degree and assess his punishment at death. Signed: Thomas W. Williams, foreman."

The judge asked, "Is this your verdict?"

Williams answered, "It is, your honor."

"So say you all?"

The jurors nodded.

"It is hereby ordered," the judge said, "and adjudged and decreed by this court that the said defendant Big Tree be taken by the sheriff and hanged until he is dead, dead, dead! And may the Lord have mercy upon his soul!

"And it is further ordered that the sheriff do take the said defendant into close custody and hold him to await the sentence of this court upon judgment herein."

They made no demonstrations but sat as if hypnotized by the processes they witnessed. At the defense table Satanta's brown eyes flicked hither and yon among them, trying to read their faces. He called out in Comanche to Horace Jones in the second row of spectators, "What are they doing? What have they said?"

Horace Jones shook his head.

"I want a chance to speak!"

Horace Jones said to him, "Not yet."

The judge said, "Counsel for the defense will control their clients! This is not a circus!"

Soward, through the dignity and severe aspect of the formalities, had become more important, for the moment, than Colonel Mackenzie. He summoned the colonel to the front, and together with him and the other officials of the court arranged for the continued trial of Case 224. Of course the prisoners would remain in the physical custody of the army.

He adjourned the court until 8:30 A.M. of the following day.

That night Satanta and Big Tree sat up a long time in their stone room behind the hospital laundry of the fort, discussing what had happened. The Kiowa people had long been known as being among the most adept at sign language among the native people of North America. Sign language had enabled them to cross a language barrier to deal in the basic feelings and ideas of human beings, whether friends or enemies. In signs they could tell complicated stories, but it required careful attention by teller and attender, to the immediate social situation, to facial expressions, to the other person's point of view. It was also true that the Kiowas for several generations had found it necessary to deal with alien people.

So it was that the two chiefs understood much about what had passed that day, not the words that came out of the legal tradition, but the feelings, motives, intentions of the individuals at this thing called a trial.

Big Tree said, "The skinny one with blond hair on his face was on our side."

"You are surely right," Satanta said. "The question is: Did they shut him up by threats or did he make a deal some way."

"It seemed that after the four men went in the little room, they talked about me," Big Tree said. "The one who talked so much kept pointing his finger at me."

"He talked about both of us, but pointed at you. There are some false things at this trial. They put Bad Hand Mackenzie among the watchers as if he had nothing to do with it, but the Tehanos have a little soldier society there to keep order and such; yet they don't hold us. Mackenzie holds us. Does Mackenzie observe for their Great Father in Washington? Could be. Every person in that room was ready to kill us except for the skinny blond one, but somehow they cannot do it now. What is it? Custom and ceremony? Washington? Some Great Father here in Texas?

"The one who talked so much is a good orator," Satanta went on. "I'm sure he was good. But he's our worst enemy. He's ambitious and selfish.

"I learned this: The great speech I planned is no good. Any justification of our people is no good. They have shut their ears. If they will let me talk I'm going to save my life any way I can. And if they will let me live, they will let you live."

They had agreed that if death became imminent Satanta would make the first move and they would attack with all their strength the most important white in their presence. But Satanta was confident that such an action would not be necessary soon; he believed that the two of them were like pawns passed back and forth in a gambling game.

Colonel Ranald Mackenzie was indeed a watcher for Washington. That evening he posted a letter to his San Antonio headquarters saying, "Big Tree was tried and sentenced to death today. Satanta, if a Jury can be impanelled, will be tried tomorrow, and as the evidence is much stronger in his case than in Big Tree's, the result is not doubtful." The letter would take days to reach San Antonio, but it would be straightway put on the wire to Washington, for the trial had become a hotly disputed cause in the federal bureaucracy. Washington was not so much concerned about the fate of two chiefs or even the settlers or the Kiowa tribe. The issue was whether the War Department or the Interior Department would control the Indian Service. Sherman had not only intruded into the domain of Interior, but he had handed some authority over to a state government. Whether the arrest and trial would stand up remained as yet a moot point.

The courtroom was gaveled into quiet at 8:30 A.M. the following day, July 6. The court quickly solved the jury problem and obviated any necessity for repetition of evidence by testing, empaneling, and truly swearing the same twelve men who had served the day before.

Lanham had one witness, Horace Jones, who had been on the piazza of the C.O.'s house that day with Sherman, Marcy, Grierson, and others when Satanta was arrested. Jones testified that the chief had freely admitted his part in the attack on the wagontrain.

The jury did not stay out so long this time. They brought in their verdict, which James Robinson read. "We the Jury find the defendant Satanta guilty of murder in the first degree and assess his punishment at death." Whereupon Judge Soward said, "It is therefore hereby ordered and adjudged and decreed by the court that the said defendant Satanta be taken by the sheriff of Jack County and hanged until he is dead, dead, dead, and God have mercy on his soul, and it is further ordered by the court that the sheriff do take the defendant into close custody and hold him to await the sentence of the court upon the judgment herein."

The court proceeded then to formal sentencing, taking Big Tree's case first. As a matter of form Ball asked for a new trial, and it appeared to the court that the law was with the State. The judge asked whether Big Tree had anything to say before he was formally sentenced. Ball shook his head. Whereupon the judge set his hanging for Friday, September 1, at "some convenient place near the courthouse at the town of Jacksboro," and when he had prayed the mercy of God on the doomed soul, it being the final disposition of this court in the case, the judge said, "Amen."

The court proceeded similarly to the sentencing of Satanta. But when the judge asked Ball whether the prisoner had aught to say before he was sentenced, Woolfolk stood up.

"Your honor," he said, "I request that the court ask Mr. Jones or the other interpreter to inquire of the defendant whether he has aught to say."

The judge obviously saw no harm in it. There was time before lunch. He asked Horace Jones to come to the defense table. Jones came and discussed the matter with the chief, then Satanta stood up.

He held up his manacled hands and turned about to show them all. He spoke in Comanche, because it was Jones's best Indian tongue, and gave ample time for interpretation.

"I cannot speak with these things upon my wrists. I am like a woman.

"Has anything been heard from the Great Father in Washington?" It was a rhetorical question, but he gave them time to ponder it.

"I have never been so near the Tehanos before. I look around me and see your men, women, and children, and I have said in my heart, if I ever get back to my people I will not again make war upon you.

"I have tried to find friendship with the white man since I was so high." He held his hands at waist level. "My tribe has even taunted me and called me a woman because I associated with the whites.

"We suffer now for the crimes of irresponsible Indians, of Lone Wolf and Kicking Bird and Big Bow and Fast Bear and Eagle Heart, and if you will let me go, I will kill the latter three with my own hand.

"I did not kill the Tehanos. I came down to Pease River, where we began the raid, as a big medicine man to doctor the wounds of the braves.

"I am an important chief among my people and have great influence among the warriors of my tribe; they know my voice and will hear my word.

"If you let me go back to my people I will withdraw all warriors from Texas. I will take them all across the Red River and that shall be the line between us and the palefaces.

"I will wash out the spots of blood and make it a white land and there shall be peace, and the Tehanos may plow and drive their cattle to the banks of Red River.

"But if you kill me it will be like a spark on the prairie. It will make a big fire. A terrible fire." After a moment of silence he sat down.

Judge Soward proceeded. "It is ordered, adjudged, and decreed by this court that the sheriff of Jack County do take the defendant Satanta on Friday, the first day of September, A.D. 1871, to some convenient place near the courthouse at the town of Jacksboro and him, the said Satanta, to hang by the neck until he is dead, dead, dead! And may God have mercy on his soul, Amen!"

The spectators were not inclined to make any demonstration. They were cowed by the awesome legality of it all. They left the courtroom in an orderly manner, convinced that they had seen history made. The soldier guard surrounded the two prisoners and took them back to their cell at the fort.

The judge and other officials remained in the courtroom for an informal discussion with the jurors and a few town leaders who had been in the audience. They considered briefly whether it would be an advantage to the frontier or a disadvantage should Governor Edmund Davis commute the sentences. Woolfolk listened and said nothing; he had realized that the judge and clerk were going to hold the trial records, perhaps destroy them, to prevent an appeal, but it appeared that Soward would keep his promise to write the governor.

The court had some further business to take care of that afternoon, then adjourned until the next regular term of court. The judge returned to Weatherford and the following Monday wrote the promised letter, trying to offer the argument for commutation and yet not clearly recommend it. He wrote in part:

> Mr. Tatum expressed a strong desire that they should be punished by imprisonment for life instead of death, but the jury thought differently. . . . I must say, here, that I concur with Mr. Tatum as to the punishment, simply, however, upon a politic view of the matter; Mr. Tatum has indicated that if they are tried, convicted and punished by imprisonment, that he would render the civil authorities all the assistance in his power to bring others of those tribes on the reservation who have been guilty of outrages in Texas, to trial and just punishment. I would have petitioned your Excellency to commute their punishment to imprisonment for life, were it not that I know a great majority of the people on the frontier demand their execution. Your Excellency, however, acting for the weal of the state at large, and free from the passions of the masses, may see fit to commute their punishment. If so, I say, Amen! . . .

CHAPTER TWELVE

PRISON

Governor Edmund J. Davis, a tall, stiff-necked man of forty-four with a well-trimmed beard and mustache, sat in his office at Austin considering a letter from one of his appointees, Charles Soward. The governor was slightly miffed at some of the wording: "I would have petitioned . . . but . . ." and "Your Excellency . . . free from the passions of the masses. . . ." The man was making a recommendation for clemency and trying to pretend that he was not. And was the man pretending that a governor did not need the votes of west Texas? Free from passion? He was trying to reconstruct this state, protect Union sympathizers, give freed blacks a fair chance, break the spirit of ex-rebels, and he was faintly beginning to wonder whether he would go down in history as the state's most hated chief executive.

Davis had come to his position by a difficult route. He had been himself a district judge in Brownsville, Texas, until 1861. A Unionist, he had campaigned for a position as delegate to the Secession Convention, but had lost and found himself in trouble when the people in the southern tip of Texas went strongly for the Confederacy. He fled to Mexico. He began to raise troops among other disgruntled Texans, and in 1862 was appointed colonel of the 1st Texas Cavalry of the Union army. Early in 1863 the Confederates thrusting into Mexico captured him and brought him back to Texas, but the governor of Tamaulipas made such strong protests and appeals that Davis was released. In the spring of 1864 he led his troops in an unsuccessful attack on the town of Laredo, and was promoted that same year to brigadier general, whereupon he took his men to Union-held New Orleans. He served out the war in Louisiana.

When he was mustered out at San Antonio in August of 1865, he turned down General Phil Sheridan's appointment as chief justice of the Texas Supreme Court, but soon entered Reconstruction politics. He was the leader of the loyalist (or as some ex-rebels preferred—scalawag) faction in writing the state constitution of 1869, and in the election that fall, supervised by General J.J. Reynolds, he won the governorship.

He was not unaware that the settlers of northwest Texas had voted for the Union ten years before, but why hadn't they fought for the North as he had? It was hard to decide whether they should be treated as ex-rebels or not. As to the trial of the two Kiowa chiefs, the army had certainly favored it, and a man could hardly go wrong siding with Sherman. On the other hand, he was aware of the jealousy of the Interior Department over control of Indians, and hanging seemed such a permanent disposition of the matter. His power in Texas surely depended upon keeping in the good graces of every federal official possible. Then, too, Soward, for all his mincing of words, made some sense in his letter concerning the Indian problem on the frontier.

On August 2 the governor ceased his procrastination and issued a proclamation.

. . .

The State of Texas

To all whom these presents shall come

Whereas at the July term 1871 of the District Court of Jack County in said State one Satanta and one Big Tree known as Indians of the Kiowa Tribe were tried and convicted on a charge of murder and sentenced therefor to suffer the penalty of Death on the 1st day of September A.D. 1871.

And whereas it is deemed that a commutation of said Sentence to imprisonment for life will be more likely to operate as a restraint on others of the Tribe to which these Indians belong.

And whereas the Killing for which these Indians were sentenced can hardly be considered, on a just consideration of the animus, as coming under the technical crime of murder under the Statute of the State, but rather as an Act of Savage warfare.

Now therefore I Edmund J. Davis Governor of Texas, by virtue of the authority vested in me by law and the Constitution of this State, do hereby commute the Sentence of the said Satanta and Big Tree to imprisonment for life at hard labor in the State Penitentiary and hereby direct the Clerk of the District of Jack County to make this commutation of Sentence a matter of record in his Office.

In testimony whereof I have hereunto signed my name and have caused the Great Seal of the State to be affixed at the City of Austin this the 2nd. day of August A.D. 1871

Edmund J. Davis
Governor

The wheels of justice turned slowly. After he had already commuted the sentence the governor got letters from federal officials asking him to do so. Apparently also some officials questioned whether a primitive western state had any formal legal processes and demanded that the federal government be given a copy of the trial records. On September 8, Clerk James Robinson, still pretending that the state had custody of the chiefs, wrote a long warrant ordering the sheriff to deliver the prisoners to the state penitentiary at Huntsville. He included in this document a complete summary of the trial with pleadings and exceptions and rulings and much legal form and language. But Robinson did not give the warrant to the sheriff; rather, he took it to the temporary C.O. at Fort Richardson (Mackenzie had gone on a campaign against marauding Indians). The officer judged that it was an adequate record of the trial to satisfy any demands of the federal government.

Four days later General Reynolds at San Antonio had printed up and issued Special Orders, No. 185, which said in part: ". . . the commanding officer, Fort Richardson, Texas, will send, under suitable guard, the Indian prisoners, *Satanta* and *Big Tree*, to Huntsville, Texas, and cause them to be delivered to the warden of the State penitentiary. . . . The commissioned officer in charge of the guard will be held directly responsible for the *sure custody*, and *entire personal safety*, of the prisoners, while *en route* and until formally delivered to the warden, and to this end all communications with the prisoners, by civilians, will be carefully prevented and strictly forbidden. . . . The Quartermaster's Department will furnish the necessary transportation."

The order was obeyed and on November 2, 1871, the army turned over the two Kiowas to the warden of the penitentiary in east Texas. For the first time the two chiefs were in the actual custody of state officials. They were duly admitted and entered in the records thus:

Name	Satanta, Kiowa Chief	Big Tree, Kiowa Chief
Number	2107	2108
Age	unknown	unknown
Nativity	Indian Country	Indian Country

Time Convicted	July Term, 1871	July Term, 1871
Offense	Murder	Murder
Occupation	none	none
Term of sentence	Life	Life
County	Jack	Jack
Education	none	none
Use tobacco	yes	yes
Height	5′ 9½″	5′ 7″
Complexion	copper	copper
Color of eyes	black	black
Color of hair	black	black
married	yes	yes
Residence	Indian Territory	Indian Territory
Money	none	none
Received	November 2, 1871	November 2, 1871
Expiration	Life	Life

That winter a writer for *Scribner's Monthly* visited Huntsville. In his article published later was this account:

> In a corridor of the penitentiary I saw a tall, finely-formed man, with bronzed complexion, and long, flowing, brown hair—a man princely in carriage, on whom even the prison garb seemed elegant,—and was told that it was Satanta, the chief of the Kiowas, who with his brother chief, Big Tree, is held to account for murder. I was presently introduced to a venerable bigamist who was Satanta's chosen boon companion, on account of his smattering of Spanish, and through this anxious prisoner was presented at court. Satanta had come into the work-room, where he was popularly supposed to labor, but where he never performed a stroke of work; and had seated himself on a pile of oakum, with his hands folded across his massive chest. His fellow prisoner explained to Satanta, in Spanish, that we desired to converse with him, whereupon he rose and suddenly stretch-

> ing out his hand gave mine a ponderous grasp, saying: "How!" He then responded, always through the aged wife-deceiver, to the few trivial questions I asked, and sat down, motioning to me to be seated, with as much dignity and grace as though he were a monarch receiving a foreign ambassador. His face was good; there was a delicate curve of pain at the lips which contrasted oddly with the strong Indian cast of his other features. Although he is much more than sixty years old, he hardly seemed forty, so erect, elastic, vigorous was he. When asked if he ever expected liberation, and what he would do if it should come, he responded "Quien sabe?" with the most stoical indifference. "Big Tree" was briskly at work plaiting a chair seat in another apartment, and chewing tobacco vigorously. His face was clear cut and handsome, his coal-black hair swept his shoulders, and he only paused to brush it back and give us a swift glance as we entered, then briskly plaited as before. The course pursued toward these Indians seems the correct one; it is only by imposing upon them the penalties to which other residents of the State are subject that they can be taught their obligations to the mass of citizens.

Satanta was thinking about his obligations to certain people who had considered him a leader in tribal affairs, in war, in diplomacy.

Now that he had seen more of the white-man's country and ways and strengths, it was more clear than ever that Indians must some day accommodate themselves to change. Also, the danger of lack of unity impressed itself further upon him. He had an ability, by the force of his personality and conviction, to influence his guards and the officials of the prison, and through his Spanish-speaking friend he argued that if he were released he could bring all the Indian troubles of the south plains to an end. He was not insincere; he thought he could convince the

Comanches, Kiowas, Kiowa-Apaches, Cheyennes, and Arapahos to move first to strength through unity, then peace. Surely if anyone could, he could. Finally, the officials gave in and allowed him to dictate in Spanish a letter to be written in English to Agent Tatum. In this letter he asserted that he believed that he could, if released, act almost as effectively as if he were the principal chief of all the warrior Indians of the south plains. He got no answer and no result from the letter.

They did not ordinarily treat him badly in prison. The greatest difficulties were things they probably did not even know about, the humid air, the lack of freedom, the oppression of stone walls, the heavy, crude shoes which he could never get used to and which rubbed blisters on his feet. He felt disdain for their work and for the petty ways they sometimes used against him, withholding tobacco and other privileges, but he advised Big Tree to work and learn as much as possible about their occupations.

For a short time early in the following year he and Big Tree went out on a railroad work gang to help complete the Houston and Texas Central Railroad from Corsicana into Dallas. It was backbreaking work, something he was not used to, but he felt constrained to do his share; if he did not hold up his part of a steel rail or crosstie another of the gang had to take the weight in his own hands. He worked and his middle-aged muscles knew it.

He was aware that the prisoners around him were outcasts, rebels, irresponsibles, of white society. He observed them and learned such English words as he could and as much as he could of their peculiar thought patterns.

On that day when the three chiefs had been arrested by orders of General Sherman, the Kiowa bands had fled west sixty miles or more into the land of the headwaters of Red River. They had got sure word of the death of Chief Tsatangya and rumors that Chief Satanta and Big Tree had been killed on the way to Texas or later. They wished the Cheyennes and Comanches to declare all-out war along with them against the whites, but were unable to convince these allies that it would be feasible.

The Kiowas had split into two main factions: the militants under Principal Chief Lone Wolf and the peacemakers under Kicking Bird. In August 1871, Kicking Bird brought to the agency eleven mules, but Stone Head Tatum would accept only two of them; the others were inferior. Later that month the chief brought in thirty-eight more mules and one horse to satisfy the claim of the freighting firm of Warren and DuBose.

Tsatangya's eldest living son, An-pay-kau-te, began a war of his own. He placed a high value on the life of his father and began to collect when and where he could from any white. In less than a year he took the lives of one soldier and three civilians, the last a cattle worker named Frank Lee killed north of Fort Sill just four days short of the first anniversary of his father's death. Lee had come from New York to the romantic West to learn to be a cowboy, and did not even try to escape as Tsatangya's son and three other Indians came toward him. They shot him and knifed him and took off his scalp and one ear. Then An-pay-kau-te's passion for vengeance was satisfied.

Others of the Lone Wolf faction raided into Texas that spring. In April they struck a wagontrain carrying small arms and ammunition for the government at a place called Howard's Wells on the San Antonio–El Paso road. Seventeen teamsters, Mexican-Americans, were killed and their cargo taken. When two troops of the 9th Cavalry chased them, the Indians set up an ambush, killed one officer, and made the pony soldiers retreat.

Kiowas also attacked a ranch on the Brazos River east of Fort Griffin, killing three whites and capturing three children.

At a council in the summer of 1872, called so that Indians of more peaceful tribes might admonish their wild western brothers concerning their warlike ways, one Kiowa stated that he intended to kill Stone Head Tatum. Fortunately Tatum, who had considered the council useless, had already left the meeting site. Cyrus Beede, Quaker clerk of Indian Superintendent Enoch Hoag, was present, and he demanded that the Kiowas give up their raiding and their captives and all government property they had taken. Lone Wolf replied that the government must move Fort Sill and get all white soldiers out of Indian country. The reservation must be extended to the Rio Grande on the south and the Missouri River on the north. Satanta must be brought so that they could see his face and know that he was alive, and he must be given back to his people. Then the Kiowas would think of peace.

Kicking Bird, who had not spoken at the council, came to Beede afterward and said that he would do all in his power to influence his people toward peace. The Quaker clerk reported to his superiors that the Peace Policy seemed to be working, and he indicated that the Indians seemed to be showing a friendly attitude.

That same summer Judge Soward of Weatherford, frustrated that he had gotten no more Indians to try, wrote President U.S. Grant a strong letter, saying that the

> . . . depredations have been growing from bad to worse until they are perfectly alarming to our people. I might give your Excellency scores of instances of recent date of murder, rape, and robbery which they have committed alone in the counties composing my Judicial District. It has been but a few days

> since the whole Lee family consisting of six persons were inhumanly butchered, three of them being females were ravished, murdered and most terribly mutilated. Then Mr. Dobs, Justice of Peace of Palo Pinto County was but last week murdered and scalped, his ears and nose were cut off. Mr. Peoples and Mr. Crawford of said county met the same fate. Wm. McClusky was but yesterday shot down by those same bloody Quaker Pets upon his own threshold. I write to your Excellency, as one who from your Exalted Position in our nation *can* if you *will* protect us from this inhuman butchery. . . .
>
> . . . Your humble correspondent believes your Excellency to be endowed with at least a moderate amount of human feeling and a mind that cannot be trammeled by this one dread *Insane* Pseudo humanitarian Policy: called the "Quaker Indian Peace Policy." Am I mistaken?

It was hardly a proper letter to write a president, and the judge had his facts partly wrong regarding the Lee family, but the letter demonstrated the frustration of the settlers.

Meanwhile the government had decided to bring representatives of south-plains Indian tribes to Washington. The purpose of the trip was summed up thus by the Commissioner of Indian Affairs: ". . . it is at once cheaper and more humane to bring the savages to a realizing sense of their weakness and the impossibility of long contending with the government, by giving a few chiefs and braves free rides on railways and Broadway omnibuses, than by surprising their camps on winter nights and shooting down men, women, and children together in the snow. . . ." Two special commissioners, Henry Alvord, ex-captain of calvary, and Professor Edward Parrish of Philadelphia, were sent to persuade the Indians to make the trip. Parrish, an elderly man, became ill and died at Lawrie Tatum's agency on September 9, and the task was left for Alvord alone.

One great stumbling block stood in the way. Lone Wolf,

speaking for the Kiowas, was adamant about seeing Satanta and Big Tree. He did not intend to cooperate in any project whatsoever unless it were proved to him that they were alive. Captain Alvord immediately directed toward Governor Edmund Davis whatever power of persuasion he could summon. Alvord's request was extraordinary; let the federal government use his two most famous prisoners for a short time. Davis, still aware that his position in Texas depended upon pleasing as many officials in Washington as possible, consented. He had journeyed to Washington recently, had talked with Secretary Columbus Delano at some length, and had decided that his own interests lay more with pleasing the Interior Department than with pleasing the War Department. Now he went to Huntsville for a long talk with Satanta, then made arrangements for the loan of the two chiefs.

The prisoners were sent to Dallas over the railroad they had helped to construct and were transferred to an army ambulance under cavalry guard for the trip north. At first it was intended to take them to Fort Sill, but the plan seemed dangerous. No one knew exactly how much power Satanta had. The sight of him might cause an Indian demonstration, even an uprising; at least it would tempt some Indians to try to free him. It was decided that the meeting between the delegation to Washington and the two prisoners must take place well out of Indian Territory.

Captain Alvord persuaded thirty-seven Indian men and eleven Indian women to go east with him under the clear guarantee that they would see Chiefs Satanta and Big Tree. Kiowas Lone Wolf, Son of the Sun, Sleeping Wolf, and Dog Eater, and the wives of two of them, all skeptical, fearing white duplicity, agreed to go. The delegation traveled east by wagon to the end of the M K & T Railroad, which had been built south to a point near the small town of Boggy Depot, and took a special pullman car for St. Louis. Satanta and Big Tree and their army guards came to the same railhead and took the train a day later.

It was rainy and chilly when the delegation arrived in St. Louis on the afternoon of Saturday, September 28. The Indians were issued red and blue blankets and were put up at a good hotel, the Everett House. They were being watched over and assisted by Captain Alvord, Friend Enoch Hoag, who was the Indian Superintendent from Lawrence, Kansas, interpreter Horace Jones, and a Colonel Campbell of St. Louis.

A reporter for the *Missouri Republican* had become interested in the situation. Shortly after Satanta and Big Tree arrived in town he wangled an interview with them. The two had just learned that their request to go all the way to Washington had been refused, and they were disappointed. Satanta said that he had important ideas about peace that he would like to explain to the President.

Then the reporter went to the large basement dining hall of Everett House, where that Sunday morning the council would be held to prove that Satanta was alive. The tables had been shunted aside and chairs arranged all around the walls, leaving a large hollow square in the center. The forty-eight Indians from the south plains, men and women, were seated, waiting. The faces of some of the chiefs were painted vermillion. Some Indians were barefoot; some wore moccasins. Their dress made a motley variety. Nearly all were wrapped in their new blankets of red or blue. They wore beads, brooches, breastplates, earrings, trinkets, feathers of variegated colors in their hair.

At eleven o'clock that morning Alvord, Campbell, and Hoag entered, and Alvord introduced the other two as counselors on Indian affairs to the Great White Father. Campbell spoke briefly, saying that he wished justice and peace. Hoag talked about the good road of peace and prosperity. He said, "Two of your principal chiefs followed the bad road and were overtaken and thrown into prison. They were sentenced to death. . . ." Then, erroneously, but probably sincerely, he claimed the credit for the commutation of the sentence. "I interceded with the Great Father at Washington to spare their lives, and their lives were spared, and they are here today, and you will see them. . . ."

Alvord said that he would ask Satanta to speak to them first in Comanche, which many understood, then in his native tongue.

An opening was made in the crowd, and Satanta entered with light elastic step, followed by Big Tree. They wore prison stripes, but had blue blankets wrapped around their bodies under their arm pits. The Indian watchers gasped in surprise and delight. Satanta came to the center of the square and shaded his eyes against the ceiling lights with his right hand, looking around to see whom he could recognize.

In one corner Lone Wolf and the Kiowas, from the strain of riding a train, from the bustle of a city, from all the strangeness, from now seeing their old friends, buried their faces in their hands and wept like children.

At length Satanta said, "I feel like one who has risen from the dead to see my people once more."

Turning to the Comanches and addressing one in particular named Milky Way, he said, "Brother, I want you to work strongly for us. I want you to take pity on us. I want you all, if you love us and desire our release, to keep your young men off the warpath.

"The governor of Texas gave me some good talk. He said that he was a great chief, but not half so great as the big chief in Washington.

"He said if you would restrain the young men from going on the warpath, we would get our liberty.

"The governor wants to be a friend of all the Indians. That

is what the governor of Texas told me, and he told me the truth.

"General Grierson of Fort Sill told the governor to cut my throat, but the governor said, no, I want to see him."

Then Chief Satanta, the diplomat, made a curious statement: "I am a Texan and I do not want our braves to go any more on the warpath in Texas." Perhaps he meant: I sympathize with the Texas settlers. Or, I see their side of it. Or, I am willing to treat with them. But the reporter took it down from the English of Horace Jones, "I am a Texan. . . ."

Satanta continued, "If you do right as I tell you, we will be released and go to you. This is the talk the governor of Texas gave me.

"He told me that our men ought to take the good road, the road marked out by the white man. I look to you and to the Great Father in Washington.

"There is no chief better known than Satanta. The sun shines on no more influential chief, and if we are released I can be of service to you all.

"I promise to do you good. You were told in the papers that we were dead, but you see that we are alive, and our hearts are strong and can stand a great deal."

Satanta and Big Tree then went around the room shaking hands and embracing old friends. Many of the members of the Indian delegation could not keep from shedding tears. The reporter wrote on his pad that their "proverbial stoicism seemed to forsake them. . . . Men who can thus weep are not totally depraved, they must have some redeeming traits."

Lone Wolf spoke briefly to the assembly, as did representatives of the Comanches, the Arapahos, and the Wichitas. Then Captain Alvord announced that the grand dining hall was needed for another purpose and the council was over. The

Indians went back to their rooms, where they were allowed some further visit and smoking with Satanta and Big Tree before continuing the journey to Washington.

The guards of Satanta and Big Tree took them back south to their Texas prison.

The reporter wrote a good story filled with details and facts, but perhaps it could not compete for interest with other news read by some of the newspaper's readers. He had said of the Indians' dress: "They were apparelled in all the fanciful costumes peculiar to their ideas of dress upon a great occasion." That day another column in the same paper carried this news of hats from New York: "The round hat is high in the crown and wonderful in the trimming. . . . With bonnets, a collar encircles the head from ear to ear, sitting at the front close to the hair and flat. Behind rises a coronal of the material, a puff, on top of this a mat of lace with a mass of flowers trailing down each side, meeting in the small of the back, where another outbreak of ribbons and lace occurs."

Captain Alvord had made considerable investigation of the situation in regard to the Indians of the south plains, in talks with Indians, with Tatum, and others. In Washington he filed his recommendations with the Department of the Interior, including this on the Kiowas:

> The Kiowas, from their present attitude and their conduct during the last two or three years, demand especial consideration. The tribes number about 1,200. In 1868 they barely avoided a serious conflict with the United States troops, and, although the larger part of them were brought to within a reasonable distance of their agency, and suitably located in the spring of 1869, they soon returned to their favorite range between the Wichita

mountains and the eastern slope of the Staked Plains, whence unrestrained they have most of the time since made frequent and successful expeditions in different directions, chiefly into Texas. To a certain extent they are subdivided into bands, and the chiefs of these have evinced different degrees of friendship, but it would be impossible to deal with them otherwise than as a tribe.

As already stated, their hostilities of the past year were pursuant to their deliberate decision, and it is safe to state that at least one-half of the terrible scenes of blood, fire, and pillage which they have caused have never yet been reported to the Department. The cold-blooded murders of inoffensive persons known to have been committed by them within two years approach a hundred, and they have now in their herds not less than a thousand stolen horses and mules, including over two hundred taken within a few months from the troops and agencies in their vicinity.

Lately they have yielded to a demand made upon them and given up the only white captives known to be among them, and there is no doubt that the present delegation, with the man at its head acknowledged as the principal chief of the tribe, will make every profession of friendship in the future and be anxious to cry quits and begin anew on peace terms. Nevertheless, while I desire to give this people all the credit they deserve, the opinion is very positively expressed that these apparently friendly acts on their part are no guarantees for the future, but simply repetitions of their conduct every autumn, when it is highly important to them to place themselves in position to receive during the winter months the material aid in subsistence and clothing afforded by the government. Gladly will they offer this fall certain terms of peace, but these will be found wholly in their favor—entire forgiveness for all past offenses, the possession of the greater portion of their stolen property, and full restoration to the rights and privileges of the plains Indians in general. But the promises of future good conduct will be utterly worthless, and, these terms granted, there will be every prospect of a renewal of their depredations as soon as the early grass recuperates their stock and they find themselves able to subsist on the prairies.

The present position of the Kiowas may not be exactly one of open hostility, but it is certainly nothing less than the most offensive insubordination. Their agent for the past three years, a sincere member of the Society of Friends, a man who has proved himself eminently fitted for the place, declares this tribe uncontrollable, and states his belief that nothing less than military authority, with perhaps some punishment by troops, will bring them into such subjection as to again render the services of a civil agent of benefit to them.

The Kiowas have no shadow of excuse for their conduct. For three years they have received their annuity goods, of proper quantity and quality; have drawn their rations regularly until their action last spring compelled their agent to refuse them; and in no way have they received any injury from the government troops or agents. The arrest of two of their chiefs under due process of law, with their subsequent trial and conviction in the state of Texas, must not be forgotten; but the government at once interceded and secured a commutation of their sentence, and the Kiowas were informed that the fate of their chiefs depended on the future action of the tribe. This can in no way be considered an excuse for them, uncivilized as they are, and as a pretext it but makes their conduct worse. . . .

I recommend that the representatives of the Kiowas now in Washington be told, in the presence of the entire delegation, that the government proposes to dictate its own terms to that tribe, and that they be the following: The entire tribe to encamp before November 30 at some suitable point near Fort Sill (for instance, Crawford's creek), where every movement can be watched by troops. All horses or mules found in their herds, . . . taken from the government and from private parties during the past two years, to be given up within the same time, . . . and

> the tribes to surrender to the proper authorities, for trial by United States courts, the three most prominent men of those engaged in the greatest atrocities during the past year. Also, that they be told that the recent conduct of the tribe prevents all present hope of the release of their two prisoner chiefs, and that the liberty of those and the others to be given up will depend entirely upon future good behavior. Also, that no annuity goods whatever be issued to them for the present year, and that hunting parties be allowed to leave camp only when accompanied by a proper detachment of troops. . . .
>
> Should these recommendations be approved, it would be well also to notify them that, having come or been forced into camp as proposed, they will be closely watched, and any movement, great or small, not fully authorized by whoever has them in charge, will subject the movers to immediate attack. . . .

But the Executive Committee of Orthodox Friends and the Quakers in the Indian Department would not admit that their policy of love and mercy might be failing. The very fact that Alvord had a military record made him suspect. The Commissioner of Indian Affairs, with the approval of Secretary of the Interior Columbus Delano, promised the Indian delegation that, with their continued good behavior, Chiefs Satanta and Big Tree would be returned to them in the coming spring. The promise was a questionable one, since the prisoners had been turned over to the state of Texas to serve life sentences.

CHAPTER THIRTEEN

THE BIG COUNCIL

General Sherman had been against any talk of ever releasing the two Kiowa chiefs since the time he had caused their arrest. He wrote that if they went free "no life from Kansas to the Rio Grande will be safe, and no soldier will ever again take a live prisoner." He had decided, as he would later write, that the south-plains Indians were "as children, needing counsel, advice, and examples, coupled with a force which commands respect and obedience from a sense of fear. . . ."

Early in 1872 cavalry out of Fort Concho engaged a group of Indian raiders and captured a Spanish-speaking boy, who shed new light on how marauding bands got guns and ammunition. Comancheros from New Mexico were trading arms and whiskey for stolen cattle and horses. They had trading stations scattered over that poorly mapped region to the west, and a good wagon road led across the Llano Estacado to settlements in New Mexico. Central to these operations were the Kwahadi Comanches, who had never signed a treaty with the United States. Militants among the other Comanche bands and the Kiowas cooperated with the Kwahadis, worked with them and through them.

In the summer of that year Mackenzie went out from Fort Richardson and rode more than six hundred miles through west Texas and New Mexico, proving that the cavalry could operate in the region and improving maps. That fall he went out again and struck against the Kwahadis, in particular a village east of present Amarillo on McClellan Creek, where he killed about twenty-three Indians, burned their 262 lodges, captured about 120 women and children, and took their immense horse herd. The warriors recovered their horses in an engagement that night, but Mackenzie delivered the captive women and children to Fort Concho, where they were held as hostages for the return of white captives and as pawns for future negotiations.

During that winter of 1872–73 the Kiowas restrained themselves and stayed on the good obedient road, looking to the promise of the release of Satanta and Big Tree. In this, the militant faction led by Lone Wolf was sincere. Whether Kicking Bird actually desired the release of Satanta is questionable.

Agent Lawrie Tatum had been in trouble with other Friends of the Indian Service since the day he cooperated with Sherman. He had written to his immediate superior, Friend Enoch Hoag, asking whether he would be sustained in demanding the arrest of three more militant Kiowas, Eagle Heart, Big Bow, and Fast Bear. Hoag had replied, "I do not deem it necessary to await special instructions from the Department as the 1st. Article of their Treaty of 1867 provides for the surrender and punishment of those committing wrong or depredation upon the person or property of any one, White, Black, or Indian subject to the authority of the United States. . . ." But he had proceeded in the same letter to state his confidence that the Indians were now inclined to lead a better life and had said, ". . . I would deem it imprudent to make further arrests at present." It was a cut-and-dried proposition; you didn't need permission to do it, but you had better not do it. Sometimes Stone Head Tatum felt that it was difficult to be a Quaker.

He would write later, ". . . to my mind the effect on the Kiowas of the promise of the release of Satanta, a daring and treacherous chief, was like a dark and rolling cloud in the Western horizon, and when he should be restored to his people in freedom, it might burst like a tornado upon innocent and unsuspecting parties." He did not analyze his reasons for thinking that Satanta in particular was dangerous, nor whether he personally were afraid on account of his part in the arrest, nor whether he had a guilty conscience from falsifying evidence, nor how he could be so directly in disagreement with other well-meaning Friends. He prayed a lot and suffered from headaches and dizziness. Finally he sent in his resignation, to take effect on March 31, 1873. If Satanta were released in the spring, whatever the result, someone else would have to handle it.

During the four years of his tenure as agent, which must have been the most hectic of his life, Lawrie Tatum had supervised the construction of agency buildings, had aided some few Indians to begin farming, had set up a school for Indian children, which was poorly attended. He was by nature a kind of salt-of-the-earth man, with whatever such characterization implies of virtue and limitation. His temperament was not suited to dealing with people of an entirely different culture, different ways, different values. He knew that his administration had not been entirely successful. Of one thing he was proud: During his last eight months at the agency he aided in the recovery of twelve Mexican captives and seven white captives from the Indians under his charge. Whether he ever asked about a baby, Milly Durgan, is not known. It was so long ago.

Another Quaker, James Haworth, was named by the Indian Office to replace Lawrie Tatum.

General Sherman was incensed at the possibility of the release of the two chiefs. In that spring of 1873 he wrote to Secretary Delano: ". . . I hope when Satanta is released and when he is actually killed at the head of a raiding party off the reservation (as certain as next year comes), you will simply decree that the Kiowas are outlawed, their property confiscated, and their most valuable reservation restored to the public domain.

". . . I believe that Satanta has done fifty murders. Indeed, my idea is that the Indian by nature can't help it. He should no more be tempted by a horse or a convenient scalp than a child should with candy." The general was sincere with the same kind of righteous sincerity that some people might have used in declaring him to be guilty of fifty thousand murders.

President Grant was being pulled to and fro; whenever anyone high in the Departments of Interior or War conferred with him, they had some argument to make about the release of Satanta. Grant decided to go along with Interior and the Quakers, and Governor Davis at Austin seemed willing to cooperate, providing he could get guarantees against Indian raiding which would vindicate his action before the voters of his state.

But in April of 1873 occurred events far to the west, near the California-Oregon line, which should have had no bearing on the Kiowa problem, but did, an uprising of certain Modoc Indians under a chief called Captain Jack. The Modocs refused to live where the government had determined that they must and retreated to a wild lava-bed fortress. Here they inflicted heavy casualties on attacking U.S. troops. In a peace conference that followed, Captain Jack drew out a pistol and shot dead General E.R.S. Canby, who was the army commander of the Department of the Columbia; a Methodist minister was killed at the same time. After this the Modocs were attacked unmercifully; Captain Jack and three of his lieutenants were hanged.

A wave of anti-Indian sentiment swept across the country on account of the killing of Canby. The Quaker Peace Policy came under criticism. The President and Delano concluded to delay the release of Satanta and Big Tree. Immediately the Quakers, aware of the folly of allowing Modoc problems to influence relations with the Kiowas, began to write letters urging that the promises to the south-plains Indians be kept. The Comanches had released sixteen white and Mexican captives; in return the army delivered back to their people the women and children Mackenzie had taken prisoner the year before.

But the release of the two Kiowa chiefs proved to be another matter; the citizens of Texas were strongly against it. In July Governor Davis went to Washington, trying to settle in his own mind where he stood with the Grant administration and how he might improve his federal backing. Texans were proving hard to reconstruct, and he felt no assurance that he could ever be reelected. The President evidently still backed the Peace Policy. It was also true that strong rumors of graft in the War Department were making it less potent politically. Davis decided to risk the ire of Sherman, and he arranged for a council at Fort Sill, during which Texas' terms for the release of Satanta and Big Tree would be discussed. He was not happy with the results he got in Washington. Interior seemed determined to do a complete land survey of the large Kiowa-Comanche Reservation in southwestern Indian Territory, and it was obvious that many Indians saw no reason for it, might even attack survey parties. Interior practically admitted that they wanted the two chiefs freed so that south-plains warriors would be pacified and their surveyors would be safe. Davis decided to do some hard bargaining before he released anybody.

Back in Texas he made arrangements for Satanta and Big Tree to be taken out of the penitentiary by the military and moved to Fort Sill, to be held in the guardhouse there to await the big council; but he wrote to General J.W. Davidson, the new commander at Sill, that he was "forced to conclude that the Kiowas and Comanches, especially the former, even while their agents are asserting their entire peacefulness, are engaged in raiding on the frontier. . . ." And he insisted to the general that no promises touching on the release would be honored except those which the Governor of Texas should make.

Within two years of the conviction of the two chiefs at Jacksboro and the commutation of their death sentences to life at hard labor, the question of their freedom had become a cause célèbre. The Legislature of Texas passed a unanimous resolution asking that they not be released. The General Council of the Indian Territory, meeting at Okmulgee, composed of Choctaws, Muscogees, Cherokees, Wyandottes, Ottowas, Senecas, Shawnees, Quapaws, and Sac and Fox, petitioned President Grant, urging on him the immediate pardon and liberation of Satanta and Big Tree.

After the Kiowa chiefs had already been taken to Fort Sill and the council to deal with their fate had been set for early October, the governor received a fat envelope, with a letter and documents, certified, from a citizen of Jacksboro. The letter, from L.J. Valentine, said in part:

> I have just returned from one of the most revolting sights I have ever witnessed—the mutilated bodies of Howell Walker, and his Son Henry, who formerly lived in this town and who were killed yesterday at "Thurman's Springs" about 7 miles S.W. from here.
>
> I have hurriedly made a "verbatim" Copy of the testimony, etc. taken at the Coroners inquest held this morning, which I enclose to you. . . .
>
> During the last month there has Scarcely a night passed without Some depredations being committed by the Indians in the

vicinity of the town, and "Fort Richardson," and throughout the Country—Some, within half a mile of the military post. As many as 150 to 200 Horses and Mules, have been taken during this period. . . .

Public Sentiment here is *intense*, and the only hope Frontiersmen now have left, is that you can induce the U.S. Government to adopt *Stringent measures* that will effectually remedy these outrages and *Compel* the Indians to remain on the reservation. If you can effect this, it will make every frontiersman, your *friend* personally, *politically*, but if Satanta and Big Tree are given up, *without adequate Security* for the protection of the frontier, the Republican Party is *defeated*—and *you* will be *unjustly censured*. . . .

Among the enclosures was a deposition from a witness reading thus:

Mortimer Stevens sworn says·

That the killing of old man Walker and his son took place yesterday morning about 8 o'clock, at the Thurman Spring on Salt Creek, about seven miles S.W. from the town of Jacksboro. They were killed by Indians.

We three the old man, his son and myself, had come from his ranch down the creek, after drinking water, to haul some in barrels to the house, deer sign were very thick about then and Mr. Walker said let us drive the wagon in under the hill, and set down and wait for deer. We saw some deer coming in from the North, we were about forty yards apart, I had showed him the deer, and when I showed him the deer he looked in the direction of the deer and then turned his head to the left, toward the bluff and started to run toward me and said "My God Steve the world is just alive with Indians" he says to me "the best thing we can do is to make that mountain." I says no let's stay right here and give them all we've got. Him and his son started for the mountain. I looked and saw four Indians, and I said "Walker come back and let's give them a fight right here." He kept on going and I struck in behind them, I was about twenty yards behind the boy, and the boy was about five or six feet behind his father. We had made a little point of timber in there about two hundred and fifty yards from the Spring. About that time, here came the Indians charging us from the direction of the Spring, the biggest portion of them came from the North side of the Spring. We then fell down on our bellies and they charged all around us. They had passed us, and we all started for the bluff in the creek, and when we got in about a hundred yards of the creek bluff the Indians charged us again. When we got down in the creek the Indians came charging right along the edge of it and commenced shooting down the creek at us. I commenced shooting and then two run around the head of the branch and got in behind us. I was shooting at the Indians in front of us and he was watching the Indians behind us. He kept raising his gun to his face and taking it down again, and while he was doing that he was shot by the two Indians that got behind us. I think the shot went through him and wounded his son, they both sung out "wounded" about the same time. The old man fell right over backwards his son was lying on his belly, and the old man was setting on his knee watching the Indians on the other side the creek. After this shot they spoke but few words to me and they were both gasping for breath.

The old man said to me "Steve if you get out alive have me buried decent, and go to Mr. Ayres and get the money that is due on the hay" the boy said "My Lord Steve I am killed" while they were gasping I shot at an Indian and he gave a yell and I started down the creek in the direction I shot, they did not follow me. I went through a black jack thicket and got lost, and struck old man Rodger's house, at about one o'clock. The Indians were well mounted. I came into town and got a detail of soldiers and went back, and got there about 11 o'clock last night. There were thirty-seven Indians I counted them, I think they had about nine Spencer guns, and the remainder I think were six-shooter pistols. The Indians had blankets of different colors and hats, government hats. Two of them had on quilts that belonged to me they had robbed my camp before they got to the Spring. There were some Spencer cartridge hulls marked H on the end found where the Indians shot at us on the hill.

his
Mortimer X Stevens
mark

Sworn to and subscribed before me this
14th day of September 1873.
Moses Wiley J.P.

When Governor Davis headed for Fort Sill toward the last of September it was with a stern determination that he would release Satanta and Big Tree on his own terms, without any soft-headed foolishness, or bring them back to serve life at hard labor.

The two chiefs had been taken from Huntsville to Fort Sill by a cavalry guard in August and had been lodged there in the newly built post guardhouse. Commissioner of Indian Affairs E.P. Smith and Indian Superintendent Enoch Hoag came to Fort Sill to take part in the planned deliberations. Governor Davis arrived on Friday, October 3, accompanied by various aides. Talks were immediately started with Indian leaders of the area to set a time and place for the council. The Indians did not wish to hold it on the post; it was a bad place and they mistrusted it since that day when the three chiefs had been arrested there. The governor, however, would consider no other location, and since it was accepted that the disposition of Satanta and Big Tree lay in his hands, it was agreed that the formal meeting should be held in front of the headquarters building at the south side of the post quadrangle on the following Monday.

Colonel J.W. Davidson, now in command of Fort Sill, made preparations. Not only did he have erected a large tent for shade at the chosen spot, but also alerted his garrison, required them to remain inconspicuous, and caused the cavalry horses to be saddled in their stables.

The officials, some army officers, various chiefs and warriors, gathered at the assigned time and place. Satanta and Big Tree were brought under a guard of black soldiers and seated on a bench. Much shade was available on the long porch of the limestone headquarters building. Davis, Smith, Hoag, and other notables sat at a table under the tent. Two hundred yards across the neat parade ground the participants could see the commanding officer's quarters where the two men now prisoners had been captured in that stormy session with Sherman less than two and a half years before, a place which symbolized to the Indians treachery, to the whites authority acting according to a valid treaty.

Commissioner Smith began the council with brief remarks, among them these idealistic words: "God has given us language to tell what we think and what we know and nothing else. Now today let there be nothing but truth between us."

Phillip McCusker was the interpreter, putting the English into Comanche, which most of the Indians understood.

Governor Davis rose and spoke. "People of the Comanche and Kiowa, I have brought back Satanta and Big Tree. They are here and we all see them.

"They were prisoners to the Texans and they could have taken their lives but did not. I have come here because the people of Texas have been suffering a long time.

"I want to have peace if possible—we are at peace with all

other of the Territory and want peace with the Kiowa if we can.

"I have come here to make my talk as to what the Texans want. I will hear your talk and then . . ."—at this point the governor began speaking to Smith and Hoag instead of to the Indians—"tell them what the Texans want them to do so that they can consider whether they want peace or war with Texas.

"Satanta and Big Tree can tell them what they have seen in Texas and how they were treated.

"They will make their talk and then we will hear what the Kiowa have to say—I will then make my talk."

From the crowd of Indians around, one pushed into the open in front of the table, a frail, aged man. It was Satanta's father, called by the whites Red Tepee. The old man put his hands on the governor's head and invoked an ancient blessing, then said: "I am an old and a poor man and I ask that you take pity on me and give me my son. You have your women and your children. I love my children as well as you love yours and I want my son." He did not say anything about the fact that he had once held captive the wife and children of the black man Britt Johnson. But his words were simple and poignant. Davis was somewhat embarrassed, as were the other officials. Smith motioned for him to withdraw and motioned for Satanta to rise and talk as the governor had asked.

The chief stood up and said in Comanche, "I speak to Lone Wolf, Kicking Bird and all and want them to pick up a good road. To the Comanches now raiding in Texas I want them to quit it and stay here on the reservation.

"This official, Mr. Smith, has come from Washington to tell them what the Great Father wants them to do.

"While in Texas in prison we were treated kindly; no one struck or abused us.

"Someone told my people I was dead, which was wrong. I mean what I say; I take my Texas father by the hand and hold him tight.

"I am part Kiowa and part Arapaho." He mentioned this fact because of the reputation the Arapahos had for their willingness to seek peace. "Whatever the white man agrees in, that is what I want my people to do.

"Strip these clothes off of me that I have worn in prison, turn me over to the Kiowas and I will live on the white man's road forever. Turn me over to my people and they will do as the white man wants them to.

"The Father in Washington has selected good men to meet our tribe and do what is good. The best thing to do for the Kiowas is to release us.

"That is what I have to say to the white people and now I will talk to my chiefs."

He changed to his native language, intending to admonish Lone Wolf and Kicking Bird that they should suppress any differences they might have and show before the whites one mind and one heart. But quickly McCusker began to talk and the white officials became excited and McCusker shouted, "Speak Comanche! So we can interpret!"

Satanta felt a flush of bitter anger; his fate lay before them and they would not even allow him to speak his own language. But it was no time to show anger. He sat down beside Big Tree.

Smith signaled to Lone Wolf that it was his turn, and the chief said, "My people have come here today to hear what the governor of Texas has to say to them and afterwards we will answer."

Davis' plan as to who would speak in what order had not been particularly logical. Evidently he realized as much, for he rose and addressed the gathering.

"Satanta and Big Tree being here alive shows that I have kept my word, that the Texans will keep their word. That as I promised about Satanta and Big Tree and what I now promise will be adhered to.

"For many years Texas has been a part of the U.S. Government and has been under the government at Washington and a part of the nation. Since when Lone Wolf was a little boy." Here the governor was exaggerating, for his state had been in the Union only twenty-eight years, while Lone Wolf now had grown children. He went on:

"The great chief at Washington was bound to protect the lives and property of Texans as well as others of his children. But all these years the Kiowa and Comanche have been killing and capturing our women and children and stealing our horses."

The governor dwelt at some length on the guilt of the Indians and the innocence of the Texans, reminded the redmen present that Texans were as numerous as the leaves in the forest, and stated his terms for the release of the prisoners. The Kiowas and Comanches must settle down on farm land near Fort Sill with a white agent in each camp to check on them daily. Who would employ these agents Davis did not say, but he was surely aware that he was laying down terms for the Indian Bureau as well as for its charges. Rations must be issued for only three days at a time and each family head must be present to draw his own. The Indians present must agree to help arrest the leaders, presumably Comanches, of recent raiders in Texas. Also, every horse stolen and any white captive still held must be delivered up.

The governor went on. "Satanta and Big Tree will remain in the guard house at Fort Sill until the commander of the post is satisfied that this arrangement is being carried out in good faith, when he will release them to go with their tribe, but it must be understood by them that they are not to be pardoned, but will be subject to re-arrest and return to the penitentiary of Texas to suffer for their old crime if at any time the Kiowa violate this arrangement.

"I have consulted the commissioner, Mr. Smith, your agent, and the commanding officer of the post and I am satisfied you can comply with these conditions if you desire peace and to live without war.

"These terms come from me as governor of Texas and not from those officers.

"If they are *not* complied with it will be better for the people of Texas who are the sufferer by the bad conduct of bad men of the Comanche and Kiowa to have open war and settle this matter at once.

"I have nothing more to say."

Commissioner Smith, Agent Haworth, and Superintendent Hoag were plainly startled by the governor's stern manner. They whispered together, then Smith stated to the assembly, "The governor of Texas has given you these terms and not the commissioner or agents, who knew nothing about the governor's terms until they heard them today." He motioned to Lone Wolf that he should speak.

Kiowa Chief Lone Wolf, thin, austere in looks, proud, understood that this was a day for agreeable words. The idea that the Comanches should accept hard terms in order to secure the release of Kiowa chiefs or that Kiowas had a responsibility to help arrest Comanche raiders seemed ridiculous, but he had heard some of Satanta's appeal for a unified front before that chief had been cut off. He rose and spoke.

"This is a good day. I have heard the talk the governor made. You made us a good talk and a wise talk and we have taken it all up and have concluded to do as you wish us to.

"I have looked through that talk and have found nothing bad in it. It is the same as I have talked to my people and I agree with it.

"My friend, you have come a long way to see us and to make a good road for us and the Texans to walk in. We intend to do just as you say.

"I am already trying to do as my agent wants me to do, and although these tribes are different ones, they are all trying to do right. These tribes are all alike, one people and one mind.

"We are like the whites; though from different sections, one people. I and my people mean what we say.

"If you will deliver up Satanta and Big Tree to us, we will do just as you say.

"My Mother Earth hears me."

It was a good speech. The answer to Davis was subtle, not calculated to challenge—let the prisoners go, and then we will meet the terms. He had spoken as the one principal chief of the Kiowas.

Kicking Bird rose to speak and caused a minor commotion. Both Satanta and Lone Wolf called out to him in Kiowa that he must help show a solid front. They were hushed by the white officials and the interpreter. Chief Kicking Bird said:

"We have met and the sun shines on us all. We have met to make a permanent peace, and I believe all the governor says to me and my people. . . .

"Along with the talk given us, which was a good strong talk, we want the prisoner chiefs given to us. . . .

"We want the chiefs given up at once, and not delayed for so long a time."

Whether Kicking Bird was sincere no one will ever know. He had made an issue of what was in fact the issue and given

Davis an opening for stubborn refusal. Kicking Bird's people could hardly blame him for his words. He went on.

"I have been trying for a long time to keep the peace between my people and the whites, but they are like boys; they sometimes do right and sometimes do not. . . ."

He complied with the plea for unity. "Although there are different people here, we are all the same; turn over the chiefs and we will quit raiding in Texas. . . ."

He spoke further and ended thus: "There are many here on the reservation who know of our efforts to restrain our tribe."

Then a Comanche chief named Horse-Back took his turn. Among other things he said:

"I am pure Comanche and in the last few years have been trying to get into the white man's road and next summer I think I will be plumb on it. . . .

"It is true that some of our foolish young men go off on the warpath yet, but then the Great Father has not kept all his promises and built houses for us as the agent had promised. . . .

"And now I ask the Texas governor to favor my friends the Kiowas and give up Satanta and Big Tree. . . ."

Following his talk, Pacer, the chief of the Kiowa-Apache band, spoke. He affirmed that his band was peaceable and asked that the two prisoners be released. He said: "We are corraled; we cannot live much longer and must be good. We want to live well, in houses, to cultivate land, and not live on the prairie.

"With houses and comfort we will be more gentle people than we have been. . . .

"We know the governor now for the first time. . . . It is true what he says—that it is better to have men watch us in our own camps.

"We are willing to be watched by the white men, but do not give us bad men who will not tell the truth about us.

"We have grown up in our Indian ways, but our little ones will grow up as white men.

"Give us houses as promised and then our children will grow up good, we want them educated as whites. . . ."

Chief Pacer showed that he had given thought to the destiny of his people and had considered the mixture of Spanish and Indian people south in Mexico in these words: "We do not want our people separated from the whites, but want to live like in Mexico where we all mix together and respect one another."

Pacer's concluding remarks were difficult to translate. He was more sincere than either the whites or the Kiowas proper, who faced each other this day as Machiavellian diplomats. He said:

"I don't want to live away from here. I want to be what you call 'good,' but my people are afraid of the whites, and so we live wild on the prairie.

"If I come here just to buy bread a soldier puts a bayonet at my breast and yells, 'Stop there! Go to the other side of the creek!'

"It is hard to understand how to be friends with the white man."

Satanta, sitting there taking it all in, finely tuned to every nuance, must have thought: Chief, you are too truthful for this world. You bare your heart in poor Comanche. You tell them your band is afraid of the whites. Do you think they will respect you for it?

The Penatuhka Comanche Asa-toyeh spoke in favor of releasing the prisoners next. Among other things he said, "I saw my Father in Washington and have been true to my promises, but am still waiting for my Father to keep his to us. . . ."

Commissioner Smith took up the accusation. "What has your Washington Father promised you?"

Asa-toyeh said, "Houses, lands, horses, plows."

Smith asked, "Have you not got a house and farming implements?"

Asa-toyeh said, "Yes! I made a good start towards building my house and was doing all right, but a white farming teacher came out and I couldn't get along with him."

A Yamparika Comanche chief, Quirts Quip, rose and spoke.

". . . I have been trying to get all my young men to do right. The agent promised houses and farms to help us live. That was last fall, but I have not heard any more of those houses and things.

"I'm just as poor now as I was then.

"Washington has lots of money, for I saw it in Washington, but I never see any of it here. I do not know what becomes of it; it must go into the ground.

"It has been repeatedly promised that Satanta and Big Tree would be given up; why then are they still in prison and why is it delayed to release them?

"The governor is too particular to want all the young men delivered up who have raided; they cannot be changed in a day. . . .

"You blame us for not getting on your road, but you have broken your promise to us about houses and farms and things, and you cannot blame us for breaking some of our promises.

"Why should I talk so much; I will try to get into the white man's road, but it cannot be done in a moment; we must have time."

He concluded, ". . . Now if you want me to be in the white man's road, let me see the things promised."

Commissioner Smith had obviously become irritated. He asked, "Did you have ground plowed for you this spring?"

Quirts Quip said, "I went out to a farm and thunder and lightning came and it looked like bad medicine to me and I left.

"Clouds came to my place only; all else was clear!"

His logic was beyond any answer the commissioner could make.

A Wichita chief of the Waco band, Buffalo Good, said: "I am a Texan and glad to see my brother the Texas chief.

"I knew Sam Houston; I was in Washington once and saw General Polk. He told me that Sam Houston was among the best of his children, and you, Governor Davis, are just like him."

The chief was good at flattery. He went on: "I hope today we succeed in doing what we came to do. I want this thing straightened out and Satanta and Big Tree released.

"The best agents we ever had were Texans. When they told us we would get lands and plows we got them.

"Washington sends agents who promise but don't do."

Commissioner Smith asked, "Did the agent send a man to show you how to plow?"

"After a lot of talk the agent sent me a man," Buffalo Good said; "I wanted the man to plow first and then I would plow."

"Yes," Smith said, "You wanted the white man to do the work and not to show you how." He probably was not aware that Buffalo Good's ancestors had farmed as long as his own. But the council was nearly getting out of hand.

Forgetting his admiration for the Texans, Buffalo Good said, "Well, the Texans have been stealing our horses."

Governor Davis asked, "When did Texans steal your horses?"

"Sometime in July."

"Did you report it to your agent?"

"Yes."

"How did you know they were Texans?"

"We've been losing them all summer and did not know for certain who was doing it. Two of my young men five nights ago found a party running off our horses, and one of my men was shot by them."

At this point Guadalupe, a chief of the Caddoes, arose. "I do not belong at this agency," he said, "but came to hear what was said at the council.

"I have time and again advised these Indians for the sake of the Caddoes to cease going on the warpath, but I am sorry to say that it has not stopped.

"I used to live out on the Brazos, and I defy any man to say that I or my people have ever raided on any one. These very Kiowas and Comanches that are here today were the cause of my tribe being removed from Texas.

"I too am tired of trifling with these raiding Indians. If they won't quit let them say so.

"My tribe had been raising cattle and hogs and farming on the Washita, and these raiders interfere with us as much as they do with the whites.

"I am dressed in the hat, pants, and boots of a white man. I did not steal them, but bought them with money from my farm.

"I talk this way to my red brothers, for I feel it's for their own good. . . .

"I would like to see settled this trouble between the state of Texas and these Indians. I think that Satanta and Big Tree have been sufficiently punished, but that is not my affair.

"It is between the Texans and Kiowas and Comanches."

It appeared that everyone had had his turn. The governor returned to the problem of white horse thieves. "In relation to the Texans reported to be stealing horses from them, if they will report the thing promptly so that troops can pursue I will answer any requisition if they escape into Texas.

"I do not wish to protect any bad Texan who is guilty of such conduct. . . .

"In answer to their request that I should release Satanta and

Big Tree this afternoon, I have to say that they are my prisoners and I only have the right to make any promise about them. . . .

"I will not change the conditions. . . . The sooner they comply the sooner these chiefs will be released." He then repeated his demand that the Indians help arrest recent raiders.

Superintendent Hoag obviously did not like the way the situation had developed. He said, "About a year ago when the delegation was in Washington the President did promise that if their people would keep out of Texas till Spring the two chiefs Satanta and Big Tree would be released.

"Lone Wolf was there and I was instructed to tell him that thing. . . . He assures us and our agents assure us that no Kiowa have been in Texas since then. . . .

"Now as their agent I appeal to His Excellency Davis on behalf of the President and Secretary of the Interior whether it is not unwise to keep them longer. . . .

"All promises their agents have made to them came through me and from Washington supposing they would be kept."

Davis said to the Indians, "I believe what the agent told you is what Mr. Hoag thought, and he has acted on the information he had. Texas has control of this matter entirely. . . .

"Your agent Mr. Hoag and Mr. Haworth want me to comply with *their* promises, but I do not agree to their request and will not do so."

Hoag said: "The governor proposes to deliver up these chiefs to the commanding officer to be surrendered to the tribes when they comply with his demands. Will he leave them on such terms with the commanding officer?"

Davis said: "I have implicit confidence in General Davidson and know he will act with discretion in the matter. In my opinion they can comply with my demands in thirty days."

Hoag said stiffly: "There is another matter I would like to

impress upon the governor, but I don't care about having it interpreted to these Indians, however, and that is this: We can place men in their camps who can control them if Satanta and Big Tree are released, but not if they are not."

The injustice of demanding that every Indian word must be interpreted and some white words not be probably did not occur to the superintendent.

Davis flared back: "If they are so warlike as that then we had better settle the matter at once."

Commissioner Smith, as the ranking federal official, apparently felt that it was time to assert himself. He said: "I have said nothing so far. I was not in Washington when you were there last year. I am your commissioner. But what the government told you then would be demanded, I am now here to demand.

"They told you that you had been raiding in Texas for many years. They told you that you had no reason to do so.

"That the government had given you a good country, rations, beef, and blankets, and you had no reason to raid in Texas and he told you that had got to stop.

"And you said it should stop and last spring when those Indian captives of the cavalry came from Texas, your agent wrote me that you had promised you would not raid if they were given up.

"You promised him you would not raid, and those women and children had hardly got in your camps when your young men went on a raid.

"Now I am here to demand those young men of you, and before the sun gets that high tomorrow." He pointed dramatically at a mid-afternoon position of the sun.

"I want those men brought here, and when those men are here you will get your captives and the governor and I will be agreed. Now go home and talk of this and talk of nothing else."

The conference was concluded upon this stern note. As the guard escorted him and Big Tree back toward confinement, Satanta was thinking: There has been no negotiation today. These whites are just like Indians, with no unity, no organization. Davis and Hoag and Smith were merely asserting their authority. But he had seen in the eyes of Lone Wolf that he and his young colleague would be rescued by force if the opportunity came.

On the following day those who had taken part in the council were busy. Fort Sill Commander Davidson asked Davis to put into writing the conditions that had to be met before he was supposed to release the two chiefs. Davis complied by hastily scribbling a letter in which he named the principal terms: that the bands have gone on permanent locations, have agents watching them, draw their rations on roll call, and have put themselves under the direction of the military to help arrest raiders.

The representatives of the Indian Bureau could not accept the general situation, for it was clear that the governor could not administer his terms, but was in effect giving an ultimatum to their branch of the federal government. Commissioner Smith searched for a way out of the dilemma, and he exchanged ideas in writing with the stubborn Texan concerning the question of administering the conditions of release.

Meanwhile the Indians were as busy as anyone. If they got another chance such as they had found on Monday they intended to take the prisoners at whatever cost. Every Kiowa warrior was to carry arms concealed under his blanket. When they found that another council was planned for Wednesday they assigned strategic posts to their braves and brought fast horses to carry Satanta and Big Tree. Governor Davis and the federal officials would be killed. It would be a costly and bloody engagement, for surely the cavalry was watchful and prepared, but they intended to free Satanta and Big Tree.

The council on Wednesday was tense. Davis read the letters exchanged between himself and Smith. These were not interpreted. But the explosion which was built up and ready did not come off. The governor told McCusker to ask Satanta and Big Tree to stand up. Then he said:

"Satanta and Big Tree and Kiowa and Comanches, since I spoke to you on Monday the government of the United States through Mr. Smith, the commissioner of Indian affairs and authorized to speak for it, has offered to become responsible to me to do that which I requested of your tribes to do.

"The government of the United States has promised me to make your tribes do what I demanded of you yourselves to do. . . .

"You heard Monday what I demanded. Satanta, Big Tree, and you Kiowas and Comanches heard what I said. The same thing the government of the United States now promises me you shall do."

He cautioned that the prisoners were not pardoned, only paroled, and said, "Now Satanta and Big Tree, you go to your tribes and remember what I told you."

Satanta knew that the governor could not understand this moment. He approached the stiff-necked, hairy, embarrassed Texan and embraced him, then turned and went to hug Lone Wolf.

Commissioner Smith began to try to keep his end of the agreement. He said: "You all now see what a load you have put on my back. The governor of Texas was going to keep Satanta and Big Tree until you did what was right and what he demanded of you.

"But I promised him that you should do what was right, and now I want you to promise me before these Texans and before these other gentlemen present that you will do what the governor wants you to do and what the authorities at Washington want you to do.

"I should be ashamed to go down to Texas or to Washington a month from now, and see that you have broken this promise.

"Now I want to see all of you down at the agency this evening, as I have something I want to say to you."

The council was over. The purpose of the commissioner in the evening meeting was to show some toughness of his own and to recruit helpers for the military in finding the "outlaw" Comanches who had been raiding. These recruits would in the days to come guide a military expedition on an extended wild-goose chase in west Texas searching for elusive Indian outlaws, and that would be the last of the governor's strict terms.

But to the camps that evening went two Kiowas, more properly designated men than chiefs in these circumstances, after more than two years of unnatural life among their enemies. They drank deep of the overflowing cups they had once known, of the voices and laughter, the smiles, the faces of friends and kin, the joking, of all the blessedness of what they had lost and regained.

People on the frontier of the south plains were incensed. They believed that the prediction of a bit of verse published in the San Antonio *Daily Herald* had come true. The bitter piece of literary effort read thus:

By Order of the President
Turn loose Satanta and Big Tree!
How can they ever vex us?
If they are set at liberty
Away down south in Texas?

They'll never take so far a stroll
To dare to face me on my throne,
In my imperial capitol,
Where everything is now my own. . . .
What do I care for murders there?
They'll never be as many fold
As you can hear yet, everywhere
Of Grant's blood-thirsty army told—
I'm used to extremes, and can smile
If homesteads burn and persons bleed,
I want a horse to trot a mile,
And who can bring me such a steed?
Turn loose Satanta and Big Tree!
To send me presents. Yet, do not tell
That, in return for liberty,
I hope they'll chastise Texans well.

The frontiersmen were not alone in their disgust. That impulsive and non-diplomatic general of the U.S. Army, W.T. Sherman, wrote to Governor Davis this reaction:

> I believe in making a tour of your frontier with a small escort, I ran the risk of my life; and I said what I now say to you, that I will not again voluntarily assume that risk in the interest of your frontier, that I believe Satanta and Big Tree will have their revenge if they have not already had it, and that if they are to have scalps, that yours is the first that should be taken.

CHAPTER FOURTEEN

A TIME OF FREEDOM

An old folk song begins:

> 'Twas in the town of Jacksboro
> In the year of '73,
> A man by the name of Crego
> Came stepping up to me,
> Saying, "How do you do, young feller,
> And how would you like to go
> And spend the summer pleasantly
> On the range of the buffalo?

The summer did not turn out to be pleasant for the hunters; angry Indians waited out there on the buffalo range. In fact, though many of the shaggy beasts roamed to the north and west of Jacksboro and its post of Fort Richardson, it was not in 1873 a major outfitting point for hide hunters; the railroad was too far away.

The great slaughter for buffalo hides had begun in western Kansas. A sportsman from England traveled thirty or forty miles along the bank of the Arkansas River east of Fort Dodge in the fall of 1873 and was appalled. He wrote: "There was a continual line of putrescent carcasses, so that the air was rendered pestilential and offensive to the last degree. The hunters had formed a line of camps along the banks of the river and had shot down the buffaloes, night and morning, as they came to drink. I counted sixty-seven carcasses on one spot covering four acres."

By the end of 1872 most of the buffalo of western Kansas and eastern Colorado had been killed. By the following year hide hunters began to push south into Kiowa and Comanche country.

Chief Satanta was released on October 8, 1873, and thereupon began the most difficult year of his life. Now that he knew better than ever the value of freedom, he felt that he must risk his own more than ever. Now that he felt that he saw clearly what Indian leaders must do, his own leadership could well send him back to prison. Though it was his nature to be flamboyant, obvious, he must work behind the scenes. He had developed a dream, as had many an Indian chief or diplomat before him, of a nation of native peoples, which would be able to slow white encroachment, so that those people could choose for themselves what they would accept or reject of white civilization. There was not much time to realize his dream. Whether it was already too late, he did not know.

On account of the agitation for his release, his name was on the lips of all the warrior people of the south plains. He hastened to exploit this interest in himself by calling for a council of Cheyennes, Arapahos, Comanches, Kiowas, and Kiowa-Apaches, to meet in the western edge of the reservation away from prying white eyes. They came together, chiefs and representatives, in the Kiowa moon of Aga-nti, or the time of waiting for winter to come soon.

Without any interpreters or clerks to write down words, Satanta spoke to them in the great meetings and in the small talks around campfires. His theme was this: We all have one mother, the earth; therefore we should have but one council fire. All he tried to tell them was implied in that theme. In the idea of the Earth Mother lay the commonality of their religion and spiritual attitudes and beliefs about land ownership and use. In regard to the one fire, they should not consider anything important in these times except those things important to all of them.

What had the reservation been when they first heard of it? Only a line drawn by Washington to keep out whites. Then they found that the line did not keep out white soldiers. Then a smart man from Washington told them they did not need to leave the reservation to hunt; the buffalo came through twice a year and that was enough. Now they were saying all bands must camp near the agency. The reservation lines did not keep out white horse thieves from Kansas or Texas or from the land of the farming Indians to the east. The line did not keep out surveyors, who went about driving stakes in the Earth Mother for reasons only a white man could understand.

One mother and one fire. Did it mean fighting? Yes, but only for a limited number of things: the buffalo, the land, the right to change their lives at their own pace and discretion. Those who wanted peace at any price were depending upon the mercy of the white man and his understanding.

One mother and one fire. It meant fighting for the things important to all the tribes as decided in a common council. No more senseless raids against the Utes. No more raids for personal glory and aggrandizement. No more raids for personal revenge.

Satanta wished that he were an even more persuasive orator than he was. Some of them understood and some did not. Some agreed and some did not.

That winter proved to be a hard one, particularly for the

1873? 1874?

obedient Indians who camped in the near vicinity of Fort Sill. The Indian Bureau did not deliver the rations they promised and put the blame on transportation difficulties. Many Indians were forced to kill horses and mules for food.

In mid-January of 1874 a raiding party returned and brought bad news to the Kiowa camps. Shortly after the Fort Sill council with Governor Davis a number of warriors, some thirty or forty, including nine Kiowas, had ridden south on an extended plundering expedition. They had made a temporary camp on the Nueces River in south Texas, then crossed into Mexico, where they killed some fourteen Mexican peons and captured more than a hundred horses and mules. Coming back into the United States, they had killed two Americans and then were attacked by a force of U.S. Cavalry. In the engagement nine of the raiders died, including two young Kiowas, Tau-ankia and Gui-tain. It seemed a disaster, for Tau-ankia was the beloved favorite son of Lone Wolf, the principal chief; Gui-tain was his nephew.

Lone Wolf was desperate with grief when the news came. He slashed himself with a knife, killed some of his horses, cut off his hair, burned his lodges. From that time, Lone Wolf was thoroughly hostile to the whites, but not in the way that Satanta would have wished. Lone Wolf longed to recover the body of his son and to have revenge.

In April the chief struck south and, guided by a member of the previous raid, found the bodies of his son and nephew. The cavalry was in close pursuit, however, and the two mourned corpses were placed in permanent burial in a cleft on a mountainside. Lone Wolf captured about twenty-five horses belonging to the infantry at Fort Concho and escaped back to the reservation.

About the same time white horse thieves from Kansas stole

forty-three horses from the Cheyennes. A party of warriors, including the son of Chief Little Robe, went in pursuit. They could not recover the horses, but took the first cattle they could find, then were attacked by cavalry near the Kansas border. Little Robe's son was killed. Another chief of the warrior people of the south plains had become militant, not in any wise and effective way, but full of grief and desire for revenge.

Satanta began to counsel with the Comanches, who had always existed as autonomous clans and bands, urging upon them the value of the annual sun dance as an aid to unity. In June of 1874 these good allies held the first and only Sun Dance during their existence as a tribe. They held it out west of the Wichita Mountains, where Elk Creek runs into the North Fork of the Red River. The ceremonies were well attended by the allied tribes and amounted to a council of war. Some seven hundred or more warriors were ready to act. A prophet, Isa-tai, had risen among the Comanches; he claimed magical powers against white bullets.

There was talk of riding down and destroying the Tonkawas, who were scouting for the cavalry in Texas. Satanta argued against it. To follow up that old feud would accomplish nothing and would waste their strength. Instead, they should strike the buffalo hunters who had gone from Dodge City to the southern hunting grounds and built a big camp near the adobe ruins on the Guadalpa River, at the place where the whites had struck the Kiowa camps ten years before. The allied warriors smoked the pipe on it, and they rode west, seven hundred to a thousand strong, in their greatest combined effort in twenty years.

They surrounded the buffalo hunters' headquarters camp, which consisted of some five rough buildings and a picket enclosure, and attacked it on the morning of June 27. The battle would prove to be a fiasco.

Satanta had agreed to blow his bugle with some trepidation. It would enable him to stay in the background, but surely would leave room for white guesses as to his involvement. He need not have worried. Here, in the same area where he had confused the troops of Kit Carson with his bugle ten years before, even though he was the only Indian in the region well known to be a bugler the whites heard his soundings of charges and retreats and wondered at it but never connected him with it.

Isa-tai's magic proved worthless. The Indians lost thirteen killed and many wounded, as well as many horses. The white hunters were excellent marksmen and fired long-range buffalo guns with telescopic sights. Satanta saw a warrior knocked off a horse by the bullet of a rifleman nearly a white-man's mile away.

He was worried little about Isa-tai's medicine failure, more about the whites' superior weapons. In his younger days the need had been for guns to match the whites. As they got the guns, the whites came up with repeating rifles. Now that the Indians were getting many repeating rifles, the whites had come up with a weapon that would shoot a mile. But what concerned him much more was the lack of organization among the allies, clear to him as he tried to bugle the orders which would be agreed to by a dozen chiefs. Individual warriors proved their bravery, particularly in picking up the wounded and carrying them out of danger, but there was no plan and no authority which could press home the attack to destroy the two dozen white defenders. As they gave up the battle in the middle of the afternoon, Satanta rode away with a heavy heart.

Most of the warriors gathered their families and moved east to a site on Kop Pepa, or the North Fork of the Red, where the Kiowas would hold their annual Sun Dance. Satanta had decided that words alone were not enough, not even beautiful words like "one mother, one fire." He tried to think of a way whereby he might dramatize at this great Kado gathering, which many Cheyennes and Arapahos and Comanches would attend, the message he was trying to convey to them all.

The medicine arrow or lance, Zebat, which he owned, had belonged originally to a warrior named Tan-guadal. The warrior had been killed on a raid, leaving the Zebat, somewhat damaged, sticking in the ground where he died. Satanta had retrieved the sacred weapon, taken it home, repaired it, and, since the first owner had been his kin by marriage, had claimed it as his own. Tan-guadal's relatives had strongly protested, but Satanta, who already had much power and prestige, had kept the Zebat as another symbol of his leadership.

The struggle for honors in which he had played such a successful part in the past now appeared to him in a different light. Warriors and chiefs had too often judged a particular warpath, not for what it might mean for the people, but for what it might mean in terms of personal glory. Ambition and rivalry were coming to seem to him the greatest weaknesses of his people. At a time when they were being surrounded on all sides by the whites, what did coups matter? What did it matter who was principal chief? What did it matter who was the keeper of the Zebat? He had a sudden insight that he had begun to understand the mysterious strength of old Tsatangya.

In a dramatic giveaway before the assembled Kiowas and the allies Satanta presented the sacred weapon to the warrior Ato-t-ain. His people knew Satanta and his nature; they marveled at his generosity. Some of them understood the meaning of the gesture and some did not.

After the Kado, Lone Wolf began to recruit a party to go to Texas in order to get revenge for his son. Satanta was against the expedition, but he could say nothing. Lone Wolf got his revenge on this raid in the killing of two Texas Rangers in the same area where Satanta's party had attacked the wagontrain three years before.

Guerrilla war sputtered intermittently over the south plains that summer. Some of it Satanta approved: the killing of buffalo hunters, the killing of wood haulers and surveyors on the reservation, the killing of teamsters hauling army supplies. Vaguely he hoped that the government would sue for peace and schedule another large council with the Indians before winter.

But in Washington the white general who had said "War is hell!" was getting permission to settle the "Indian question" in his own way. Sherman proposed a plan, which President Grant approved: Let the Indians who wanted peace separate themselves from the hostiles, enroll with their agents, and remain near their agencies with army officers. Then the army, disregarding any treaties or reservation lines, would attack the hostiles, subdue them, and send their leaders far away to the eastern seacoast as prisoners of war. Some people would have thought it a realistic plan, which it was not. Not many Indians could camp near the agencies and keep their horses, for there would not be enough grazing. More important, these Indians could not be classified merely as sheep and goats, as Sherman's plan proposed. They were people with greatly divided hearts. Some were afraid; they did not know when the cavalry might descend upon a quiet camp and slaughter everyone who could not escape. Many were proud. Some were willing to fight to the death for their way of life. All were appalled at the quick depletion of buffalo in the past two years. Some were completely innocent of understanding of the larger world around them and did not guess at their inevitable destiny.

Satanta enrolled as a friendly at the agency below Fort Sill, then went with a large group of Kiowas up to the Wichita

Agency on the Washita River, which was guarded by only one company of infantry. Here were camped Penatuhka Comanches, Wichitas, Caddoes, Delawares, and Nawkoni Comanches, the latter band considered hostile by the whites. The situation became tense when the agent would issue no beef to the Kiowas and Nawkonis. It became more tense when Colonel Davidson rode up from Sill with four companies of cavalry and demanded the arms, even bows and arrows, of the Nawkonis. Fighting erupted and continued as a confused melee for part of two days. Five civilians were killed, four soldiers wounded, one Indian killed, several wounded. The Kiowas and Comanches fled west upriver, while the Wichitas fled east. Satanta had hoped that the affair would get the farming Indians involved, but he concluded that his people had made as many enemies as friends in the minor battle.

That was a hot autumn, and plagues of grasshoppers came through the country stripping the leaves from trees and tender plants. Then violent thundershowers ripped across the plains, flooding the low places. Five white armies were in the field chasing Indians, from Forts Dodge, Sill, Richardson, and Concho, and from Fort Bascom in New Mexico Territory. No great battles resulted, only skirmishes, scatterings, flights. The warrior Indians were at a great disadvantage because they had their women and children with them.

Two and a half weeks after the affair at the Washita Agency an Indian group, including Satanta, attacked an army wagon-train guarded by soldiers on the divide between the headwaters of the Washita and the Canadian rivers. They killed a few soldiers and held up the train four days. Then they besieged a small group of white dispatch carriers hiding in a buffalo wallow, killing one of them.

Two weeks later Satanta led a band including Big Tree east

to a camp about thirty miles from the Cheyenne-Arapaho Agency near Fort Reno on the North Canadian River. He sent Big Tree in to ask questions and determine if possible their status as parolees. Satanta had seen the impossibility of continuing this guerrilla war into the winter; if the whites would talk, it must be soon. Also, he was beginning to ask himself: Could it be possible that Kicking Bird had been right the past four years? That chief had been militant until after a raid in the summer four years earlier, then had turned peaceful and insisted upon cooperation with the whites. Satanta believed that no leader had the right to sacrifice his people by fighting to the end, but how was one to know the right time? At the Cheyenne-Arapaho Agency Big Tree was arrested, and messengers were sent telling Satanta to bring his band in at once, which he did. He was arrested along with other leaders and sent to Fort Sill under guard.

Satanta had waited too long for his own personal well-being. His old nemesis Sherman was making the decisions in Washington as fast as they could be rubber-stamped by the President. He might have agreed that Satanta be sent with other militant Indians to a prison in Florida, but he had turned the chief over to Texas in the first place and had been furious at the release. Now he decreed that Satanta, this time alone, be sent back to the prison at Huntsville. It was a minor victory for the General in Chief.

At first he told himself that he had been a prisoner before. He must be patient. But the days dragged on and on forever. The stone walls, the pine forests and hills, the heavy, humid air—all drew strength out of him.

Finally he came to think less about how to heal the factionalism among the Kiowas and the problems of Indian alliance.

He did not change his mind about these matters, nor come to deny their importance; it was rather that the dull prison days wrought a change so that he was ruled by his blood or his soul rather than his mind. The change was defensive; he felt extremely lonely.

The things that occupied him were not political, nor diplomatic, nor even logical, but the simple things of the old life. He felt a horse under him with a long easy gait, his clothes, his ornaments, his braids, joggling to the movement, the prairie wind in his face. He felt himself sitting cross-legged in front of his lodge as light fades in the evening and stillness comes over the camp. Meat was propped over his fire. As it dripped on the gray coals, curling wisps of white smoke rose as high as the waist of a man and disappeared in the air. A thin haze of smoke hung in the trees and around the tops of the scattered tepees. He said something, not a certain thing, but a comment addressed to his family near him. The women laughed low and easily; the children giggled with delight. It must have been humorous what he said. They seemed precious and generous to respond so to him.

Often he felt himself sitting high on a horse so that he could see vast distances. He came west toward the headwaters of the Donpa and out ahead rose the dim blue peaks of the great mountains, a day's ride away. Again he sat his horse on a rise above the broad Guadalpa and followed with his eyes its foliage-marked sweep from the west to the far horizon in the east. Again he sat his horse down in the Tainpa, or Brazos de Dios, country, his gaze directed by the pointing of the bare brown arm and hand of a companion warrior, and saw the distinctive landmark of Double Mountain rising in the broken prairie.

It had been going on a long time before he became aware of it. They were treating him strangely. He noticed it one day when he was standing in the sun. The guard said, "Did you want to go in now or did you want to stay out here a while?" He understood enough of the words to get the sense. He looked around and saw that the exercise time was over, and the other prisoners had already been herded through the door. He followed the guard inside and thought about it. His special friend who spoke Spanish had got in the habit of patting him on the back and saying something cheerful and giving him full packages of tobacco. Then often as they sat at the long dining table he heard the ones around him saying, "You better eat, Chief. Eat. It's not so bad. You better eat more."

In the damp steamy room, mirrors hung on the wall where those who shaved their faces came to put on soap and scrape off hair, each under the watchful eye of a guard. He approached a mirror and stared at himself. He wiped at the glass with his hand. His eyes seemed to have drawn closer together, the wrinkles between them deepening. The broad cheeks were curiously hollow. With a little start he said to himself, "The mirror makes me look like an old man."

He had been aware of the changing seasons and knew that only four winters had passed and knew that he was not old. Thinking of old age made him think of Tsatangya. I should have gone with him, he thought. Things looked different then, but now I see clearly. I certainly should have gone with him. His name will live forever, but I shall finish out my days among the despised outcasts of the Tehanos and be forgotten.

He found in himself willingness to do even yet what Tsatangya had done, but these people had made it impossible. How can you stab men who bring you magazines to look at and stand aside while you pass through the door first and show sometimes in their faces that they understand that you are slowly dying a long way from home?

He would think, If I could only hear one friend speak the beautiful Kiowa tongue again maybe it would bring back my strength.

At the time of Chief Satanta's re-arrest General Sherman had been proceeding at full steam on his solution to the south-plains Indian problem, and it had not taken long. The warriors had been forced to surrender on account of their families. They were held in a large unfinished ice house at Fort Sill and were fed by the soldiers, who threw large chunks of raw beef over the stone walls, "as if we were lions," one of them said later. Kicking Bird, now made principal chief by authority of the whites, chose which Kiowas should be sent to the Florida prison: Chiefs Lone Wolf, Woman's Heart, White Horse, Double Vision, Bird Chief, and Buffalo Bull's Entrails, and nineteen warriors, including the medicine man, Mamanti, who had killed Britt Johnson and had gone with Satanta to attack Warren's wagontrain.

Shortly thereafter Kicking Bird was seized by great cramps one morning and died the same day. The Kiowas thought he had been prayed to death by Mamanti; the post surgeon at Sill recorded that he had been "poisoned by strychnia." Soon after the prisoners reached Florida, Mamanti died. Regardless of the agency of death in either case, they were victims of the deep, impossible divisions among their people.

The mid-1870s were a time of rapid change in the southern plains. The Kwahadi Comanches, who had never signed a treaty with the United States, came into Fort Sill and agreed to live on the reservation. White buffalo hunters swarmed out along the headwaters of the Canadian, Red, and Brazos rivers; they had almost destroyed the great southern herd by the end of the hunting season in 1876 and in two more years would leave only frightened scattered remnants, numbering in the hundreds. Stockmen drove their cattle out to graze the range where the buffalo had been. Several notable events occurred in 1878. In March of that year final orders were issued for the closing of Fort Richardson at Jacksboro; the frontier had passed it by. In early summer of that year the government decided to release the south-plains warrior Indians it had held in prison in Florida and take them home to the prairie land they loved. The policy of confinement had worked, at least insofar as stopping the raiding, which had been a part of their way of life.

Satanta had said in his great speech at the Medicine Lodge council, "I love to roam over the prairies. There I feel free and happy, but when we settle down we grow pale and die." On August 10, 1878, Thomas J. Goree, superintendent of the Texas penitentiary, wrote to the agent at Fort Sill that the chief was "in declining health, and very feeble. If he remains here can not live long. Will heartily second any effort made for his release." Any effort that was being made would come too late. In early October, a Mr. W. A. Morris and a Mr. Joe Bryant of Montague County in north Texas visited Satanta in prison and told him it seemed hopeless that he would ever be free again.

It was October 11, 1878, though of course he was paying no attention to the white man's calendar. He was standing alone in a room on the second floor of the prison hospital, where he went sometimes that they might give him medicine to ease his rheumatism and the other pains. Thinking how no white medicine could fill the void in his breast. Thinking about Tsatangya. Suddenly, like a gift out of nowhere, an understanding came to him. Had that old chief asked, when he started his battle there south of Fort Sill, whether he could overcome five troops of cavalry? No, he had not considered it. I have been too reasonable all my life, Satanta thought. I was once a great leader of our people; I must not be an old man here in these walls. Why should I offer myself consequences?

I'm going home!

I'm coming to see you, Tsatangya. Make a little feast for an old friend. Help me, Taime! My legs are weak. Help me, Grandmother! I must go home. Oh, Earth Mother, give me enough strength!

He ran for the light. It meant to him the open air and the prairie. He would run through the stone walls and run north. Through the door he rushed and onto the high second-story landing. The railing hit him and he went over, to fall on the hard paving below, where his body was broken.

They came and found no life in him.

A small wooden hill near the prison served as a graveyard. Many of the men who spent their last breaths in the Huntsville institution were abandoned men, whose remains were not claimed by kin. Here Chief Satanta's body was brought and buried, somewhat apart from the others, as if someone had a vague idea that the location of the grave must not be lost among the others.

Now comes a story which may be only legend or may not be. Those who told it are gone. They did not explain it or support it. As for the possibility of its being true, it is no more unlikely than that Indians should cherish and carefully rear white captive children; that warriors should chase John Wooten out on Elm Creek and save his life; that Joe Woolfolk should lay his law career on the line to defend two enemies; that Satanta should say in the St. Louis hotel dining hall, "I am a Texan"; that settlers from Montague County should visit him in prison. The story is this:

In December of the year when the chief died, a woman, dressed in black and heavily veiled, appeared at the marble yards of Thomas E. Byrne of Houston, Texas, just as he was closing his office for the day. She would not give her name. She bought a monument and made arrangements for him to erect it, telling him the exact spot where the grave could be found. She gave him a slip of paper showing him the inscription he must cut: "Satanta, Chief of the Kiowas." Then some Latin (or was it Spanish?) which he could not translate. The woman paid him, and he gave her a receipt reading: "A stone for Indian Chief, $127.00. Paid in cash." The monument stood at the head of Satanta's grave for many years, then was carried off by thoughtless vandals.

If the story be true, one would like to know what the Latin or Spanish said.

CHAPTER FIFTEEN

THE ALLIANCE

The three chiefs who were arrested that summer day at Sherman's orders, shackled, and thrown in the dungeon were of three distinct generations, being born in about the years 1801, 1821, and 1849. As Tsatangya grew to manhood the whites were mostly a rumor, an infrequent trapper or trader, certainly not the arbiter of anyone's destiny. Tsatangya had lived faithful to Kiowa religion and ideals and warrior ethic, one of nature's rare noble savages. Toward the end of his life he surely saw the inevitable fate of his people, but he was able to leave a testimony to Kiowa bravery, loyalty, integrity. Satanta lived a more tragic life. A man of competence, destined to be a leader, he knew well the old-time ways, but saw them through most of his manhood against the background of white encroachment. Had he been a white man, with his vigor and daring and intelligence, he would have been an important political leader; but throughout his prime he lived somewhat in the backwaters of destiny and fought a losing battle.

Big Tree was a different case, on account of his birth in a later era and also, perhaps, because of a different temperament. He had worked hard during his two years in prison, and had studied, in his own quiet way, the habits and ideas of whites. After the skirmishes of 1874, the authorities did not revoke his parole, nor was he sent away to Florida with the other prisoners.

In 1879 the Kiowa-Comanche agent solved the long-time problem of slow delivery of rations, annuities, and supplies by himself accepting the responsibility of transportation (as Tatum should have done in the fall of 1870) and by hiring Indians as teamsters to do the hauling. He put Big Tree, now about thirty and a man who had the respect of other Indians because of his fighting record and his chieftainship, in charge of some of the wagontrains. As many as fifty wagons were used in this operation, freighting from the railheads in Kansas. The supplies were delivered in good time and in good condition.

Big Tree was not made a chief by white men, nor did he cater to them. He objected to the government's plan to break up the reservation in the 1890s, and history has proved his judgment correct, for the Kiowa and Comanche descendants would be fortunate had they held onto the large reservation. But at some point Big Tree decided that any violent opposition to the whites was a mistake and that his people must do their best to find what was good in the new way of life.

In the autumn of 1893 an official of the American Baptist Home Mission Society called a meeting of Kiowas at the agency, now relocated forty miles north on the Washita River (near present Anadarko), to get permission to send missionaries onto the reservation. The Indians showed such interest that the agent's office was too small to hold the gathering and it had to move to the sawmill building. Big Tree spoke strongly in favor of the Baptist missionaries. Because of his attitude a mission and church were established near his camp northwest of the Wichita Mountains at a place called Rainy Mountain.

He welcomed the church, but was reluctant to become involved in it during its first years. His wife, Om-boke, made up her mind sooner. She said publicly: "The Jesus way is the best for the Indians to travel. I do not know about those of our fathers who never heard of the Jesus Road, but if we who have heard of it turn away from it, we will have no one but ourselves to be blamed."

When old Chief Tsatangya was killed in 1871 he left two small children, a boy called Buckskin and a girl, still a baby, called Spliced Hair. As a teen-ager Buckskin was sent east to study at Carlisle Institute in Pennsylvania. The school physician, Dr. Joshua Given, was attracted to the bright youngster, became something of a foster-father to him, and gave him his own name, Joshua Given. Joshua persuaded his little sister, Spliced Hair, to come to Carlisle, and she became Julia Given. Joshua got a good education and studied theology; then he married a white girl from Connecticut and went back to the Kiowa people in southwestern Oklahoma as an Episcopal minister. Julia felt the same kind of commitment. She returned to become interpreter for the new Baptist mission at Rainy Mountain.

In 1897 some of the Kiowas near Rainy Mountain were Christians, and others held to the beliefs of their forefathers. One man, Sanko, had taken the Jesus Road, but his one-time friend and mentor, Tone-a-koy, strongly believed in the old faith and insisted that Sanko give up Christianity. Tone-a-koy knew how to make bad medicine to harm his enemies—in fact, it was thought that he knew how to pray a person to death—and he threatened Sanko with serious consequences. Finally, Tone-a-koy set up a medicine lodge at the foot of Rainy Mountain with the one purpose of punishing Sanko for his Chistianity. Sanko fled to the mission, exceedingly frightened. The whites laughed at the danger and ridiculed Sanko's superstition, but

Julia Given took him seriously and told her colleagues that Kiowa beliefs could not be so easily dismissed. The missionaries and Sanko and Julia (Tsatangya's baby girl) prayed and wept at great length over the problem. On a chosen day, with a considerable Kiowa audience gathered, Tone-a-koy tried to make good his threats. Sanko could not stand the evil dancing, the shrill prayers, the rattle shaking, the sinister songs, so he fell unconscious. Unfortunately for the medicine man Tone-a-koy, he became too frenzied in his efforts, had a heart attack, and died in front of his audience. Sanko awoke from his faint and announced that his God had won.

The incident had a strong effect on the Kiowas, for different reasons. Some of them truly thought it had been a contest of gods. Some of them saw in it the foolishness of certain old practices which could only be described as witchcraft. They were a religious people and seriously needed a religion after their great Sun Dance, the Kado, had been forbidden by the government. They were feeling the imperfections of white justice and mercy which Satanta had foreseen long ago. Could it be that this God, conceived by a primitive people, the Jews, could be what they meant by the Great Spirit? The women were more amenable than the men. The great horse-buffalo culture of the plains had rewarded the hunter, the raider, the warrior. What woman could make a home while they were constantly on the move and never camped two winters in the same place? Perhaps, also, the idea of a baby, born in a manger, actually the Christ, appealed to them.

One of the converts who came forward in 1897 was Big Tree. Described by a satirical D. A. Lanham as a "tiger demon," the warrior who had counted first coup in the long-ago attack on Warren's wagontrain, he took the Jesus Road, was baptized, and joined the Rainy Mountain Baptist Church. As he learned the

Bible and the tenets of his faith, he became a deacon and a Sunday-school teacher, teaching the adult men's class.

America had always been fascinated by its Indian component and heritage in a strange, ambiguous way. In 1859 it minted its Indian-head penny. In 1907 it issued its ten-dollar gold piece, upon which the Goddess of Liberty wore a feathered plains Indian bonnet. In those years an artist, James Earle Fraser, was making portrait busts of Indians, and his work eventually resulted in an engraving of an Indian on the buffalo nickel, issued in 1913. Fraser wrote that the head was a composite of three Indians, one Irontail, one Two Moons, and the third he could not remember. His wife's memory was better. She later stated that the third was a Kiowa chief, Big Tree.

The minds of military men varied greatly in those years of the Indian Wars and in those uncertain years that followed. When the Indian prisoners were sent from Fort Sill to St. Augustine, Florida, in 1875, along with them went Lieutenant R. H. Pratt. He remained with them in their confinement. The lieutenant had the ability to see his charges as human beings and put himself in their moccasins; he gained their respect and affection. After the period of imprisonment he took several of them as a nucleus of students to Carlisle, Pennsylvania, to found the famous Indian school.

Another officer who was able to establish close rapport with Indians was young Captain (later General) H. L. Scott. He was made commanding officer of Troop L, 7th Cavalry, which was enlisted at Fort Sill in 1891. This old regiment had been Custer's, had been nearly wiped out at the Little Bighorn, had massacred the Sioux at Wounded Knee; but all of the new Troop L were Indians, mostly Kiowas. Chief Satanta, when he died, had left three sons and five daughters. The two younger sons, Odle-pah and Auchiah, joined Troop L and served with distinction. The Kiowa people needed religion; the men also needed something to fill the great void that had resulted from the destruction of their way of life. They needed to belong to something, they needed pageantry, they needed a uniform. The cavalry served them as they served it. Later it would become a mark of high honor to have been in Troop L.

After the mid-1870s the frontier rapidly passed the Jack County-Young County area. Young County was reorganized in 1874. One of the first acts of citizens meeting at Belknap was to pass this resolution:

> That the County Court of Jack County be required to turn over or cause to be turned over, to the officers legally entitled to possession of the same all books, papers and records and maps, which belong or otherwise appertain to Young County or Young County Land District and now in possession of the officers of Jack County, and that W.T. Ditto be and is hereby authorized to make the demand. . . .

The county went back into business. The town of Belknap was rebuilt among its ruins, but it would never be able to compete with the new, flourishing towns like Olney, or Newcastle, where coal was discovered, or Graham, ten miles southwest of where Warren's wagontrain tried to circle that day.

Those who had lived in the area in the 1850s and 1860s and the early 1870s saw that they were old-timers. All these strangers coming in—they were Johnny-come-latelies, who did not know about the troubles, pain, violence, glory, of the past. The old-timers formed Pioneer Associations of Indian Fighters and had gatherings to feast themselves and remember and tell true stories and lies about the way it used to be. The forts, Richardson on the edge of Jacksboro, Belknap on the Brazos, Griffin down to the southwest, stood lonely, dropping the stones off their walls one by one, but testifying that not all the stories were lies, that once the blue-coat cavalry rode over this country and aggressive white pioneers contested with aggressive redmen.

As the decades passed the old-timers became white-haired and saw themselves dying one by one. Soon no one would remember the way it used to be. But wait! What is an Indian Fighter? It might be one who fights Indians or it might be an Indian who fights. Those people wouldn't come down here, would they? We could barbecue some beeves and there is plenty of room to camp around old Fort Belknap. They wouldn't come, would they?

They would and did. No one loves gathering and feasting and camping out and celebrating history more than the Kiowas and other plains Indians. They came to Texas to attend Pioneer Association outings, old-timer reunions, Fourth of July parades. They contributed to the pageantry by drumming and dancing. The Texans were as limited linguistically as they had ever been; fortunately many of the Indians had learned to speak English.

In 1930, sixty-six years after the Elm Creek Raid, Milly Durgan came home. Or not exactly *home*; she came back to Young County.

Captured at the age of eighteen months she had quickly forgotten any English words she knew, including her white name, and began the process of becoming a good Kiowa. She had seen some history made. She had, for example, seen Colonel Kit Carson and his regiment march out onto the plains in the winter of 1864, in the vicinity of Adobe Walls, to attack and burn a Kiowa camp. Her frantic foster-mother had hid her during the battle in a clump of bushes. But Milly was a fortunate girl. Her foster-father, Aperian Crow, was a member of the elite Koitsenkya, the Society of the Ten Bravest. He sired no children, but gave all his paternal concern to her in those chaotic years when she grew up. She became a good horsewoman. At sixteen she married into a good family, the Goombis. Now her name was not Milly Durgan, but Saint-To-Hoodle Goombi, and she had forty-nine children, grandchildren, and great-grandchildren, all good Kiowas.

She visited Texas a number of times. The Kutch-Manning Pioneer Association had been formed by the white veterans of a particular fight between the men of a cow outfit and Indians in 1869; it later expanded to include all Indian Fighters and met yearly at the camp grounds at Newcastle, three miles north of old Belknap. On July 17, 1931, Mrs. Goombi, her five children, thirty-two grandchildren, and twelve great-grandchildren were made honorary members of the Association. In 1932 she toured Texas schools, telling through her son's interpretation the story of her life; perhaps she thought of herself as a kind of missionary to the whites with a subtle message. That year she visited the capitol at Austin, sat in Governor Dan Moody's chair, and when asked what the state of Texas could do for her, replied that she only wished to go back to Oklahoma and live with her people. In 1933 she was taken by her Texas hosts to the grave of her mother, who had been killed and stripped and scalped in front of the burning house that day long ago; the newspaper reporter who watched her wrote that the old woman's usually placid face was "relieved by a look of childish wonder."

Her story was like that of Cynthia Ann Parker, the white girl captured by the Comanches who gave birth to the great chief Quanah. These two women, Cynthia Ann and Milly, accomplished in their lives a peace and alliance which men, for all their logic and diplomacy, could not reach.

. . .

In 1963 the Legislature of Texas passed a concurrent resolution which was about as near an apology as a governing agency permits itself. It read thus in part:

> Whereas, The remains of a historic Indian figure, known as Setainte or White Bear and popularly called Satanta, lie buried in a special plot in the cemetery of the State penitentiary at Huntsville, Texas; and
>
> Whereas, White Bear was a leader of the Kiowa Indians and was their foremost representative in councils with white men. He was also a brave and cunning warrior, and has been described as the Indian most hated and feared by such Generals as Philip Sheridan, William Tecumseh Sherman, and George Custer; and . . .
>
> Whereas, History has been kinder to White Bear than his white opponents were and there have been proposals to dignify his memory; and
>
> Whereas, His descendants, the Kiowa Indians of Oklahoma, have offered precious relics to a Texas museum in exchange for the remains of Setainte. This request has come from James Auchiah, a grandson of the great red man; now, therefore, be it
>
> Resolved by the House of Representatives of the Fifty-eighth Legislature of the State of Texas, the Senate concurring, That the Director of Corrections of the Texas Department of Corrections is hereby authorized and directed to accede to the wishes of the Kiowa Indians of Oklahoma, and to take whatever steps are necessary to allow for the removal of the bones of Setainte and for their return to his people.

In the Fort Sill Military Reservation, not far from the old fort and not far from where Lawrie Tatum had his agency, is a cemetery, and in it is an area called Chief's Knoll, where a number of Indians are buried. Here James Auchiah and others brought the remains of Satanta and laid them to rest. Following the reburial, thousands of whites and Indians, military and civilian, held the "Chief Satanta Historical Celebration." Bands played, gifts were presented, speeches were made. Satanta was called the Indian Patrick Henry, the redman's Clarence Darrow, the Kiowas' Winston Churchill of his era.

Chief's Knoll is a somewhat lonely place, and thought-provoking. Satanta's grave lies only ten feet south of that of old Tsatangya. It was here that the old man's bullet-ridden body was brought on that summer day in 1871. It took Satanta ninety-two years to come back beside him. The history of humankind back through the millennia is filled with the stories of peoples who were different and could not see all the ways in which they were the same and could not reconcile their differences in any kind and generous way; no one has known more clearly the anguish of the problem than some of the men buried here.

A person may think strange private thoughts on a small hill where old chiefs lie, imagining how the world looked to them. It is an appropriate incongruity that a white civilian is buried here on Chief's Knoll—Horace Jones, the interpreter. But one remembers that Satanta spoke five languages, and feels humble.

SOURCES

Letters in manuscript are cited by sender, receiver, and date; since there is no particular logic as to the archival location of many items, I give the source, using the abbreviations shown below. Certain books are cited again and again, and in widely separated places in the text; it has seemed convenient to refer to such works by the authors' last names. Both types of abbreviations are shown in the following list:

AAG—Assistant Adjutant General. Army officers in filing a report which is not directed to a particular individual may address the AAG or AG by name or title. In some cases I have used simply the lower headquarters, such as San Antonio, as the receiver of a letter.

AG—Adjutant General, Washington, D.C.

AGO:NA—Records of the Adjutant General's office in the National Archives.

Battey—Thomas C. Battey, *The Life and Adventures of a Quaker Among the Indians* (Norman: University of Oklahoma Press, 1968).

Carter—Robert Goldthwaite Carter, *On the Border with Mackenzie* (Washington, D.C.: Eynon Printing Company, 1935).

Corwin—Hugh D. Corwin, *The Kiowa Indians; Their History and Life Stories* (Lawton, Oklahoma: 1958).

Crouch—Carrie J. Crouch, *A History of Young County, Texas* (Austin: Texas State Historical Association, 1956).

Horton—Thomas F. Horton, *History of Jack County* (Jacksboro: Gazette Print, 1933).

Huckabay—Ida Lasater Huckabay, *Ninety-four Years in Jack County: 1854–1948* (Austin: The Steck Company, 1949).

Jones—Douglas C. Jones, *The Treaty of Medicine Lodge* (Norman: University of Oklahoma Press, 1966.)

LC—Library of Congress as an archival repository.

Leckie—William H. Leckie, *The Military Conquest of the Southern Plains* (Norman: University of Oklahoma Press, 1963).

Marriott—Alice Marriott, *The Ten Grandmothers* (Norman: University of Oklahoma Press, 1945).

Mayhall—Mildred P. Mayhall, *The Kiowas* (Norman: University of Oklahoma Press, 1962).

McConnell—H.H. McConnell, *Five Years a Cavalryman* (Jacksboro, Texas: Herald Publishing Company, 1963).

Mooney—James Mooney, "Calendar History of the Kiowa Indians," *Seventeenth Annual Report* (Washington: Bureau of Ethnology, 1898).

Nunn—W.C. Nunn, *Texas under the Carpetbaggers* (Austin: University of Texas Press, 1962).

Nye—W.S. Nye, *Carbine and Lance* (Norman: University of Oklahoma Press, 1937).

OHS—Oklahoma Historical Society as an archival repository of Indian records.

OIA:NA—Records of the Office of Indian Affairs in the National Archives.

PR Griffin, May 1871—the monthly report or Post Returns of Fort Griffin, and the month and/or year may be omitted if obvious. These are all AGO:NA records.

Smythe—H. Smythe, *Historical Sketch of Parker County and Weatherford, Texas* (St. Louis: L.C. Lavat, 1877).

Tatum—Lawrie Tatum, *Our Red Brothers* (Lincoln: University of Nebraska Press, 1970).

TIP—Dorman H. Winfrey and James M. Day, editors, *The Indian Papers of Texas and the Southwest, 1825–1916* (Austin: The Pemberton Press, 1966). I refer in every case to vol. IV, which covers 1860–1916.

Wilbarger—J.W. Wilbarger, *Indian Depredations in Texas* (Austin: Hutchings Printing House, 1889).

In instances where I refer to other books by the writers mentioned above, the title and other information is given, in addition to the author's name. My notes are not comprehensive. They are intended to deal with controversial points, as a defense of my inferences and deductions, and as justification for information not covered in previous accounts. In the case of published material, editions most easily available to me have been used.

NOTES

CHAPTER ONE

THE RAIDERS

I am deliberately inconsistent in choosing to spell the two names "Satanta" and "Tsatangya." It should be noted that it is impossible to record Kiowa sounds with the alphabet used here, but the two names have come to be spelled "Satanta" and "Satank" through long usage. Since the names translate "White Bear" and "Sitting Bear," the original syllable should be the same in each name. The trouble is that the similarity has clouded the stories of these two men for a long time. As early as 1887 an ironic example of the confusion comes to us; Tsatangya's son, Joshua Given, was given this note from the Commissioner of Indian Affairs to the Adjutant General, on January 7 of that year: "The bearer of this note is a Kiowa, Joshua Given, who desires to obtain the exact date of the death of his father and the circumstances attending it. . . . He gives the name of his father as Satanka while in the account of what seems to be his capture and death he is referred to as Satanta." See records of the OIA, microcopy 234, roll 377. The Commissioner had probably referred to the *Annual Report of the Commissioner of Indian Affairs, 1871* (see p. 503), in which the two men are confused. The great ethnologist Mooney confuses the two men;

compare *Calendar History*, p. 208, with Jones's account of Tsatangya's good-bye speech, pp. 155–157. *The New York Times* confuses them, June 27, 1873, p. 2. Even such a careful modern historian as David Lavender confuses the two men; see *Bent's Fort* (Garden City: Dolphin Books, 1954), the notes to Chapter XX. Therefore, I have determined to avoid the previous difficulties by spelling the names "Satanta" and "Tsatangya."

Tsatangya's name has been spelled "Satank," "Set-Ankeah," "Satanka," "Setangya," and other ways.

Big Tree has generally been called by the English translation. The approximate Kiowa sound is "Addo-Eta" or "Aht-do-Eta." He was also known as Ba-Tsope.

Satanta's name is spelled "Satana" on the state marker where the Warren wagontrain attack occurred. It has also been spelled "Set-Tainte," "Sate-Tyne-day," "Set-ainte," "Tsait-ante," and other ways. Satanta may have been the "Comanche" who was a troublesome visitor to the Brasos Reservation and was called "Santa Anna." Mrs. Claude Roach, who grew up in Jacksboro, has pointed out to me that local citizens were apt to confuse "Satanta" with the name of the Mexican general "Santa Anna." Many frontiersmen made errors in identifying Indian tribes; the state marker referred to above erroneously identifies "Satana, Satank, and Big Tree" as Kiowa *and Comanche* chiefs. "Santanta" is mistakenly called the "head chief of the Comanches" in the *Dallas Herald* of Sept. 28, 1872, p. 2.

My spelling of Kiowa words is usually adapted from Mooney. The description of the Kiowa language as given by John P. Harrington in *Vocabulary of the Kiowa Language* (Washington: Bureau of American Ethnology, Bulletin 84, 1928) seems abstruse to a nonlinguist, and Harrington's vocabulary is quite limited in the number of words given.

The ages I give for Tsatangya, Satanta, and Big Tree are those given by Corwin, p. 53. These ages must be close. For Tsatangya, for example, whose age is most difficult to fix, we have these considerations: He led a large party in defense of their hunting grounds against the Cheyennes in 1837; see Wilbur S. Nye, *Bad Medicine and Good* (Norman: University of Oklahoma Press, 1962), p. x. I suggest that no people selects a very young military leader to protect their homeland; this tends to set an early date for his birth. He sired a daughter, later called Julia Given, about 1869 (see Corwin, p. 68); this tends to set a later date for his birth. Perhaps 1801 would fit both considerations. A good print of the Soulé photograph of 1870 shows Tsatangya to have been about seventy at that time.

Satanta's grandson, James Auchiah, has given me various pieces of information used in this chapter, most importantly the fact that his grandfather spoke five languages; the prominence of Satanta at Medicine Lodge supports the fact. From James Auchiah also comes the description of the chief's arrow-lance and of Big Tree's quiver and shield. James Auchiah has had a longtime interest in the history of the south plains and a broad knowledge of Indian dress and accouterment. He painted murals in the Muskogee Federal Building, 1934; Northeastern Teachers College of Oklahoma Administration Building, 1934; Fort Sill Indian School Gym Building, 1938; Department of Interior Building in Washington, D.C., 1939. See *Who's Who in the Central States* (Chicago: Larkin, Roosevelt & Larkin, Ltd., 1947), p. 39.

. . . war party . . . forded Red River. A participant later told Nye (see p. 126) that this war party gathered near the site of Granite, Oklahoma. Satanta said, as will be shown later, that they went down to Pease River; likely, it would have been at a point near where the Pease runs into the Red. If they were concerned about the condition of their horses, they may well have camped overnight on Beaver Creek, on the North Fork of the Little Wichita, on the West Fork of the Trinity, making only twenty to thirty miles a day. Their route is still today lonely and little populated; they would have passed near the later small villages of Harrold, Dundee, Anarene, Farmer, and Loving. I am acquainted with the country, having spent the first sixteen years of my life there.

. . . the cavalry . . . patrolled this river . . . Colonel Grierson at Fort Sill wrote May 13, 1871, to the AAG, Department of Missouri (OIA:NA): "Two companies of the 10th Cavalry, Major McKibben commanding, were ordered March 29 to the mouth of Cache Creek and have since that time been engaged in patroling along the line of Red River." The fact that Satanta's party was not detected by these cavalrymen is evidence that Satanta was using scouts himself; this matter will be dealt with further in notes to a later chapter.

. . . It has been written that Chief Satanta. . . . The quotations describing Satanta come from the following sources: Nye, pp. 40–41; Smythe, p. 268; Mooney, p. 208 (two quotations); and De B.R. Keim as quoted by Mooney, p. 209.

. . . and sacred shield. . . . The shield is now owned by the museum of the University of California. It was given by Satanta's eldest son to Captain Hugh L. Scott, who gave it to the museum. See Scott's notes, LC, an interview with Taybodl in 1897.

. . . Tsatangya . . . a thin mustache. . . . Some examples of the thin Kiowa mustache may still be seen. I saw a beautiful silvery one on a Kiowa man, quite old, at the Tia-piah Pow Wow north of Lawton on July 4, 1970. The man was identified to me as Little Chief.

. . . senior member of the Koitsenkga. . . . This military society is described by Mooney, pp. 284–285. Its importance can be judged by the number of times it is mentioned in the calendar compilations by Marriott, pp. 292–305.

. . . selected another man, Lone Wolf. . . . Some observers thought Satanta was the principal chief toward the end of the 1860s. Lone Wolf did not sign the Medicine Lodge Treaty of 1867, but was considered principal chief by the Kiowas by the time this narrative opens.

. . . mother, who was an Arapaho captive. . . . Satanta said, "I am half Kiowa and half Arapaho." See TIP, p. 351. One cannot be sure that the interpreter was capable of rendering the word "half" accurately.

. . . The second day . . . open country. . . . Mesquite brush did not spread thickly into this area until after the turn of the century.

. . . Britt Johnson! . . . A rather complete account of this unusual black man is given in "Britt Johnson, Negro Frontiersman," by Barbara Ledbetter, *The Graham News*, June 3, 1965. A contemporary account of his death is given in the *Dallas Herald* of March 11, 1871.

CHAPTER TWO

THE ARMY

The main sources for the facts of Sherman's tour and his concerns at the time are letters he wrote from forts Concho, Griffin, Richardson, and Sill, in LC; PR May 1871 of the forts; and the daily journal of Marcy in LC (Sherman papers). The escort of seventeen men has been called "cavalry" in some accounts, but Sherman to Reynolds, May 18, identifies them as infantry, and PR Richardson, May, calls them "17 enlisted men (Infantry from San Antonio)." Marcy calls them "seventeen men of the Tenth Infantry." Since accounts from civilians call them "cavalry" it seems likely that they were mounted. Both the 10th Cavalry and the 10th Infantry were operating on the south plains.

A beautiful account of the meeting between Lincoln, Grant, and Sherman at City Point can be found in Bruce Catton's *A Stillness at Appomattox* (Garden City: Doubleday, 1953), pp. 338–341.

The existence of the "amateur historian" at Griffin is speculative, but his account of Lee at Camp Cooper is fact. Local historians repeat the story that Sherman got lost after leaving Griffin, but no one seems to have wondered how it was possible. Since the road to Belknap would have been the only traveled and maintained road, he could hardly have gotten lost without deliberately leaving the road, and there is no other place of interest but Camp Cooper.

Previous writers have not carefully studied the movements of troops in the area during Sherman's tour. The evidence is overwhelming that local commanders went to great lengths, unofficially, to guard the General in Chief and that he angrily rejected the protection in cases where he discovered it. Marcy recorded May 4: "Camped at Cold Spring, twenty-three miles west of Fredericksburg. . . . Met a detachment of Negro Infantry at our camp. They had been scouting the country between Fort McKavett and here." What was this patrol doing seventy miles east of the frontier line? I believe they were guarding Sherman. On May 11, Reynolds telegraphed AGO (NA): "General Sherman and party arrived safely at Fort McKavett. . . . All well . . . ." From Griffin, Sherman wrote to Reynolds: "We camped with the cavalry detachment from Fort Concho the three first nights out, and then came in leaving them to follow more at leisure." This detachment is shown on PR Griffin thus: "Captain Clarence C. Manck, 4th Cav. in command of his Company "B" 4th Cav, arrived at Post as escort to Gen'l Sherman and left post on same duty May 16, it being enroute to change stations from Fort Concho, Tex. to Fort Richardson, Tex." But he neither came nor went with the general; PR Richardson shows Sherman escorted only by the seventeen enlisted men, and Manck did not join the post until the day after Sherman arrived. On May 27 Reynolds telegraphed AGO (NA): "General Sherman and party at Fort Griffin fifteenth all well," and two days later Reynolds reported the General in Chief at Richardson. The most outlandish attempt at protecting Sherman and concealing the fact is the case of Companies B and F of the 6th Cavalry. This regiment had already moved toward Fort Harker, Kansas, in two parties on March 20 and April 20; see McConnell, pp. 232, 233. PR Griffin shows "May 17, Co's 'B' & 'F' 6th U.S. Cavalry, under command of Captain Joseph Kevin, 6th Cavalry, left post for Fort Richardson, Texas, enroute for Fort Sill. . . ." Presumably changing stations he would have departed early in the morning of the 17th. The next we hear of Captain Kevin he is camped on Salt Creek about dark on the 19th; see Mackenzie to Aide-de-camp McCoy of that date in Sherman papers, LC. Kevin officially has made about forty miles in three days; perhaps the truth is that some of his cavalry horses had carried scouts two or three hundred miles during that time. Sherman refers to Kevin's troops as "the two companies of the 6th Cavalry left at Griffin to escort me" in Sherman to Mackenzie, May 19. He knows what the troops were doing there a month behind their outfit, knows that Mackenzie will recognize the identification "to escort me," this in the face of the clear record, PR Griffin, May, that Kevin did not leave the post with Sherman. No interpretation other than the one I give seems to fit the facts. Evidently Kevin did not wish to face the red-headed General in Chief again, for the PR Richardson shows that he did not arrive at the post until the 21st, the day after Sherman left. In addition to the above instances there is the oft-repeated story from the memoirs of Lieutenant R.G. Carter in which the general deliberately rejects the escort from Rock Creek Station to Fort Richardson. That Sherman would not accept army quarters also seems part of a pattern of determination not to disrupt the regular duties of the army on the frontier; Marcy recorded at Fort Sill, May 23, that they "for the first time since leaving San Antonio went into quarters." They had been living in tents twenty-one days in seventeen different camping spots. On June 7, Reynolds telegraphed AGO, his news now two weeks behind events on account of poor communications: "Gen'l Sherman and party at Fort Sill. . . . All well," and one can imagine Reynolds heaving a sigh of relief that the responsibility had passed to another departmental commander.

. . . mapped parts of northwest Texas. . . . Marcy had been in charge of an expedition in 1852 in which George McClellan took part and during which the Hundredth Meridian was located at a point near Red River. McClellan evidently was responsible for the surveying. The meridian was located fifty miles in error. See W. Eugene Hollon, *Beyond the Cross Timbers* (Norman: University of Oklahoma Press, 1955), p. 136.

. . . superintendent of a military academy. . . . This school became Louisiana State University.

At Fort Concho. . . . Fort Concho was located at the forks of the Concho River, where the city of San Angelo now stands.

. . . pre-war forts, now in ruins. . . . The two forts north of Concho were Chadbourne and Phantom Hill.

. . . party reached Fort Griffin. . . . The town of Griffin became important as a buffalo-hide gathering center and as a supply point on the Western Cattle Trail, faded after the railroad bypassed it in the 1880s. See Carl Coke Rister, *Fort Griffin on the Texas Frontier* (Norman: University of Oklahoma Press, 1956).

. . . to Camp Cooper . . . the 2nd Cavalry. . . . The commanding officer of the 2nd Cavalry was Colonel Albert Sidney Johnson, but he left Lee in command at Camp Cooper. He, like Lee, was offered command of the Union armies in the spring of 1861, but refused. He bled to death after Shiloh.

. . . desolate town and fort of Belknap. . . . Crouch, p. 55, mentions five families who supposedly lived in or near Belknap at this time.

. . . intended to suggest to that gentleman. . . . Sherman to Reynolds, May 24, says: "I should suppose you could not do a better thing than to take pretty much the same outfit and follow my course, for I assure you it makes plain what is otherwise incomprehensible."

CHAPTER THREE

THE FREIGHTERS

Edwin Lanham in his novel *The Wind Blew West* (New York, 1935) presents a fair picture of Weatherford in the 1870s, calling it "Rutherford." The novel presumes to deal with some of the same subject matter as this book, but is unreliable in facts and interpretation.

Little is known about Nathan Long other than that he was the wagonmaster; Wilbarger and Smythe say that he was from Clay County, Missouri. My characterization of him is imaginary. The biographical data on Warren come from Huckabay, pp. 172, 173. Since, after Long's death, Tom Brazeal took the role of a leader, notifying the authorities and testifying at the ensuing trial, I have assumed that he was second in command of the wagontrain.

Dependable sources agree that there were ten wagons, but disagree as to the number of mules. There seems no doubt that it was demanded of the Kiowas that they return forty-one; see, for example, Marcy's journal entry of May 27. Mules were not raised by the Indians and could not be caught wild; therefore, it would have been a strange demand to ask more than they actually drove away. Agent Tatum to Agent Jonathan Richards, May 30, 1871 (OHS), quotes Satanta as saying they "drove off about 41 mules." Five mules were killed at the attack site; see Mackenzie's letter at 9 P.M. on the 19th, written at the site (Sherman papers, LC). Thus the total of mules lost was forty-six. I assume that three of the wagons must have required six-mule teams, and seven, four-mule teams.

G.A. Holland, *History of Parker County and The Double Log Cabin* (Weatherford: Herald Publishing Company, 1937), gives some background on Weatherford, including the fact that bankers Couts and Fain backed the Warren freighting firm.

CHAPTER FOUR

ATTACK

The idea that Satanta was merely lucky in bringing his party in, striking the most inviting target and returning unchallenged, is unbelievable; he had not lived to be a fifty-year-old leader at guerrilla war through being unaware of the tactical situation. In addition to the army parties mentioned in the notes to Chapter 2, these also were out: Lieutenant Peter Boehm with part of F Company, 4th Cavalry, to "scout after Indians between Fort Richardson and Fort Griffin. . . . Left Post May 10, 1871"; see PR Richardson, May. "Three Tonkawa Indian Scouts detailed to accompany Capt. Sansone, Texas State Troops, in search of hostile Indians, returned May 23, '71"; see PR Griffin, May. Another small group was out to escort a wagontrain to Sill; another to escort a paymaster. Add to these the 10th Cavalry along Red River mentioned in the notes to Chapter 1. Events indicate not only that Satanta used scouts, but that they must have been more efficient than the army's. It should be noted that Lieutenant Boehm did locate four stragglers from Satanta's party on May 20; see Major J.K. Mizner to San Antonio, June 11, 1871, OIA:NA.

I do not use the story of Mamanti's prophecy as reported by Nye, pp. 127, 128, in which the medicine man said two parties would pass and only the second should be attacked. The story as reported does not conform to the facts as to who passed on the road and when. Also, to follow superstition in such a matter does not fit Satanta's character. In the mid-1930s Nye (pp. 126–131) got the Indian's story of the attack from Yellow Wolf, Hunting Horse, George Hunt, and Ay-tah, the wife of Set-maunte. Yellow Wolf was presumed to be the last surviving participant. Of course the Indians were searching back in their memories to events of more than sixty years before. For evidence that some Kiowas were confused or misinformed about the raid, see Marriott, pp. 114–121, also Corwin, p. 54. James Mooney, though he obtained much information from Kiowa informants in the 1890s, got few details about the attack; by the 1890s the Kiowas had made a surprisingly strong "peace" or "alliance" with the U.S. Cavalry, but they had not reconciled this situation with their own recent history. I believe that a strange love-hate relationship existed for several decades, resulting in a warping of Kiowa history and a downgrading of Satanta and other militants.

Some contemporary accounts of the attack exist: for example, the report of Major J.K. Mizner to San Antonio, May 20, 1871, OIA:NA, and the *Dallas Herald*, June 3, 1871.

Nye's account has Sherman pass the attack site about three hours before the attack on May 18; his story is so well written that it has been followed by later writers. Mooney, p. 329, places the attack on May 17. The *Dallas Herald*, June 3, places the attack on May 12, and says that Sherman had "passed the point at which the massacre occurred a few hours previously." None of these accounts is correct as to the dates; Sherman passed the site about noon on the 17th and the attack took place about 3 P.M. on the 18th. I present my explanation for the origin of the error in the text of Chapter 5 and document my chronology in the text and notes to that chapter.

I take some biographical data on R.G. Carter from J.C. Dykes's foreword to the 1961 edition by Antiquarian Press, Ltd., of the Carter book. The interpretation of Carter's character and his relation to the other officers is entirely my own. I invite anyone who is dubious of my version to read Carter's account of the aborted cannon salute to Sherman and try to imagine exactly what happened. Carter did not know the difference between history and a dime novel.

In regard to the clouds and the weather, Chapters 1 through 4, all that can be documented is the dry spring and the heavy rains beginning May 18. According to Nye's informants the rain began just at the time of the attack. The weather development I present is typical. This country is in the southern end of a tornado or cyclone belt which angles across the United States from west Texas through Illinois, and spring thunderstorms can seem surprisingly violent, especially when the observer is out in the open. Writers have been impressed and have tried to describe the storms since Washington Irving in *A Tour on the Prairies*. For a modern attempt see *The Trail to Ogallala*, by Benjamin Capps.

Near the site of Rock Creek Station one can still see the washed tracks of the transcontinental Butterfield Trail. To reach the site, turn off state highway 199 just east of Jermyn, go south toward Bryson; at three miles a fenced dirt county road leads west (about four miles north of Bryson). Turn down it and note Cox Mountain ahead, called Sugarloaf Mountain on Map Q160-XVII (NA); one can see here east of it the shape which gave it that name. At one mile on this dirt road is the site of Rock Creek Station. Parallel to the dirt road and south as little as thirty feet can be seen the remnants of the Butterfield Trail. Proceeding west around the north edge of Cox Mountain this dirt road probably follows exactly the old trail in many places, because the timber and rocks leave little choice of a route. At 4.2 miles this dirt road jogs .1 mile north, and at 6.2 one is just north of the attack site. Nye's map, p. 92, is quite accurate, and its scale figures out about 1.6 miles to the inch.

. . . a lariat . . . dragged him on the ground. . . H. L. Scott papers, LC, notes on an interview with Taybodl.

. . . across the bridge of Lost Creek. . . . Lost Creek was referred to by some early settlers as Los or Loss Creek. Possibly that was its name, but such a name could not survive the well-meaning efforts of map makers, schoolmarms, and writers.

. . . "General Ranald Mackenzie . . . his compliments, sir. . . . Carter would call him "General" since he had been appointed brigadier general and breveted major general, though his actual rank at this time was full colonel. There is no consistency in the old records insofar as the use of brevet and temporary ranks is concerned.

. . . wagontrain . . . passed the last ranch house. . . . The last house out from Weatherford was Crawford's, sixteen miles out on the road; see McConnell, p 121.

. . . a thin oasis with springs. . . . Huckabay, p. 253, reports that there were eighteen springs within a mile radius of Jacksboro. All this country had many more springs a hundred years ago, before the advent of the deep well on the high plains to the west.

. . . big Yankee general. . . . tents were pitched on the creek. . . . One can make a valid guess as to where Sherman camped. In *Circular 4*, Surgeon General's Office, Barracks and Hospitals, with Descriptions of Military Posts, Washington, GPO, 1870, Assistant Surgeon J.H. Patzki describes Fort Richardson and provides a map of the post; *Circular 4* is reprinted in W.W. Bill Dennis, *Fort Richardson, Texas (1867–1878) and the Mackenzie Trail* (Jacksboro, 1964). Marcy's journal entry for the 17th concludes: "Camped *near* the fort" (italics mine). To the west Sherman would have been among the camp followers; to the north, near the stables or the saloons; to the south, near the row of toilets behind the officers' houses. A logical place might have been behind post headquarters on the east, but since at Concho they camped at "the immediate forks of the two Conchos, half a mile below the fort" (Sherman to Reynolds, May 10), I conclude that they camped at the northeast corner of Fort Richardson, near the springs.

. . . Two others were wounded. . . . Sherman to Wood, May 19, says one was wounded. Sherman to commanding officer, Richardson, May 28, refers to "the man" who described the attack. Major Mizner's report to San Antonio, May 20, OIA:NA, says three. Evidently only Brazeal came to the post, and Mizner had time during the 19th and 20th to discover more details. The *Dallas Herald*, June 3, 1871, says three.

. . . Behind them they left . . . James Williams. . . . Sources disagree on the teamsters' names. The state historical marker at the site of the attack is apparently in error in listing Thomas Williams, and the error seems to have originated in the *Dallas Herald*, June 3; no other source lists such a name.

. . . the remnants of Chief Black Kettle's stricken band. . . . It is not certain that Satanta inspected the Custer-Washita battleground of 1868, but he had time to do so, and the council, at which he would have been an important speaker, was held only about twenty-five miles southwest of the battleground; see Nye, pp. 71, 72.

CHAPTER FIVE

PURSUIT

Since the present account overturns several previous accounts in regard to who did what on what day, and since I reject what Marcy recorded in his journal on May 19, 1871, the facts are in issue; but in truth the facts are clear to anyone who will consider all the evidence. Incidentally, a calendar is useful in checking the sequence of events, May–July 1871, and the days of the week match the days of the month in 1967 the same as they did in 1871.

Sherman's party went from Belknap to Richardson on May 17; the attack occurred on May 18; to establish this sequence beyond question is crucial to the judging of sources for a later chapter. Following is sufficient proof:

Sherman to Reynolds, May 18, from Richardson: "As I wrote you from Fort Griffin, we left there on Tuesday morning [May 16] and traveled 35 miles to old Fort Belknap, and yesterday [May 17] came 38 miles to this place."

Marcy's journal entry, May 17: "Left Belknap at 6 A.M. and traveled . . . Fort Richardson, where we arrived in the afternoon."

PR Griffin, May: "May 16: General Sherman and Staff left for Fort Richardson."

PR Richardson, May: "General Sherman . . . arrived at the post on the 17th."

Major J. K. Mizner to San Antonio, May 20, OIA:NA: "A war party of Indians . . . attacked . . . on the afternoon of the 18th."

Indictment published by Huckabay, p. 180: ". . . the 18th day of May . . . Satanta and Big Tree . . . malice aforethought made an assault. . . ."

Sherman to Pope, May 24: "The day after we passed from Fort Griffin to Richardson a large force of Indians attacked a train. . . ."

Further, the two Sherman letters of the 18th mentioned in the text, to Reynolds and to John Sherman, definitely establish the sequence of inspecting the post, writing a letter, reading copies of the *Herald*, receiving the citizens, writing another letter; Sherman certainly had no time for traveling on the 18th. The Patzki report at the site is evidence, as are Sherman's orders to Wood and Mackenzie. Mackenzie's letter written in pencil at the site was not dated, but was dated the 19th in copies made at his headquarters. Further evidence can be had from the PRs of Griffin and Richardson when distance and travel time are considered. All manner of secondary evidence exists, including the granite marker standing today at the attack site, dating the event May 18, 1871.

The principal error in regard to dates has been that Sherman and the wagontrain were both on Salt Creek Prairie the same day. The error has traveled thus: Smythe got it from Marcy's journal on March 27, 1877 (see marginal note on copy in Sherman's papers, LC, opposite May 27 entry). Wilbarger got it from Smythe. Nye, a first-rate scholar usually, made the mistake of following Wilbarger. Nye's has been accepted as the definitive account from the army's and the Kiowas' point of view and has been followed by modern writers, including another usually first-rate scholar, Mayhall. That Mayhall followed Nye is not clear from her notes, but is highly likely from the fact that she also picked up two other minor Nye errors, namely (p. 229) that the freighting firm's name was Warren and *Duposes* and that it came from the *railroad* at Weatherford. The moral of the traveling error seems to be that no writer with a large general subject can adequately check all the facts and that skepticism about the facts of history is a valid attitude.

That Marcy was indisposed on May 19 is deduced from his strange journal entries of that date. For suggestions that he felt at home among a group of drinking officers, see W.E. Strong, *A Trip to the Yellowstone National Park* (Norman: University of Oklahoma Press, 1968), pp. xvii, 17, 20. For his story telling see pp. 22, 26, 43, 136 of the same book. For the availability of liquor around Fort Richardson see McConnell, pp. 60, 61, 160. That Marcy got his information about what had happened from the Sherman-to-Wood letter seems likely because of these common facts and figures in the letter and his journal: ten miles, seven men, five, one wounded (erroneous), at once, 150 cavalry, a month, one hundred Indians. The "at once" is logical in Sherman's letter; the "immediately" is less logical in Marcy's journal, for probably eight hours passed between Brazeal's entering the post and Mackenzie's leaving. It seems likely that had Marcy read the orders to Mackenzie with the words ". . . who yesterday attacked . . ." and ". . . five men who escaped from the train and reported its capture to us this morning . . ." then he would have better understood the situation.

There is no stream named Soloman uniting with the North Fork of Little Wichita on modern maps. Professor Don R. Swadley, who grew up at Dundee, Texas, has studied Map Q 160, NA, compiled in 1860, and Oklahoma Map 9, NA, compiled in 1875, and believes that the Soloman was the stream known today as Slippery Creek, which at infrequent intervals carries a considerable volume of water. I concur with Swadley's opinion. This means that the "high Prairie just north" refers to what would later be called Black Flat and would prove to be excellent farm land. The necessity for meeting the Griffin contingent at this point would limit Mackenzie's freedom of movement and cause him to face more flooded streams than he would had he gone farther west. For a Marcy map of the area in question see "Map of the Country upon the Brazos and Big Wichita Rivers, Explored in 1854, Capt. R.B. Marcy," reproduced in W. Eugene Hollon, *Beyond the Cross Timbers* (Norman: University of Oklahoma Press, 1955).

. . . buildings lined up around a parade ground. . . . See *Circular 4*, previously cited. Several of the stone buildings still stand today, including the hospital. One of the officers' quarters houses, made of cottonwood lumber, still stands.

. . . a committee of leading citizens. . . . The affidavits and information about the committee may be found in the records of OIA, recorded in microcopy 234, roll 377. Apparently Sherman took the material to Washington and, in the wrangling that followed, it was presented by the War Department to the Department of the Interior. The committee consisted of W.M. McConnell, chairman, Dr. J. McCarthy, D.L. Ayres, H.J. Thompson, H. Horton, S.W. Eastin, W.N. McKaime, Peter Snyder, James Robinson, W.D. Kirk, R.J. Wynder, Stanley Cooper, Edw. Eastburn, Peter Hart, and Jas. Dosier.

. . . voting on secession from the Union. . . . See Horton, p. 16. Huckabay, p. 77, has not included the Union votes from small precincts 2 and 3. That this vote, not surprising from a west Texas county, was in the minds of local citizens is certain; that they mentioned it to Sherman is speculation.

. . . a certain Daniel Waggoner. . . . Dan Waggoner was one of the patriarchs of western ranching in the United States and with his son Tom would establish the large 3-Ds ranch some eighty miles to the northwest.

. . . Two women. . . . wanted their children. . . . Nye, p. 134, note, identifies one of these women as Mrs. Elizabeth Clifton and says that she was the grandmother of "Millie Durgan." The woman compounds the difficulty of researching her story by having been married at least three times, thus having had at least four surnames. Harry A. Stroud, *Conquest of the Prairies* (Waco: Texian Press, 1968), p. 200, says that one of her names was Clifton. For an exhaustive search of local records regarding the background of the captive infant Milly, see "Who Was Saint-To-Hoodle Goombi?" by Barbara Neal Ledbetter, in *West Texas Historical Association Yearbook*, vol. XLI, pp. 103–119, which establishes that Owen Durgan or Durkin could not have been the father of baby Milly. But it establishes nothing about the existence of Milly or her name, since none of the searched records would have dealt with an eighteen-month-old baby. The scene with Sherman as I present it is speculative, but not illogical. Mrs. Elizabeth Fitzpatrick had been through serious differences with her daughter Milly Susan, had seen that daughter slain, had herself suffered the indignities of captivity, then been ransomed; Mrs. Fitzpatrick may well have been hysterical when she appealed to Sherman.

. . . Corn, pieces of harness . . . littered the place. . . . Nye, p. 131. M.L. Johnson in *Trail Blazing* (Dallas: Mathis Publishing Company, 1935), pp. 66, 67, says he witnessed the scene shortly after the Indians left, but I do not believe him, for some of his errors, such as identifying "Captain" Carter as the commander at Fort Richardson, indicate that he got his adventures from books rather than from memory.

. . . Griffin . . . send along about forty cavalrymen. . . . Colonel Wood dispatched two lieutenants and forty men. PR Griffn, May.

. . . east along the lumber road. . . . Marcy's journal entries, May 20–23, describe the route.

. . . "There is no doubt . . . Indians. . . ." Sherman to Pope, OIA:NA.

CHAPTER SIX

OLD STONE HEAD TATUM

Much of the first portion of this chapter is taken from Tatum and Nye. The latter leaned heavily upon the Quaker's book, but also checked extensively into old army records. Various others, such as Mayhall and Leckie, give the general history of the Quaker Indian policy. My biographical data on Tatum come from the Foreword by Richard N. Ellis in Tatum's book.

I intend to imply that the Quakers suffered psychosomatic illnesses caused by the contrast in their ideals and the reality they faced in the field. Tatum mentions the "severe mental strain" of the work, p. 160, and his indefinite sickness, pp. 55, 161. He was succeeded in the position by Quaker James Haworth, whose health failed; see Tatum, p. 200. Quaker Brinton Darlington died in the work; Tatum says of him, p. 223: "The mental and physical strain on him was more than he could stand. His health gave way, and he peacefully passed away May 1st, 1872, aged 68 years." Thomas Battey shows, pp. 6 and 39, that he left the work on account of ill health and mentions his sick spells in a half dozen other places in his book.

For Tatum's defense of his clerk, Smith, see Tatum to Hoag, January 24, 1872, OIA:NA. The OIA:NA records show investigation of Smith through 1871, but his activity seems to have been unethical rather than illegal; to be precise, he was selling corn to himself as acting Indian Agent. On November 3, 1871, when Tatum was present on the reservation, Smith signed a letter (OIA:NA) as "Acting Agent, Kiowa Agency."

The exact dates of Tatum's absence in the winter of 1870–71 are unclear; the meeting was in December and he says, p. 55, that he returned to the agency in March. In his letter to Hoag of January 24, 1872, defending Smith, the Quaker agent estimates corn as worth $1.75 or $2.00 a bushel; in his budget estimate for the first quarter of 1872 (OIA:NA), it is $2.00 a bushel. This corn price should be contrasted with the price for beef on the hoof of less than two cents a pound being paid about the same time. In January of 1871 Grierson wrote to departmental headquarters (Nye, p. 122) that corn prices were exorbitant because contractors were forming combines to raise the price. Smith remained at the agency as long as Tatum did and then went to Washington, probably with the Quaker's recommendation, to work in the Treasury Department.

Probably no one can judge Tatum without going through the same experiences he did. I have not included in the text the most serious evidence against him. On pp. 238 and 239 he defends Quaker Agent J.D. Miles, who "had an interest in a cattle herd which was very lucrative, but it did not interfere with his official business as Indian agent." This in the face of the fact of the previous graft in the Indian Service, supposedly to be corrected by the Quakers. Then on pp. 293–295 Tatum records how, in trying to finally settle his own accounts with the government, a suit was brought against him; he settled out of court by making a payment of one hundred dollars plus the costs of the legal action. I do not believe Tatum stole a penny, but the combination of his gullibility and the authority he had accepted raises a serious moral question.

. . . wild-acting Kiowas . . . attacked the herd. . . . Tatum, p. 34. Also see W.S. Nye, *Plains Indian Raiders* (Norman: University of Oklahoma Press, 1968), p. 156. Tatum says one herder was killed. Nye, who had access to more records in this case, does not mention any herders being killed.

. . . He left his clerk . . . in charge. . . . Tatum, p. 53. Grierson to AAG, Department of Missouri, May 13, 1871, OIA:NA, says: "In December and about the time the annuities were expected here, Mr. Tatum, the Agent, went North to his home in Iowa, leaving a clerk in charge of his business. . . ."

. . . That was an unusually cold winter. . . . Tatum, p. 53. Nye, p. 121. Medicine Bluff Creek, just north of Fort Sill, froze solid.

. . . The blankets and other annuities . . . arrived. . . . Grierson to AAG, May 13, 1871, OIA:NA, says ". . . the annuities arrived last month—six months after they should have been issued. . . ." Grierson apparently was more concerned with making good the word of the United States than was Tatum.

. . . files were jammed with . . . claims. . . . These documents are all in the claims files of OHS. Various letters in the OHS archives indicate that the claims from the Choctaw and Chickasaw Nations were not specifically brought to Tatum's attention until July of 1871; thus the matter would be out of the time sequence I present.

. . . One such case had been for a modest amount. . . . Affidavit made at Kiowa Agency, June 8, 1870, OHS.

. . . flowing up and down in the red-tape channels. . . . Hoag to Tatum, February 22, 1871, OHS.

. . . a daring departure from the policy of loving. . . . Tatum, pp. 115, 116. The letter three days later repeating the question is Tatum to Hoag, May 25, 1871, OIA:NA.

. . . a man called . . . dressed in civilian clothes. . . . In his journal entry for May 23, 1871, Marcy mentions the Sherman-Tatum interview. Marcy says the agent called on the general; Tatum, p. 116, says Sherman "called at my office." Since it was known that Sherman would be at Fort Sill several days, it seems unlikely that Tatum would have approached him immediately. Given Sherman's energy and determination, it does seem likely that he would have called on the agent. Sherman to Pope, May 24, 1871, OIA:NA, says: ". . . Mr. Tatum admits that . . . Satanta with a large party of Indians is now off in Texas."

. . . he wrote to his friend Jonathan Richards. . . . Tatum to Richards, May 25, 1871, OHS.

CHAPTER SEVEN

CONFRONTATION

It seems likely that Mackenzie never picked up Satanta's tracks at all. Major J. K. Mizner to San Antonio, June 11, 1871, OIA:NA, reports that Lieutenant P. M. Boehm had just returned with twenty-five men from a thirty-day scout and that they ". . . on the narrow divide between the Brazos and Big Wichita struck a hunting party of four Indians killing one. . . . This occurred on the 20th of May. . . ." Mizner's report confirms the killing of Tomasi as related by Quitan to George Hunt, cited by Nye, p. 132. The narrow divide mentioned is some ten miles west of present Seymour and some thirty-five miles west of where Mackenzie was to meet the Griffin cavalry (see notes to Chapter 5). What was done with the forty-one mules is not known; after having a chance to ask some questions around Fort Sill, Sherman wrote to General John Pope, May 24, 1871, OIA:NA, "I am now satisfied that many of these murders and depredations have been done by Indians from this Reservation, and that a system exists of trading the stolen horses and mules to Kansas and New Mexico for arms and ammunition. . . ."

The principal events of this chapter are taken from Marcy's journal entry of May 27; a seven-page letter, Tatum to Richards, May 30, 1871, OHS; and from the books by Tatum, Nye, and Leckie.

I do not know whether Satanta in his speech named Big Tree as accompanying him on the raid, nor does anyone else; notes taken during conferences with Indians were much less exact and complete than is often supposed. It is interesting to contrast the letters presented by Leckie, p. 150, and by Nye, p. 136. They are ostensibly the same letter, the one sent by Tatum to the fort immediately after Satanta's "confession," but one contains Big Tree's name; the other does not. I suggest that the Nye letter is the real one, that Sherman, already knowing his importance in history, took it along with him, or a copy of it, for his papers, and that the other letter, which Leckie found in the agency papers, had been tampered with. Nye seems to accept the idea, p. 136, that Lone Wolf implicated Big Tree, but there is some logical inconsistency here, for on the previous page Nye has reproduced, from Tatum, the "confession" in which Big Tree is already implicated. It is also true that Tatum and Lone Wolf were not at all on confidential terms at the time. No one seems to doubt that Big Tree took part in the raid; the question is whether there was any legal evidence that he had done so. My interpretation of the difference in the two letters is given in Chapter 11, "The Trial," and its notes.

In regard to the Custer-Kiowa confrontation of December 1868, Leckie presents it in pp. 108–110, and Nye in pp. 71–75. Something of Nye's point of view can be seen in that he shows as humorous the Kiowas' attempt to communicate with Custer in English. Dee Brown in *Bury My Heart at Wounded Knee* (New York: Holt, Rinehart, and Winston, 1970), p. 244, repeats the funny story from Nye about Walking Bird calling Custer a "Heap big nice sonabitch. Heap sonabitch!" Neither pro-military Nye nor ostensibly pro-Indian Brown appears to wonder whether Walking Bird knew exactly what he was saying, and neither notes the irony that Custer faced a man, Satanta, who could speak five languages plus sign language and yet could hardly communicate with him.

For the complete story of Custer's treachery in arresting Satanta and Lone Wolf after they had come to him under a white flag, see G.A. Custer, *My Life on the Plains* (New York: Sheldon and Company, 1874), Chapter 13. Check Custer's account against William B. Hazen, "Some Corrections of *Life on the Plains*," *Chronicles of Oklahoma*, vol. III (Dec. 1925). The actual meeting between the Kiowa chiefs and Custer and his men is the subject of a detailed painting by Charles Schreyvogel, completed and shown in 1903. As a result of a hassle over the "historical correctness" of the painting (reported in the New York *Herald* in April and May 1903) the painting was established as authentic, even as to details of clothing; see James D. Horan, *The Life and Art of Charles Schreyvogel* (New York: Crown Publishers, 1969), pp. 33–40.

Corwin, p. 54, says that it is evident to him that some of the older Kiowas confused Custer and Sherman in their memory. Perhaps it was because each of the officers arrested Satanta through deception.

. . . raid by the whites . . . old adobe trading post. . . . Carson's attack on the Kiowas near Adobe Walls in 1864 is taken from Mildred P. Mayhall, *Indian Wars of Texas* (Waco: Texian Press, 1965), pp. 166, 167. Also from Mayhall, pp. 200–204, and Nye, p. 36.

". . . white man become a child . . . kill and not eat?" . . . For Satanta's anger at the buffalo slaughter, see Mooney, p. 207, and Jones, pp. 67–69.

. . . What do you have to do to get them to understand? . . . Tatum, p. 34, certainly did not get the message. Nor did Nye; see his *Plains Indian Raiders* (Norman: University of Oklahoma Press, 1968), p. 156.

. . . Tatum acted strangely. . . . The agent and the army cooperated in the trickery to arrest the chiefs. Nye says, p. 135, that Tatum tried to gain time by telling Satanta that a great soldier chief was at the fort. Sherman to AG, May 28, 1871, OIA:NA, says, "We manoeuvered a little till we could get all who were concerned in that particular affair." Sherman to his son Tom, May 29, 1871 (*Chronicles of Oklahoma*, vol. XLVII, no. 2, p. 126) says, "I resolved at once to arrest them and told Gen. Grierson quietly to have his horses saddled and his men under arms."

. . . to the veranda of Grierson's house. . . . This building is still the quarters of the commanding officer at Fort Sill.

. . . Are you the man . . . ? Sherman to C.O., Richardson, May 28, 1871, LC, says that Satanta ". . . openly admitted the whole affair, and described exactly the attack. . . ."

. . . Kicking Bird . . . say no more about it. . . . Informants told Nye (see p. 138) that Kicking Bird privately told the Indians not to say any more. The best sources, i.e. Marcy, Sherman, and Tatum, who were present and described the scene in writing soon afterward, do not say that anyone was implicated by Satanta at the front-porch council other than himself.

CHAPTER EIGHT

THE DUNGEON

The post guardhouse was not completed until 1873. The chiefs were kept in a cellar underneath the south end of one of the long barracks. The entrance is at the southwest corner of the old quadrangle. The door, now mortared up, can be plainly distinguished. Evidently some soil has been added to the lawn in this area so that the lintel appears even lower than it was in 1871.

In regard to the possibility of rescue out of the dungeon or later, it seems likely that the bulk of the Kiowa warriors had gone far to the west. Tatum to Richards, May 30, 1871, OHS, says, "Last night there was supposed to be about 200 Indians in the timber back of the Post. But it may be a false report. No one knows what to look for from the Indians." I suspect that the Kiowas had at least some scouts in the vicinity, but they probably gave up all ideas of rescue when Mackenzie came in with six companies on June 4. By 1871 these Indians had become fearful of a surprise attack on their women and children. James Auchiah informs me that the stories of old men indicate that they were already taking precautions at Medicine Lodge in 1867; there the Kiowas had three camps, and the women and children were kept in the one farthest from the white soldiers.

The visit of Caddo Chief Washington to the cell is inferred from a diary entry by Quaker school teacher Josiah Butler as given by Corwin, p. 62. Butler wrote: "6th Month, 8th., Washington, the Caddo chief, is still here and, about time for school, word came for all Indians to go see the prisoners, as it was expected that they were to be started on their journey to Texas for trial. So I placed the children in Washington's care and he took all but four. (I afterwards learned that it had not been intended to send for the school children)." Note that the words "word came" are quite indefinite. None of the children in the school were Kiowa. Indeed, what official, army or agency, would have sent for any Indians "to go see the prisoners"? Also, since Tsatangya turned up with a knife on June 8 and since he must have been searched when first made prisoner, one must infer a visitor.

. . . the correspondent H.J. Budd . . . wrote this. . . . Tsatangya's speech and Budd's reaction are shown in Jones, pp. 156–157.

. . . He felt like a blind, crippled man. . . . Sherman to Mackenzie, May 29, 1871, LC, says that the prisoners are in "double irons."

. . . asked Big Tree how he had been captured. . . . The capture of Big Tree is told in Tatum to Butler, August 14, 1872, as reproduced in Corwin, p. 58. Also in Nye, pp. 139, 140.

. . . The young warrior Tsatangya rode out with his lance. . . . This incident is told in Corwin, pp. 66, 67.

. . . He, himself, had killed . . . tribe knew it. . . . Papers of Hugh L. Scott, LC, interview with Taybodl.

. . . Cheyenne band of forty-eight elite warriors. . . . W.S. Nye, *Bad Medicine & Good* (Norman: University of Oklahoma Press, 1962), pp. x, xi.

. . . years of fighting the Cheyennes ended in a great peace-making. . . . A good account of the south-plains Indians' peace of 1840 is given in George Bird Grinnell, *The Fighting Cheyennes* (Norman: University of Oklahoma Press, 1971), chapter 6.

. . . why had they named years after Tsatangya? . . . An interesting comparison is given of four Kiowa calendars in the appendix of Marriott. The years referred to here can be seen in pp. 293–298.

CHAPTER NINE

THE MEMBER WHO WORE THE BLACK SASH

This chapter is adapted from a number of sources, including Mooney, Corwin, Carter, and Nye. Carter may have been more than usually accurate in describing the death of Tsatangya, for he had a long letter about the event from ex-Corporal Charlton, which he quotes.

Apparently little was known about the Koitsenkga by the whites until Mooney made his investigations in the 1890s. He presents the song addressing the sun and the earth on p. 329. A somewhat different version of Tsatangya's song was obtained from his granddaughter by Alice Marriott and is given in Marriott, p. 124. It is not known whether the old chief wore his badge of office, the black elkskin sash, that day, for no observer who left a written record would have known the significance of it. If Tsatangya did not wear the sash, he pinned it symbolically, for as Mooney states, p. 284, he "deliberately invited death in accordance with the obligation of his office." The importance of the matter to the Kiowas can be seen from the fact that in the Marriott calendar compilation, pp. 293–305, the Koitsenkga is mentioned eleven times, whereas only one other warrior society is mentioned and that only once. After the death of Tsatangya the Sun Dance was not held for two years; however, this could have followed from the death of another man, the Taime keeper, as pointed out by Mayhall, p. 169.

No one will ever know how many bullets were fired toward or into Tsatangya. Lieutenant Thurston's report as cited by Nye, pp. 145, 146, says, "several pieces were discharged." Then after the old man regained his feet: "I immediately gave the order to fire upon him again, and drew my pistol and fired one shot myself. Several shots were fired in rapid succession. . . ." Then he makes the peculiar guess that the total shots fired were "probably seven or eight." I suggest a more realistic picture of what happened can be imagined by noting that the mounted teamster Bordello was seriously wounded about fifteen feet from Tsatangya. Thurston explains it thus: "This teamster remained mounted on his nigh wheeler during the firing, and, owing to the wagon sheet could not be seen by those firing at the Indian from the rear. He should have dismounted." I believe that if they could not see the teamster they could not see the Indian. In fact, I would have hated to have been in the lieutenant's shoes, trying to explain this engagement, the number of shots fired, the knife, the exit of the two guards from the wagon. The *Dallas Herald* of June 24, 1871, says that Tsatangya was "filled with balls." Horton (this writer was a fourteen-year-old resident of Jacksboro that spring of 1871) says that Tsatangya was "riddled with bullets."

The tobacco chewing, spitting trooper who narrates the principal event is nearly an imaginary character. Orin Given, grandson of Tsatangya, told Corwin (see pp. 69, 70) about a story he had heard in 1905, in which one of the guards ". . . was chewing tobacco, and he turned around and spit in, or at, the old man's face." I have tried to imagine the event as it might have looked through the eyes of this hearsay character.

. . . orders said to shoot them dead. . . . Sherman to his son, May 29, 1871, *op. cit.*, p. 126, says ". . . on the least display, the guard will shoot these three prisoners dead."

. . . The old one . . . stumbled or lurched. . . . This may have been a gambit on Tsatangya's part to avoid a careful search of his person.

. . . he could see a single mounted Indian. . . . It is not known what Kiowas, if any, observed Tsatangya's death. In Marriott's semi-legendary account, pp. 112–125, Eagle Plume, or Frank Given, the chief's eldest living son, saw the events of this chapter from a distance.

. . . Help me, oh, Taime. . . . The Taime was a stone image, in the likeness of a small person, a central part of the Sun Dance ceremonies. See H.L. Scott's "Notes on the Kado or Sun Dance of the Kiowa," *American Anthropologist*, vol. XIII, no. 3 (July–Sept. 1911), p. 345.

. . . Oh, Grandmother, I'm too old. . . . Tsatangya owned one of the ten sacred grandmother bundles; see Marriott, p. 41.

. . . He *is* loose. . . . James Auchiah says that old Kiowa story tellers believe Tsatangya had in a pouch some bow-string tallow, which he used to help slip the irons. Thurston says in his report, ". . . he succeeded in slipping his handcuffs, severely lacerating his hands. . . ." Tatum, p. 121, mentions his skinned hands.

. . . "I don't want any smart-Alec nonsense. . . . McConnell, p. 165, says that Patzki was "well posted" in his rights and held his own against the commanding officer.

. . . Carter . . . occupied with paper work. . . . PR, Richardson, May and June, clearly show that Carter did not go with Mackenzie.

. . . exactly five feet, nine and one-half inches. . . . Bureau of Records and Identification, Texas Department of Corrections.

CHAPTER TEN

THE SETTLERS

The ten informal points of policy which I present as having been adopted by Judge Soward and others in regard to the trial cannot be specifically documented, but they will be seen as a fair summary of motives and intentions as the facts of the trial are presented.

Information on the Elm Creek Raid is taken from Crouch; from Mildred P. Mayhall, *Indian Wars of Texas* (Waco: The Texian Press, 1965); from J. Evetts Haley, *Charles Goodnight, Cowman and Plainsman* (Norman: University of Oklahoma Press, 1949); from Kenneth F. Neighbors, "Elm Creek Raid in Young County, 1864," *West Texas Historical Association Yearbook*, XL (Oct. 1964), pp. 83–89; and from an eyewitness account by Thornton Hamby, reprinted by Barbara Neal Ledbetter, *The Fort Belknap of Yesterday and Today, 1851–1963* (Newcastle, 1963), pp. 37–39. The accounts agree substantially.

The most complete account of Britt Johnson is in Barbara Ledbetter, "Britt Johnson, Negro Frontiersman," *The Graham News*, June 3, 1965. More details about Britt's recovery of captives may be found in Crouch, pp. 41, 42. The *Dallas Herald* story of March 11, 1871, mentioned in the text, gives details of his death.

The publishing history of Lanham's "speech" begins with Smythe in 1877. That writer presented it as a speech actually given at the trial, as has every writer since who reprinted it. Before I understood the nature and source of the "speech," it gave me much concern in my search for the truth about the trial. Anyone who reads Smythe with discrimination will perceive that the language of the "speech" is not that of Smythe, but of a competent, energetic young D.A., who will someday be a congressman and governor. Furthermore, a writer in Weatherford would not dare concoct out of the whole cloth, only six years later, a speech by a well-known local citizen. Lanham must have written the speech.

Still, the speech is full of errors which Lanham would have known to be errors on July 5, when the trial opened. Most notable perhaps is the fact that Lanham is summing up a trial of two men, when there is no doubt that the two men were tried separately (see the confirmed "minutes" of the trial cited in the notes to Chapter 11). Also notable is that Lanham speaks of Sherman's ". . . personal observation of the *debris* of the scene of slaughter. . . ." Sherman saw no *debris* since he passed the site about twenty-six hours before the attack, as we have established. Could Lanham have conducted the prosecution in ignorance of the sequence of events in the Belknap-Jacksboro area on May 17, 18, 19? No. The D.A. was assisted in the trial by certain local citizens, including one W.M. McConnell (see *Dallas Herald*, July 22, 1871, p. 2). OIA records previously cited show that McConnell was chairman of the committee which appealed to Sherman at Fort Richardson on May 18; he certainly understood the sequence of events, since he was telling Sherman of atrocities at about the same time as the attack on Warren's wagontrain. But McConnell was gone to Sill during June 26 through July 2 (see the same *Dallas Herald* story). These dates are confirmed by the fact that it was regularly a three-day trip, or six-day round trip, to Sill, and that Tatum wrote a letter, dated June 29, for the citizens' committee to take back to Jacksboro. McConnell is only one example; many citizens of Jacksboro, unlike latter-day writers, would have known the true sequence of events in the Belknap-Jacksboro area on May 17, 18, 19.

An erroneous presumption that has proceeded from the mistaken interpretation of Lanham's speech is that Tatum was a witness. Tatum was not a witness at the trial. He says (Tatum, p. 121): "M. Leeper, my interpreter . . . and H.P. Jones, the post interpreter, attended the trial. . . ." He says in Tatum to Hoag, July 1, 1871, OIA:NA, "By request of Col. Mackenzie, Col. Grierson and I have sent our Interpreters to Jacksboro as witnesses in the cases of Satanta and Big Tree."

. . . exterminating the "red devils." . . . Extermination is clearly advocated in the issue of July 30, 1871.

. . . common cause with . . . authorities on the frontier. . . . For Soward's partisanship see Soward to Davis, July 10, 1871, as printed in Smythe, pp. 275–276; Soward to Tatum, September 19, 1871, OHS; and Soward to Grant, July 15, 1871, as quoted in Nunn, p. 181.

. . . swamped the general with affidavits . . . and the man had been impressed. . . . Sherman to E.D. Townsend, May 28, 1871, OIA:NA, says, "Texas has Sheriffs and Courts and all the machinery of a criminal code. . . ."

. . . A handful of arrows from the scene. . . . The story of the three kinds of arrows is in the *Dallas Herald*, June 3, 1871.

. . . Fort Murray north of the river. . . . Spelled "Murrah" in some accounts and the spelling may be correct, since Pendleton Murrah was a Confederate governor of Texas.

. . . official report of the engagement, Lieutenant Carson. . . . As given in Mayhall's *Indian Wars of Texas, op. cit.*

. . . Elizabeth . . . disagreements . . . with her daughter Susan. . . . For the trouble between Elizabeth and Susan see Barbara Neal Ledbetter, "Who Was Saint-To-Hoodle Goombi?" *op cit.* A court had declared Elizabeth incompetent to be guardian of her own son at the demand of Susan.

. . . officials of the Thirteenth Judicial District took the stage to Jacksboro. . . . Smythe, p. 275, and Huckabay, p. 187, reprint a letter by Soward in which he says, "Upon arriving at Jacksborough, we dispatched a posse of five citizens to Fort Sill. . . ." Court opened and the citizens left for Fort Sill on the 26th, according to the *Dallas Herald* of July 22, 1871.

. . . The colonel wrote a letter to Agent Tatum. . . . Mackenzie to Tatum, June 25, 1871, OHS.

. . . Satanta and Big Tree . . . eight-by-twelve stone room. . . . Patzki's description in *Circular 4, op. cit.*, shows the laundry as picket and canvas. Patzki's report was published in 1870. I am assuming that the stone laundry and morgue was built by June 1871; a picture of it can be seen in the W.W. Bill Dennis pamphlet, *op. cit.*, p. 6.

The thoughts of Satanta are conjecture, of course. The story of the Kiowas giving meat to the cave people was told me by James Auchiah.

. . . Lanham lacked a few days being twenty-five. . . . For the early life of S.W.T. Lanham see anonymous, *History of Texas, Together with a Biographical History of Tarrant and Parker Counties* (Chicago: The Lewis Publishing Company, 1895).

. . . he intended to be governor. . . . Lanham was elected to the U.S. Congress in November 1882, and served until March 4, 1893. He was elected governor of Texas and served from January 20, 1903 until January 15, 1907.

CHAPTER ELEVEN

THE TRIAL

The two versions of the Tatum to Grierson letter of May 27, 1871, can be seen in Nye, p. 136, from LC, and Leckie, p. 150, from OHS. That Tatum and probably others fraudulently made evidence here is a surmise, but I see no other interpretation. Could the variation be merely the error of a copying clerk? A name (Big Tree) might be inadvertently dropped in copying—that makes the OHS letter the original; the copier then must have inadvertently added "three," which word makes only limited sense if it were used in haste in the original letter and as an accidental addition would have required the copier to go back accidentally and count some names before he added it.

The question of what trial records have existed and been available to historians has presented an interesting challenge. Smythe reports, p. 274, "W.H. Mitchell, clerk of the district court of Jack County, wrote May 4, 1877, that the papers in the Satanta case 'have been lost and cannot be found.'" I presume that Judge Soward and Clerk Robinson withheld the records for some years, then placed some of them in the courthouse at Jacksboro, where they remained until at least 1929. No records of the trial exist today in the district clerk's office, nor in the files of the Texas Court of Criminal Appeals, nor in the Texas State Archives. Some time in the 1920s old court records were ordered destroyed by a resolution of the legislature, but this order must not have been obeyed before July of 1929 in Jack County.

There are extant two valid copies of the trial records in archival repositories: one of which might be called the "Rister Minutes," the other the "Warrant Minutes." On July 23, 1929, Carl Coke Rister got a "full and complete" certified copy of the trial, verdict, sentence, and commutation from the court clerk of the district, which had at that date changed from the Thirteenth to the Forty-third District. Rister changed the certified copy to a typescript; what happened to the certified copy is anybody's guess. The typescript is located in the Southwest Collection at Texas Tech University. It has certain careless errors in it: Woolfolk's name is misspelled, in one place "Monday" is written instead of "Thursday," the word "animus" is produced as "Americans," and Davis' first name is given as "Edwin" instead of "Edmund." One might speculate that Professor Rister had a student assistant do his typing.

The other valid copy of the trial records exists in the National Archives filed under Letters Received, Fort Richardson, Texas. It purports to be a warrant issued by Clerk James Robinson on September 8, 1871, ordering the sheriff to convey the two prisoners to the penitentiary at Huntsville, but is much longer than such a warrant would need to be. It consists of ten legal-size sheets and gives all the principal actions, the motions, pleas, etc., of both trials. One can be sure that the sheriff did not ordinarily file his papers in Letters Received out at the fort. This document was Jack County's answer to the federal government's demand for trial records; undoubtedly Mackenzie had been instructed never to release custody of the chiefs until he got the records.

The Rister Minutes and the Warrant Minutes confirm each other. They were certainly copied from the same source. Where the prosecution is called "plaintiff" in one it is so called in the other; where it is called "the state" in one it is so called in the other. Where a word such as "defendant" is abbreviated to "deft" in one it is the same in the other. Both sets of minutes show the verdict as to Big Tree signed "Thos. W. Williams, Foreman of Jury." The Rister Minutes show the verdict as to Satanta "Not signed by Foreman." The Warrant Minutes simply give the exact verdict and ignore the question of a signature, though the signature had been noted for the first trial. Incidentally, this kind of fact, that the jury foreman should forget to sign a verdict, appears to me to be precisely the kind of thing that does happen and not at all the kind of thing that is made up.

Woolfolk's name has often been incorrectly spelled "Woolfork." Biographical data on him is taken from "Frontier Lawyer Led Full Life," by Barbara Ledbetter, pp. 20, 21, in *Scrapbook of Young County* (Graham: The Graham News, 1966). Also from James Cox, *Historical and Biographical Record of the Cattle Industry and the Cattlemen of Texas and Adjacent Territory* (St. Louis: Woodward & Tierman Printing Co., 1895).

That Woolfolk was a rebel at the trial is surmise. The minutes clearly suggest that someone was making the kinds of objections in the early part of the trial as if he were truly working for his clients' interests. The move for the severance is the best example; a severance was not necessary for the appearance of legality. Yet not long after the severance is granted, the defense accepts the jury with such an interested party as Peter Lynn on it. A "deal" is strongly suggested.

Why do I choose Woolfolk as the rebel rather than Ball? For several reasons. 1. Woolfolk did not sign the hypocritical petition to Soward not to hold the term of court. 2. In the book by James Cox, above, data for the biographies were supplied by the subjects themselves (see p. 297) and yet Woolfolk says nothing about the famous trial; one might conclude that he was not proud of it. 3. The *Dallas Herald* story of July 1871, covering the trial, calls him W. Woolfork; evidently he was not talking to reporters. 4 The same newspaper story reports that Ball spoke eloquently for the Indians. Such a defense may have been a good show, but the only effective defense would have been to attack the evidence and to make a record on the basis of valid technicalities. 5. Charles Goodnight described Woolfolk in Haley, *op. cit.*, p. 70, as "peppery" and said he "suffered some unpopularity in his own right." 6. Early records from Belknap show an assault-and-battery charge against Woolfolk; see the pamphlet by Barbara Neal Ledbetter, published in 1968, *Young County, Texas, Records*, vol. 2, p. 4.

The erroneous idea of many writers that the trial lasted through July 8 can be traced to Smythe's presentation, p. 276, of a letter by Soward, wherein the judge says, "I passed sentence upon them on the 8th of July. . . ." Smythe's book is poorly proofread, and Soward's handwriting is atrocious.

. . . agreed to send his interpreter . . . as requested. . . . Mackenzie to Tatum, June 25, 1871, OHS.

. . . getting letters from influential Quakers. . . . The letters from Nicholson, Garrett, and Rhoads are all from OHS.

. . . a history-gathering general had taken a copy. . . . Sherman to Reynolds, May 24, 1871, LC, says, "Please send me at Washington copies of all my letters. . . ." Sherman even had a copy of Marcy's journal made for himself.

. . . grand jury . . . indicted Satanta and Big Tree. . . . Huckabay, pp. 180–181, gives the indictment, but her source is indefinite and it does not seem certain that hers is a true copy.

. . . courthouse . . . made of stone. . . . A photograph of the courthouse is given in the W.W. Bill Dennis pamphlet, *op. cit.*, p. 30. Records concerning its building are given in Huckabay, pp. 138, 139.

. . . also, improperly . . . stored there the records of Young County. . . . These records are taken from two pamphlets compiled and published by Barbara Neal Ledbetter at Graham, Texas—*Civil War Days in Young County, Texas, 1861–1865* (published 1965) and vol. 2, cited above.

. . . Thomas W. Williams . . . jury foreman. . . . Information on Williams is taken from scattered references in Horton and Huckabay.

. . . Another juror who came was Peter Lynn. . . . Data on Peter Lynn and the Mason-Cambren killings come from Huckabay, pp. 35–39, also pp. 474–475; from Horton, pp. 33–35; and from Haley's biography of Goodnight, *op. cit.*, pp. 22–25, also pp. 50–51 and p. 62.

. . . another juror . . . William Hensley. . . . Horton, p. 57.

. . . prisoners . . . remain in the custody of the army. . . . Reynolds to Townsend, July 13, 1871, AGO:NA, says, "Have directed that they be held by the military until the orders of the President can be received." Also, Reynolds to AG, July 13, 1871, OIA:NA, says that the C.O. of Fort Richardson has instructions to "hold the Indian prisoners in strict military custody until the orders of the President can be received in the premises."

. . . mounted cavalrymen . . . surrounding the wagon. . . . Huckabay, p. 181.

. . . passed the two girls on the prairie! . . . From G.A. Holland, *History of Parker County and The Double Log Cabin* (Weatherford: Herald Publishing Company, 1937), p. 63.

. . . The Kiowa people . . . adept at sign language. . . . Richard I. Dodge, *Our Wild Indians* (New York: Archer House, 1959),

p. 385, says: "The Plains Indians themselves believe that the sign language was invented by the Kiowas. . . ."

. . . Mackenzie . . . posted a letter. . . . Excerpted in Reynolds to AG, July 13, 1871, OIA:NA. A copy also exists in AGO:NA.

. . . then Satanta stood up. . . . Satanta's speech is from Smythe, pp. 273, 274. Because Smythe says the speech is not literally reproduced and because of the limitations of all translations, I have made some nonfactual changes, e.g. "squaw" to "woman."

. . . The judge . . . wrote the promised letter. . . Soward to Davis, July 10, 1871, given in Smythe, pp. 275–277.

CHAPTER TWELVE

PRISON

Background on Edmund Davis is taken from Mark M. Boatner, *The Civil War Dictionary* (New York: David McKay, 1959); from Rupert N. Richardson, *Texas, The Lone Star State* (Englewood Cliffs, N.J.: Prentice-Hall, 1958); and from Nunn. R. Henderson Shuffler, "How Two Great Chiefs Became Political Pawns," *Texas Magazine* (July 17, 1966), attributes political motives to most of Davis' actions in the Satanta-Big Tree case at this time and later; and I am inclined to agree with him. The commutation proclamation is appended to both copies of the trial minutes mentioned previously.

Special Orders No. 185, dealing with the transfer of the chiefs to Huntsville and into civilian custody, can be found in the files of the Texas Department of Corrections at Huntsville, as can the admission records of Satanta and Big Tree.

The *Scribner's* article quoted is Edward King, "Glimpses of Texas—II," *Scribner's Monthly*, VII (Feb. 1874). Some further information on the prison life of the chiefs is given in the *Dallas Herald* of September 28, 1872; the newspaper reporter interviewed a Colonel Dewey, who was one owner of the company which leased and operated the penitentiary in those years. Clarence Wharton, *Satanta, The Great Chief of the Kiowas and His People* (Dallas: Banks Upshaw, 1935), gives some details of prison life, but the book is generally unreliable. That the chiefs worked on the railroad seems confirmed by a story told by Big Tree in later life; see W.W. Bill Dennis, *op. cit.*, p. 37.

Carter has led various writers astray with his account of escorting Satanta and Big Tree north before the Missouri meeting. Carter did not command the guard escort; it was commanded by a Major Webb of the 10th U.S. Cavalry. Carter's dates are wrong; also, the Indians did not meet at Atoka Station as he says. See *The Missouri Republican*, published in St. Louis, of September 27–30, 1872; also the *Dallas Herald*, September 28, 1872.

... a letter to be written in English to Agent Tatum. ... I have no direct evidence that Satanta wrote to Tatum, but it is clear that the chief was thinking along the lines indicated and that Tatum learned of it; see Tatum, p. 131.

... brought in thirty-eight more mules and one horse. ... From Tatum to Hoag, August 5, 1871, OIA:NA, and Tatum, pp. 122–125.

... An-pay-kau-te's passion for vengeance was satisfied. ... From G.W. Schofield to AAG, San Antonio, June 12, 1872, OIA:NA. Also from Mayhall, p. 237, Nye, p. 154 and Nye's *Plains Indians Raiders, op. cit.*, p. 214.

... I write to your Excellency. ... Soward to Grant, July 15, 1872, as quoted in Nunn, pp. 180, 181.

... summed up thus by the Commissioner of Indian Affairs. ... *Report of Commissioner of Indian Affairs, 1872*, p. 99, as quoted in Nye, p. 158.

... Davis ... had journeyed to Washington recently. ... See Alvord to Davis, September 22, 1873, in TIP, p. 348.

... Alvord ... filed his recommendations. ... Alvord's report is quoted from Mooney, pp. 193–195.

CHAPTER THIRTEEN

THE BIG COUNCIL

Most of the information about the actual council, where the issue was the release of Satanta and Big Tree, I have taken from TIP, pp. 350–363, which is a transcript of actual words spoken by the various participants, brought back to Texas by Davis. I've also used some facts from Battey, pp. 199–205; Leckie, pp. 175–179; and Nye, pp. 168–176.

Part of the transcript has been left out to reduce repetition and irrelevance, but I have tried to include enough to show the diversity of thought and conflict of interest between the various parties. I have altered the transcript in some cases to say what I believe was said. A simple example is in the words of Red Tree shown thus: "You have your squaws and your children." The man was thinking Kiowa, speaking Comanche, and having it recorded in English, none of which languages has the word "squaw" in it; why not translate it "woman."

Another example easily seen is in the words of Kiowa-Apache Chief Pacer. Again it should be remembered that he is speaking a foreign language, Comanche. The interpreter got certain significant words, but did not put the sense into good English. The Davis transcript shows Pacer saying, "We are all old and grown, but our little ones will grow up as white men." It is apparent that he said in his own mind something approximately as I have put it: "We have grown up in our Indian ways, but our little ones will grow up as white men."

. . . He wrote . . . would later write. . . . The two quotations in the first paragraph of this chapter are from Sherman to Townsend, May 28, 1871, as quoted by Leckie, p. 155, and Dodge, *Our Wild Indians*, *op. cit.*, p. xxxvii.

. . . Mackenzie went out from Fort Richardson and rode. . . . From Leckie, pp. 167–172, and Nye, pp. 160–163.

. . . Hoag had replied, "I do not deem it necessary. . . ." Hoag to Tatum, June 26, 1871, OHS.

. . . release of Satanta . . . a dark and rolling cloud. . . . Tatum, p. 160.

. . . he aided in the recovery of . . . captives. . . . Tatum, p. 154. Battey, p. 138, says the total of captives recovered was eighteen.

. . . General Sherman was incensed at the possibility. . . . Sherman to Delano, April 23, 1873, from Nunn, pp. 187, 188.

. . . Grant was being pulled to and fro. . . . Delano to Davis, May 27, 1873, OHS, says that the matter "has received the full and frequent consideration of the President and myself."

. . . Davis . . . wrote to General J.W. Davidson. . . . Davis to Davidson, August 14, 1873, OHS.

. . . General Council of the Indian Territory. . . . See "Resolution relating to the Kiowas, Cheyennes and other tribes of the plains." Also p. 25 of "Journal of the Fourth Annual Session of the General Council." Both from OHS.

. . . the governor received a fat envelope. . . . From TIP, pp. 342–348.

. . . to set a time and place for the council. . . . Item 223, pp. 349, 350, TIP, obviously was written by Davis inside the post to Indians outside of it and refers to the location of the council.

. . . Colonel J.W. Davidson . . . caused the cavalry horses to be saddled. . . . From Nye, pp. 168, 169, and Leckie, pp. 176, 177.

. . . long porch of the limestone headquarters building. . . . The Fort Sill museum office is in this building today.

. . . captive the wife and children of the black man. . . . That the black captives once held by Red Tepee were Britt Johnson's family is a thoughtful guess. See Corwin, p. 28.

. . . Davis . . . a letter in which he named the principal terms. . . . Davis to Davidson, October 7, 1873, TIP, p. 361.

. . . the prediction of a bit of verse. . . . From Nunn, pp. 189, 190.

. . . yours is the first that should be taken. . . . Sherman to Davis, February 16, 1874, as quoted in Nunn, p. 190.

CHAPTER FOURTEEN

A TIME OF FREEDOM

The evidence for Satanta's council is indirect, but persuasive, and comes primarily from Battey, pp. 219, 220. Lone Wolf told Battey that some Osages had come among them and called a big council of Comanches, Cheyennes, Arapahos, Kiowas, and Apaches. The

Osages preached for one mother and one fire, against surveyors and the white killing of buffalo. In fact, the Osages had no power to call such a council; they had, for example, furnished the scouts for Custer's attack against the Cheyennes on the Washita in 1868. Lone Wolf told Battey this story on December 5, 1873, just two months after Satanta's release. Battey's gullibility and the Indians' awareness of it is apparent from a careful reading of his book. See, for example, his account of the second battle of Adobe Walls, in which all the white defenders are wiped out, pp. 310, 311.

Later in December of that year the Cheyenne Little Robe reported that Satanta was stirring up a full-scale war for the next spring with the Cheyennes and Comanches assisting the Kiowas; see Leckie, p. 184.

That Satanta urged upon the Comanches the value of an annual Sun Dance as an aid to unity is also speculative, but it appears that the south-plains warrior Indians acted more in concert during the year following Satanta's release than they ever had before. If my theory about him is correct, his influence would have been concealed by his friends, lest he be sent back to prison. Speculation along this line leads one to wonder whether the Comanche prophet Isa-tai had as much influence as he has been credited with. Anyone with a sense of Comanche character knows that the prophet did not "order" all Comanches to attend a Sun Dance as Nye says, p. 190. Another interesting question, which I have not pursued, is whether the rapprochement between the plains Indians and the Apaches (we are not speaking of the Kiowa-Apaches, of course) began during the year of Satanta's freedom.

My account of the Zebat is a combination of information supplied by James Auchiah and the Kiowa calendar interpretations as given by Mayhall, p. 171, and Marriott, p. 300. Some differences of opinion remain as to when Satanta gave away the medicine arrow and whether it was a permanent gift. There may have been two such arrows in the Kiowa tribe. The Zebat used in modern ceremonies is a replica.

Much of the general summary of events in this chapter comes from Nye, Leckie, and Mayhall; however, the interpretation is entirely my own.

. . . sportsman from England . . . wrote. . . . Quoted in Wayne Gard, *The Great Buffalo Hunt* (Lincoln: University of Nebraska Press, 1959), p. 131; also in E. Douglas Branch, *The Hunting of the Buffalo* (Lincoln: University of Nebraska Press, 1962), pp. 156, 157.

. . . knocked off a horse . . . a white-man's mile away. . . . The distance was later measured as 1538 yards, about seven-eighths of a mile.

. . . gave up the battle in the middle of the afternoon. . . . In addition to the general sources mentioned above, I have considered Mayhall's account in *Indian Wars of Texas, op. cit.*, pp. 10–15, and Grinnell's account in *The Fighting Cheyennes, op. cit.*, pp. 319–324.

. . . up to the Wichita Agency. . . . The present site of Anadarko, Oklahoma.

. . . His old nemesis Sherman was making the decisions. . . . Nye, p. 220, credits the decision to send Satanta back to Huntsville to Sheridan, while Leckie, p. 219, credits it to Sherman. Even if Sheridan made the immediate decision he certainly knew well his superior's involvement and views.

. . . when we settle down we grow pale and die. . . . From Mooney, p. 208.

. . . superintendent of the Texas penitentiary wrote. . . . Goree to P.B. Hunt, August 10, 1878, OHS.

. . . visited Satanta in prison and told him. . . . This comes from Huckabay, p. 202. The story about the veiled woman and the tombstone comes from the same place. The story is unexplainable, but seems elaborate and too much detailed to have no basis.

CHAPTER FIFTEEN

THE ALLIANCE

Some sources state that Joshua Given got his name at the school near Fort Sill. His son Orin Given told Corwin (see p. 69) that his father got it at Carlisle. Joshua died when Orin was very young, but Orin's mother would have known where her husband got his name.

Information on the return of Milly Durgan is taken from Ledbetter and Stroud as cited in the notes to Chapter Five of this book. I reiterate that the well-researched article by Barbara Neal Ledbetter shows nothing about the existence of baby Milly or about her being the same person as Saint-To-Hoodle Goombi; but that the best evidence in regard to these questions is the memory of old-timers, white-skinned and red-skinned, especially the testimony of the Kiowa warrior Mokeen. I have also used the Ledbetter booklet *The Fort Belknap of Yesterday and Today*, pp. 41–43, and Mayhall, p. 199.

. . . by hiring Indians as teamsters to do the hauling. . . . Tatum, p. 233.

. . . the American Baptist . . . Society called a meeting. . . . The involvement of Big Tree and his wife comes from Corwin, p. 14.

. . . Tone-a-koy knew how to . . . pray a person to death. . . . This story comes from Nye's *Bad Medicine and Good*, *op. cit.*, p. 267 ff. The date 1897 is inferred from Huckabay, p. 206.

. . . Fraser . . . engraving of an Indian on the buffalo nickel. . . . For the general background of the use of Indians on American coins see John C. Ewers, *Indian Life on the Upper Missouri* (Norman: University of Oklahoma Press, 1968), p. 202. For Big Tree's claim as a model see a feature article in the *Dallas Times Herald*, May 28, 1971, under the headline "World of Coins."

. . . commanding officer of Troop L, 7th Cavalry. . . . Information on Troop L and its members was supplied by James Auchiah.

. . . first acts of citizens meeting at Belknap. . . . This resolution is presented in Crouch, p. 57.

. . . hid her during the battle in a clump of bushes. . . . Mayhall, p. 199.

. . . "Whereas, The remains of a historic Indian. . . . H.C.R. No. 67 of the 58th Legislature.

INDEX

ABOUT THE AUTHOR

Born in Dundee, Texas, Benjamin Capps moved with his family at the age of eight to a ranch in Archer County, where he lived till he entered Texas Tech. In 1939, he joined the Civilian Conservation Corps in Colorado and later worked as a surveyor there and in his home state.

Capps was commissioned a second lieutenant in the Air Corps in 1944, subsequently flying forty bombing missions as navigator of a B-24 in the Pacific. At war's end, he completed his education at the University of Texas at Austin, graduating Phi Beta Kappa in 1948 and receiving his M.A. the following year.

Capps is the author of eight novels, of which *Sam Chance*, *The Trail to Ogallala*, and *The White Man's Road* have won the Spur Award as best western novel of the year from Western Writers of America. For the general contribution of his work to the body of western literature the same organization has honored Capps with its prestigious Levi Strauss Golden Saddleman Award, and he has also received two Wrangler Awards from The Cowboy Hall of Fame and Western Heritage Center.

Benjamin Capps lives now in Grand Prairie, Texas.